T5-AGB-231

PEARSON

ALWAYS LEARNING

Holly Moore

MATLAB® for Engineers

Second Custom Edition for Penn State University

Taken from:
MATLAB® for Engineers, Fifth Edition
by Holly Moore

Cover Art: Courtesy of Pearson Learning Solutions.

Taken from:

MATLAB® for Engineers, Fifth Edition
by Holly Moore
Copyright © 2018, 2015, 2012, 2009, 2007 by Pearson Education, Inc.
New York, New York 10013

All rights reserved. No part of this book may be reproduced, in any form or by any means, without permission in writing from the publisher.

This special edition published in cooperation with Pearson Education, Inc.

All trademarks, service marks, registered trademarks, and registered service marks are the property of their respective owners and are used herein for identification purposes only.

Pearson Education, Inc., 330 Hudson Street, New York, New York 10013
A Pearson Education Company
www.pearsoned.com

Printed in the United States of America

1   17

000200010272105933

LB

ISBN 10: 1-323-76921-8
ISBN 13: 978-1-323-76921-8

Contents

8 • LOGICAL FUNCTIONS AND SELECTION STRUCTURES   276

9 • REPETITION STRUCTURES   318

INDEX   663

1

About MATLAB®

Objectives

After reading this chapter, you should be able to:

- Understand what MATLAB® is and why it is widely used in engineering and science.

- Understand the advantages and limitations of the student edition of MATLAB®.
- Formulate problems using a structured problem-solving approach.

1.1 WHAT IS MATLAB®?

MATLAB® is one of a number of commercially available mathematical computation tools, which also include Maple, Mathematica, and MathCad. Despite what proponents may claim, no single one of these tools is "the best." Each has strengths and weaknesses. Each allows you to perform basic mathematical computations. They differ in the way they handle symbolic calculations and more complicated mathematical processes, such as matrix manipulation. For example, MATLAB® (short for **Mat**rix **Lab**oratory) excels at computations involving matrices, whereas Maple excels at symbolic calculations. At a fundamental level, you can think of these applications as sophisticated computer-based calculators. They can perform the same functions as your scientific calculator—and many more. If you have a computer on your desk, you may find yourself using MATLAB® instead of your calculator for even the simplest mathematical applications such as balancing your checkbook. In many engineering classes, the use of applications such as MATLAB® to perform computations is replacing more traditional computer programming. Although applications such as MATLAB® have become standards tool for engineers and scientists, this doesn't mean that you shouldn't learn a high-level language such as C++, Java, or Fortran.

Because MATLAB® is so easy to use, you can perform many programming tasks with it, but it isn't always the best tool for a programming task. It excels at numerical calculations—especially matrix calculations—and graphics, but you wouldn't want to use it to write a word-processing program. For large applications, such as operating systems or design software, C++, Java, or Fortran would be the applications of choice. (In fact, MATLAB®, which *is* a large application, was originally written in Fortran and later rewritten in C, a precursor of C++.) Usually, high-level applications do not offer easy access to graphing—a task at which MATLAB® excels. The primary area of overlap between MATLAB® and high-level applications is "number crunching"—repetitive calculations or the processing of large quantities of data. Both MATLAB® and high-level applications are good at processing numbers. A "number-crunching" program is generally easier to write in MATLAB®, but usually it will execute faster in C++ or Fortran. The one exception to this rule is calculations involving matrices. MATLAB® is optimized for matrices. Thus, if a problem can be formulated with a matrix solution, MATLAB® executes substantially faster than a similar program in a high-level language.

KEY IDEA
MATLAB® is optimized for matrix calculations.

MATLAB® is available as both professional and student versions. The professional version is probably installed in your college or university computer laboratory, but you may enjoy having the student version at home. MATLAB® is updated regularly; this textbook is based on MATLAB® 9.1. If you are using earlier versions, you will notice a significant difference in the layout of the graphical user interface; however, the differences in coding approaches are minor. There are substantial differences in versions that predate MATLAB® 5.5.

The standard installation of the professional version of MATLAB® is capable of solving various technical problems. Additional capability is available in the form of function toolboxes. These toolboxes are purchased separately, and they may or may not be available to you. You can find a complete list of the MATLAB® product family at The MathWorks website, www.mathworks.com.

1.2 STUDENT EDITION OF MATLAB®

KEY IDEA
MATLAB® is regularly updated.

The professional and student editions of MATLAB® are very similar. Beginning students probably won't be able to tell the difference. Student editions are available for Microsoft Windows, Mac, and Linux operating systems, and can be purchased from college bookstores or online from MathWorks at www.mathworks.com.

MathWorks packages its software in groups called *releases*, and MATLAB® 9.1 is featured, along with other products, such as Simulink, in Release R2016b®. New versions are released every six months. Students may purchase just MATLAB, or a bundle that includes the following products:

- Full MATLAB®
- Simulink, with the ability to build models with up to 1000 blocks (the professional version allows an unlimited number of blocks)
- Symbolic Math Toolbox
- Control Systems Toolbox
- Data Acquisition Toolbox
- Instrument Control Toolbox
- Simulink Control Design
- Signal Processing Toolbox
- DSP System Toolbox
- Statistics and Machine Learning Toolbox
- Optimization Toolbox
- Image Processing Toolbox
- A single-user license, limited to students for use in their classwork (The professional version is licensed either singly or to a group).

Toolboxes other than those included with the student edition may be purchased separately. You should be aware that if you are using a professional installation of MATLAB®, all of the toolboxes available in the student edition may not be available to you.

The biggest difference you should notice between the professional and student editions is the command prompt, which is

>>

in the professional version, and

EDU>>

in the student edition.

1.3 HOW IS MATLAB® USED IN INDUSTRY?

The ability to use tools such as MATLAB® is quickly becoming a requirement for many engineering positions. A recent job search on Monster.com found the following advertisement:

> . . . is looking for a System Test Engineer with Avionics experience. Responsibilities include modification of MATLAB® scripts, execution of Simulink simulations, and analysis of the results data. Candidate MUST be very familiar with MATLAB®, Simulink, and C++ . . .

This advertisement isn't unusual. The same search turned up 771 different companies that specifically required MATLAB® skills for entry-level engineers. Widely used in engineering and science fields, MATLAB® is particularly popular for electrical engineering applications. The sections that follow outline a few of the many applications currently using MATLAB®.

KEY IDEA
MATLAB® is widely used in engineering.

1.3.1 Electrical Engineering

MATLAB® is used in electrical engineering for a wide variety of applications. For example, Figure 1.1 includes several images created to help visualize the arrangements of electromagnetic fields in space and time. These images represent real physical situations with practical applications. Cellular communications, medical diagnostics, and home computers are just a few of the technologies that exist thanks to our understanding of this beautiful phenomenon.

1.3.2 Biomedical Engineering

Medical images are usually saved as dicom files (the Digital Imaging and Communications in Medicine standard). Dicom files use the file extension .dcm. The MathWorks

Figure 1.1
Arrangements of electromagnetic fields. (a) surface plasmon polariton; (b) light scattering by a circular metal cylinder; (c) beam forming by a six-element dipole array. (Used with permission of Dr. James R. Nagel, University of Utah Department of Electrical and Computer Engineering.)

(a)   (b)   (c)

Figure 1.2
Horizontal slices through the brain, based on the sample data file included with MATLAB®.

offers an Image Processing Toolbox that can read these files, making their data available to MATLAB®. (The Image Processing Toolbox is included with the student edition, and is optional with the professional edition.) The Image Processing Toolbox also includes a wide range of functions, many of them especially appropriate for medical imaging. A limited MRI data set that has already been converted to a format compatible with MATLAB® ships with the standard MATLAB® program. This data set allows you to try out some of the imaging functions available both with the standard MATLAB® installation and with the expanded imaging toolbox, if you have it installed on your computer. Figure 1.2 shows six images of horizontal slices through the brain based on the MRI data set.

The same data set can be used to construct a three-dimensional image, such as either of those shown in Figure 1.3. Detailed instructions on how to create these images are included in the MATLAB® tutorial, accessed from the help button on the MATLAB® toolbar.

1.3.3 Fluid Dynamics

Calculations describing fluid velocities (speeds and directions) are important in a number of different fields. Aerospace engineers in particular are interested in the

Figure 1.3
Three-dimensional visualization of MRI data, based on the sample data set included with MATLAB®.

Figure 1.4
Quiver plot of gas behavior
in a thrust-vector control
device.

Flow Velocities from a Plenum into a Curved Pipe

behavior of gases, both outside an aircraft or space vehicle and inside the combustion chambers. Visualizing the three-dimensional behavior of fluids is tricky, but MATLAB® offers a number of tools that make it easier. Figure 1.4 represents the flow-field calculation results for a thrust-vector control device as a quiver plot. Thrust-vector control is the process of changing the direction in which a nozzle points (and hence the direction a rocket travels) by pushing on an actuator (a piston-cylinder device). The model in the figure represents a high-pressure reservoir of gas (a plenum) that eventually feeds into the piston and thus controls the length of the actuator.

1.4 PROBLEM SOLVING IN ENGINEERING AND SCIENCE

A consistent approach to solving technical problems is important throughout engineering, science, and computer programming disciplines. The approach we outline here is useful in courses as diverse as chemistry, physics, thermodynamics, and engineering design. It also applies to the social sciences, such as economics and sociology. Different authors may formulate their problem-solving schemes differently, but they all have the same basic format:

KEY IDEA

Always use a systematic
problem-solving strategy.

- **State the problem.**
  - Drawing a picture is often helpful in this step.
  - If you do not have a clear understanding of the problem, you are not likely to be able to solve it.
- **Describe the input** values (knowns) and the required **outputs** (unknowns).
  - Be careful to include units as you describe the input and output values. Sloppy handling of units often leads to wrong answers.
  - Identify constants you may need in the calculation, such as the ideal gas constant and the acceleration due to gravity.

- o If appropriate, label a sketch with the values you have identified, or group them into a table.
- **Develop an algorithm** to solve the problem. In computer applications, this can often be accomplished with a **hand example**. You'll need to:
  - o Identify any equations relating the knowns and unknowns.
  - o Work through a simplified version of the problem by hand or with a calculator.
- **Solve** the problem. In this book, this step involves creating a **MATLAB® solution**.
- **Test the solution.**
  - o Do your results make sense physically?
  - o Do they match your sample calculations?
  - o Is your answer really what was asked for?
  - o Graphs are often useful ways to check your calculations for reasonableness.

If you consistently use a structured problem-solving approach, such as the one just outlined, you'll find that "story" problems become much easier to solve. Example 1.1 illustrates this problem-solving strategy.

EXAMPLE 1.1

THE CONVERSION OF MATTER TO ENERGY

Albert Einstein (Figure 1.5) is arguably the most famous physicist of the 20th century. He was born in Germany in 1879 and attended school in both Germany and Switzerland. While working as a patent clerk in Bern, he developed his famous theory of relativity. Perhaps the best-known physics equation today is his

$$E = mc^2.$$

This astonishingly simple equation links the previously separate worlds of matter and energy, and can be used to find the amount of energy released as matter is changed in form in both natural and human-made nuclear reactions.

The sun radiates 385×10^{24} J/s of energy, all of which is generated by nuclear reactions converting matter to energy. Use MATLAB® and Einstein's equation to determine how much matter must be converted to energy to produce this much radiation in one day.

1. State the problem
   Find the amount of matter necessary to produce the amount of energy radiated by the sun every day.
2. Describe the input and output

   Input
   Energy: $E = 385 \times 10^{24}$ J/s, which must be converted into the total energy radiated during one day
   Speed of light: $c = 3.0 \times 10^8$ m/s

   Output
   Mass m in kg

3. Develop a hand example
   The energy radiated in one day is

$$385 \times 10^{24} \text{ J/s} \times 3600 \text{ s/h} \times 24 \text{ h/day} \times 1 \text{ day} = 3.33 \times 10^{31} \text{ J}.$$

Figure 1.5
Albert Einstein.
(GL Archive/Alamy)

The equation $E = mc^2$ must be solved for m and the values for E and c substituted. Thus,

$$m = \frac{E}{c^2}$$

$$m = \frac{3.33 \times 10^{31}\,\text{J}}{(3.0 \times 10^8\,\text{m/s})^2}$$

$$= 3.7 \times 10^{14}\,\text{J/m}^2\text{s}^2.$$

We can see from the output criteria that we want the mass in kg, so what went wrong? We need to do one more unit conversion:

$$1\text{J} = 1\,\text{kg m}^2/\text{s}^2$$

$$= 3.7 \times 10^{14}\frac{J}{\text{m}^2/\text{s}^2} \times \frac{\text{kg m}^2/\text{s}^2}{J} = 3.7 \times 10^{14}\,\text{kg}$$

4. Develop a MATLAB® solution

At this point, you have not learned how to create MATLAB® code. However, you should be able to see from the following sample code that MATLAB® syntax is similar to that used in most algebraic scientific calculators. MATLAB® commands are entered at the prompt (>>), and the results are reported on the next line. The code is as follows:

```
>> E=385e24   The user types in this information
E =

   3.8500e+026    This is the computer's response
>> E=E*3600*24
E =
   3.3264e+031
>> c=3e8
```

```
c =
    300000000
>> m=E/c^2
m =
    3.6960e+014
```

From this point on, we will not show the prompt when describing interactions in the command window.

5. Test the solution

The MATLAB® solution matches the hand calculation, but do the numbers make sense? Anything times 10^{14} is a really large number. Consider, however, that the mass of the sun is 2×10^3 kg. We can calculate how long it would take to consume the mass of the sun completely at a rate of 3.7×10^{14} kg/day. We have

$$\text{Time} = \frac{\text{Mass of the sun}}{\text{Rate of consumption}}$$

$$\text{Time} = \frac{2 \times 10^{30}\ \text{kg}}{3.7 \times 10^{14}\ \text{kg/day}} \times \frac{\text{year}}{365\ \text{days}} = 1.5 \times 10^{13}\ \text{years}.$$

That's 15 trillion years! We don't need to worry about the sun running out of matter to convert to energy in our lifetimes.

2

MATLAB® Environment

Objectives

After reading this chapter, you should be able to:

- Start the MATLAB® program and solve simple problems in the command window.
- Understand MATLAB®'s use of matrices.
- Identify and use the various MATLAB® windows.
- Define and use simple matrices.
- Name and use variables.
- Understand the order of operation used in MATLAB®.

- Understand the difference between scalar, array, and matrix calculations in MATLAB®.
- Express numbers in either floating-point or scientific notation.
- Adjust the format used to display numbers in the command window.
- Save the value of variables used in a MATLAB® session.
- Save a series of commands in a script M-file.
- Use Section mode.

2.1 GETTING STARTED

Using MATLAB® for the first time is easy; mastering it can take years. In this chapter, we will introduce you to the MATLAB® environment and show you how to perform basic mathematical computations. After reading this chapter, you should be able to start using MATLAB® for homework assignments or on the job. Of course, you will be able to do more as you complete the rest of the chapters.

Because the procedure for installing MATLAB® depends upon your operating system and your computing environment, we will assume that you have already installed MATLAB® on your computer, or that you are working in a computing laboratory with MATLAB® already installed. To start MATLAB® in either the Windows or Mac environment, double-click on the icon on the desktop, or use the start menu to find the

Figure 2.1

MATLAB® 2016a opening window. The MATLAB® environment consists of a number of windows, three of which open in the default view. Others open as needed during a MATLAB® session.

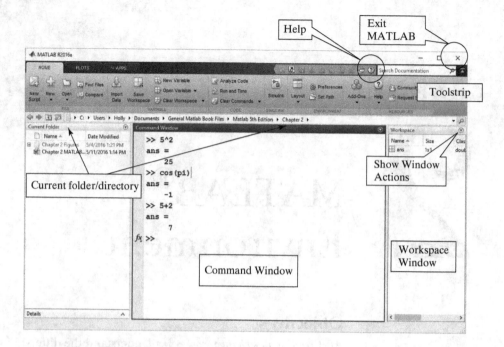

program. In the UNIX environment, type Matlab at the shell prompt. No matter how you start it, once MATLAB® opens, you should see the MATLAB® prompt (>> or EDU>>), which tells you MATLAB® is ready for you to enter a command. When you have finished your MATLAB® session, you can exit MATLAB® by typing quit or exit at the MATLAB® prompt. MATLAB® also uses the standard Windows menu bar, so you can exit the program by selecting the close icon (**x**) at the upper right-hand corner of the screen. The default MATLAB® screen, which opens each time you start the program, is shown in Figure 2.1. (There are minor differences in the MATLAB® desktop, depending on the release.)

To start using MATLAB®, you need be concerned only with the command window (in the center of the screen). You can perform calculations in the command window in a manner similar to the way you perform calculations on a scientific calculator. Even most of the syntax is the same. For example, to compute the value of 5 squared, type the command

    5^2.

The following output will be displayed:

    ans =

            25.

Or, to find the value of $\cos(\pi)$, type

    cos(pi)

which results in the output

    ans =

            -1.

KEY IDEA

MATLAB® uses the standard algebraic rules for order of operation.

MATLAB® uses the standard algebraic rules for order of operation, which becomes important when you chain calculations together. These rules will be discussed in Section 2.3.2. Notice that the value of pi is built into MATLAB®, so you do not have to enter it yourself.

HINT

You may think some of the examples are too simple to type in yourself—that just reading the material is sufficient. However, you will remember the material better if you both read it and type it!

Before going any further, try Practice Exercise 2.1.

PRACTICE EXERCISE 2.1

Type the following expressions into MATLAB® at the command prompt, and observe the results. The correct answers can be found on the Pearson website.

1. $5 + 2$
2. $5*2$
3. $5/2$
4. $3 + 2*(4 + 3)$
5. $2.54*8/2.6$
6. $6.3 - 2.1045$
7. 3.6^2
8. $1+2^2$
9. sqrt(5)
10. cos(pi)

HINT

You may find it frustrating to learn that when you make a mistake, you cannot just overwrite your command after you have executed it. This occurs because the command window is creating a list of all the commands you have entered. You cannot "un-execute" a command, or "un-create" it. What you can do is enter the command correctly, then execute your new version. MATLAB® offers several ways to make this easier for you. One way is to use the arrow keys, usually located on the right-hand side of your keyboard. The up arrow, ↑, allows you to move through the list of commands you have executed. Once you find the appropriate command, you can edit it, then execute your new version.

2.2 MATLAB® WINDOWS

MATLAB® uses several display windows. The default view, shown in Figure 2.1, includes in the middle, a large *command window*, located on the right, the *workspace* window, and located on the left the *current folder window*. In addition, the *command history window*, *document windows*, *graphics windows*, and *editing windows* will automatically open when needed. Each will be described in the sections that follow. MATLAB® also includes a built-in help tutorial that can be accessed from the toolstrip by selecting the question mark icon, as shown in Figure 2.1. To personalize your desktop, you can resize any of these windows, stack them on top of each other, close the ones you are not using, or "undock" them from the desktop by using the "Show Workspace Actions" menu located in the upper right-hand corner of each window.

You can restore the default configuration by selecting Layout on the toolstrip, then selecting Default, or you can add additional windows by selecting Layout and choosing the windows you would like to see.

2.2.1 Command Window

The command window is located in the center pane of the default view of the MATLAB® screen, as shown in Figure 2.1. The command window offers an environment similar to a scratch pad. Using it allows you to save the values you calculate, but not the *commands* used to generate those values. If you want to save the command sequence, you will need to use the editing window to create an a script stored as an *M-file*. Scripts are will be described in Section 2.4.2. Both approaches are valuable. Before we introduce scripts, we will concentrate on using the command window.

KEY IDEA

The command window is similar to a scratch pad.

2.2.2 Command History

The command history window records the commands you issued in the command window. It does not open in the default view in MATLAB 2016b, but you can add it to your desktop by selecting Layout → Command History and checking "docked." The examples in this book will show the Command History in a docked configuration. When you exit MATLAB®, or when you issue the `clc` command, the command window is cleared, but the command history window retains a list of all your commands. You may clear the command history from the "Show Command History Actions" drop-down menu, located in the upper right-hand corner of the window. If you work on a public computer, as a security precaution, MATLAB®'s defaults may be set to clear the history when you exit MATLAB®. If you entered the earlier sample commands listed in this book, notice that they are repeated in the command history window. This window is valuable for a number of reasons, including allowing you to review previous MATLAB® sessions. It can also be used to transfer commands to the command window. For example, first clear the contents of the command window by typing

KEY IDEA

The command history records all of the commands issued in the command window.

```
clc.
```

This action clears the command window but leaves the data in the command history window intact. You can transfer any command from the command history window to the command window by double-clicking (which also executes the command), or by clicking and dragging the line of code into the command window. Try double-clicking

```
cos(pi)
```

in the command history window. The command is copied into the command window and executed. It should return

```
ans =
    -1.
```

Now click and drag

```
5^2
```

from the command history window into the command window. The command will not execute until you hit Enter, and then you will get the result:

```
ans =
   25
```

You will find the command history useful as you perform more complicated calculations in the command window.

KEY IDEA
The workspace window lists information describing all the variables created by the program.

2.2.3 Workspace Window

The workspace window keeps track of the *variables* you have defined as you execute commands in the command window. These variables represent values stored in the computer memory, which are available for you to use. If you have been doing the examples, the workspace window should show just one variable, ans, and indicate that it has a value of 25, and is a double array:

Name	Size	Class	Value
ans	1×1	double	25

(Your view of the workspace window may be slightly different, depending on how your installation of MATLAB® is configured.)

Set the workspace window to show more about the displayed variables by right-clicking on the bar with the column labels. Check bytes, in addition to name, value, class and size. Your workspace window should now display the following information, although you may need to resize the window to see all the columns:

Name	Size	Class	Bytes	Value
ans	1×1	double	8	25

KEY IDEA
The default data type is double-precision floating-point numbers stored in a matrix.

The yellow grid-like symbol indicates that the variable **ans** is an array. The size, 1×1, tells us that it is a single value (one row by one column) and therefore a scalar. The array uses 8 bytes of memory. MATLAB® was written in C, and the class designation tells us that in the C language, ans is a double-precision floating-point array. For our needs, it is enough to know that the variable ans can store a floating-point number (a number with a decimal point). Actually, MATLAB® considers every number you enter to be a floating-point number, whether you insert a decimal point or not.

In addition to information about the size of the arrays and type of data stored in them, you can also choose to display statistical information about the data. Once again, right click the bar in the workspace window that displays the column headings. Notice that you can select from a number of different statistical measures, such as the max, min, and standard deviation.

You can define additional variables in the command window, and they will be listed in the workspace window. For example, typing

    A = 5

returns

    A =
        5.

Notice that the variable **A** has been added to the workspace window, which lists variables in alphabetical order. Variables beginning with lowercase letters are listed first, followed by variables starting with capital letters.

Name	Size	Class	Bytes	Value
ans	1×1	double	8	25
A	1×1	double	8	5

In Section 2.3.2, we will discuss in detail how to enter matrices into MATLAB®. For now, you can enter a simple one-dimensional matrix by typing

```
B = [1, 2, 3, 4].
```

This command returns

```
B =
    1 2 3 4.
```

The commas are optional; you would get the same result with

```
B = [1 2 3 4]
B =
    1 2 3 4.
```

Notice that the variable **B** has been added to the workspace window, and that it is a 1×4 array:

Name	Size	Class	Bytes	Value
ans	1×1	double	8	25
A	1×1	double	8	5
B	1×4	double	32	[1, 2, 3, 4]

You can define two-dimensional matrices in a similar fashion. Semicolons are used to separate rows. For example,

```
C = [1 2 3 4; 10 20 30 40; 5 10 15 20]
```

returns

```
C =
     1    2    3    4
    10   20   30   40
     5   10   15   20.
```

Name	Size	Class	Bytes	Value
ans	1×1	double	8	25
A	1×1	double	8	5
B	1×4	double	32	[1, 2, 3, 4]
C	3×4	double	96	<3 × 4 double >

Notice that **C** appears in the workspace window as a 3×4 matrix. To conserve space, the values stored in the matrix are not listed.

You can recall the values for any variable by typing in the variable name. For example, entering

```
A
```

returns

```
A =
    5.
```

Although the only variables we have introduced are matrices containing numbers, other types of variables are possible.

In describing the command window, we introduced the clc command. This command clears the command window, leaving a blank page for you to work on. However, it does not delete from memory the actual variables you have created. The clear command deletes all of the saved variables, which is reflected in the workspace window. Try it out by typing

```
clear
```

in the command window. The workspace window is now empty:

Name	Value	Size	Bytes	Class

If you suppress the workspace window (closing it either from the Layout menu on the toolstrip, or from the Window Action menu in the upper right-hand corner of the window), you can still find out which variables have been defined by using the whos command:

```
whos.
```

If executed before we entered the clear command, whos would have returned

Name	Size	Bytes	Class
A	1 × 1	8	double
B	1 × 4	32	double
C	3 × 4	96	double
ans	1 × 1	8	double

2.2.4 Current Folder Window

The current folder window lists all the files in the active directory. When MATLAB® either accesses files or saves information, it uses the current folder (also called the current directory) unless told differently. The default for the location of the current folder varies with your version of the software and the way it was installed. However, the current folder is listed at the top of the main window. The current folder can be changed by selecting another directory from the drop-down list located next to the directory listing, or by browsing through your computer files. Browsing is performed with the browse button, located next to the drop-down list (see Figure 2.2).

2.2.5 Document Window

Double-clicking on any variable listed in the workspace window automatically launches a document window, containing the *variable editor*. Values stored in the variable are displayed in a spreadsheet format. You can change values in the variable editor, or you can add new values. For example, if you have not already entered the two-dimensional matrix C, enter the following command in the command window:

```
C = [1 2 3 4; 10 20 30 40; 5 10 15 20];
```

KEY IDEA
A semicolon suppresses the output from commands issued in the command window.

Placing a semicolon at the end of the command suppresses the output so that it is not repeated in the command window. However, **C** should now be listed in the workspace window. If you double-click on it, a document window will open above the command window, as shown in Figure 2.3. You can now add more values to the

Figure 2.2
The current folder window lists all the files in the active directory. You can change the current folder by using the drop-down menu or the browse button.

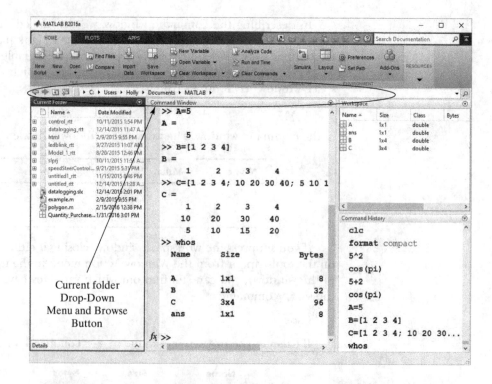

Current folder Drop-Down Menu and Browse Button

Figure 2.3
The document window displays the *variable editor*.

C matrix or change existing values. Notice that the toolstrip automatically opens the variable tab, which includes options that allow you to manipulate the data in the editor.

The document window/array editor can also be used in conjunction with the workspace window action menu to create entirely new arrays. Right click on the workspace title bar, select new from the menu, and a new variable called *unnamed* should appear on the variable list. You can change its name by right-clicking and selecting

rename from the pop-up menu. To add values to this new variable, double-click on it and add your data from the variable editor window. When you are finished creating new variables, close the array editor by selecting the close window icon in the upper right-hand corner of the window.

2.2.6 Graphics Window

The graphics window launches automatically when you request a graph. To demonstrate this feature, first create an array of x values in the command window:

```
x = [1 2 3 4 5];
```

(Remember, the semicolon suppresses the output from this command; however, a new variable, x, appears in the workspace window.)

Now create a list of y values:

```
y = [10 20 30 40 50];
```

To create a graph, use the plot command:

```
plot(x,y)
```

Figure 2.4
MATLAB® makes it easy to create graphs.

KEY IDEA
Always add a title and axis labels to graphs.

The graphics window opens automatically (see Figure 2.4). Notice that a new window label appears on the task bar at the bottom of the windows screen. It will be titled either **<Student Version> Figure...** or simply **Figure 1**, depending on whether you are using the student or professional version, respectively, of the software. Any additional graphs you create will overwrite Figure 1, unless you specifically command MATLAB® to open a new graphics window.

MATLAB® makes it easy to modify graphs by adding titles, x and y labels, multiple lines, and so on. Annotating graphs will be covered in a separate chapter on plotting. Engineers and scientists **never** present a graph without labels!

2.2.7 Edit Window

To open the edit window, choose either New Script or New from the toolstrip. This window allows you to type and save a series of commands without executing them. Most of your work in MATLAB® will probably be done in an editing window. You may also open the edit window by typing **edit** at the command. Notice than the editor tab automatically opens on the toolstrip.

2.3 SOLVING PROBLEMS WITH MATLAB®

The command window and editing window environment are powerful tools for solving engineering problems. To use then effectively, you will need to understand more about how MATLAB® works.

2.3.1 Using Variables

Although you can solve many problems by using MATLAB® like a calculator, it is usually more convenient to give names to the values you are using. MATLAB® uses the naming conventions that are common to most computer programs:

- All names must start with a letter. The names can be of any length, but only the first 63 characters are used in MATLAB®. (Use the namelengthmax command to confirm this.) Although MATLAB® will let you create long variable names, excessive length creates a significant opportunity for error. A common guideline is to use lowercase letters and numbers in variable names, and to use capital letters for the names of constants. However, if a constant is traditionally expressed as a lowercase letter, feel free to follow that convention. For example, in physics textbooks, the speed of light is always lowercase c. Names should be short enough to remember and should be descriptive.

- The only allowable characters are letters, numbers, and the underscore. You can check to see if a variable name is allowed by using the isvarname command. As is standard in computer languages, the number 1 means that something is true, and the number 0 means false. Hence,

```
isvarname time
ans =
      1
```

indicates that time is a legitimate variable name, and

```
isvarname cool-beans
ans =
      0
```

tells us that cool-beans is not a legitimate variable name. (Recall that the dash is not an allowed character.)

- Names are case sensitive. The variable **x** is different from the variable **X**.
- MATLAB® reserves a list of keywords for use by the program, which you cannot assign as variable names. The iskeyword command causes MATLAB® to list these reserved names:

```
iskeyword
ans =
    'break'
    'case'
    'catch'
    'classdef'
    'continue'
    'else'
    'elseif'
    'end'
    'for'
    'function'
    'global'
    'if'
    'otherwise'
    'parfor'
    'persistent'
    'return'
    'spmd'
    'switch'
    'try'
    'while'
```

- MATLAB® allows you to reassign built-in function names as variable names. For example, you could create a new variable called sin with the command

```
sin = 4
```

which returns

```
sin =
      4.
```

This is clearly a dangerous practice, since the `sin` (i.e., sine) function is no longer available. If you try to use the overwritten function, you'll get an error statement:

```
sin(3)
??? Index exceeds matrix dimensions.
```

You can check to see if a variable is a built-in MATLAB® function by using the `which` command:

```
which sin
sin is a variable.
```

You can reset `sin` back to a function by typing

```
clear sin.
```

Now when you ask

```
which sin
```

the response is

```
built-in (C:\ProgramFiles\MATLAB\R2011a\toolbox\matlab\elfun\
@double\sin)
% double method
```

which tells us the location of the built-in function.

PRACTICE EXERCISE 2.2

Which of the following names are allowed in MATLAB®? Make your predictions, then test them with the `isvarname`, `iskeyword`, and `which` commands. The correct answers can be found on the Pearson website.

1. test
2. Test
3. if
4. my-book
5. my_book
6. Thisisoneverylongnamebutisitstillallowed?
7. 1stgroup
8. group_one
9. zzaAbc
10. z34wAwy?12#
11. sin
12. log

KEY IDEA
The matrix is the primary data type in MATLAB® and can hold numeric as well as other types of information.

VECTOR
A matrix composed of a single row or a single column.

SCALAR
A single-valued matrix.

2.3.2 Matrices in MATLAB®

The basic data type used in MATLAB® is the *matrix*. A single value, called a *scalar*, is represented as a 1×1 matrix. A list of values, arranged in either a column or a row, is a one-dimensional matrix called a *vector*. A table of values is represented as a two-dimensional matrix. Although we'll limit ourselves to scalars, vectors, and two-dimensional matrices in this chapter, MATLAB® can handle higher order arrays. (The terms matrix and array are used interchangeably by MATLAB® users, even though they are technically different in a mathematical context.)

In mathematical nomenclature, matrices are represented as rows and columns inside square brackets:

$$A = [5] \quad B = [25] \quad C = \begin{bmatrix} 1 & 2 \\ 5 & 7 \end{bmatrix}$$

In this example, A is a 1×1 matrix, B is a 1×2 matrix, and C is a 2×2 matrix. The advantage in using matrix representation is that whole groups of information can be represented with a single name. Most people feel more comfortable assigning a name to a single value, so we'll start by explaining how MATLAB® handles scalars, then move on to more complicated matrices.

Scalar Operations

MATLAB® handles arithmetic operations between two scalars much the same as other computer programs and even your calculator. The syntax for addition, subtraction, multiplication, division, and exponentiation is shown in Table 2.1. The command

```
a = 1 + 2
```

should be read as "**a** is assigned a value of 1 plus 2," which is the addition of two scalar quantities. Arithmetic operations between two scalar variables use the same syntax. Suppose, for example, that you have defined **a** in the previous statement and that **b** has a value of 5:

```
b = 5
```

Then

```
x = a + b
```

returns the following result:

```
x =
    8
```

A single equals sign (=) is called an assignment operator in MATLAB®. The assignment operator causes the result of your calculations to be stored in a computer

Table 2.1 Arithmetic Operations Between Two Scalars (Binary Operations)

Operation	Algebraic Syntax	MATLAB® Syntax
Addition	$a + b$	**a+b**
Subtraction	$a - b$	**a−b**
Multiplication	$a \times b$	**a*b**
Division	$\frac{a}{b}$ or $a \div b$	**a/b**
Exponentiation	a^b	**a^b**

memory location. In the preceding example, **x** is assigned a value of 8. If you enter the variable name

    x

into MATLAB®, you get the following result:

    x =
        8

KEY IDEA
The assignment operator is different from an equality.

The assignment operator is significantly different from an equality. Consider the statement

    x = x + 1.

This is not a valid algebraic statement, since **x** is clearly not equal to **x + 1**. However, when interpreted as an assignment statement, it tells us to replace the current value of **x** stored in memory with a new value that is equal to the old **x** plus 1.

Since the value stored in **x** was originally 8, the statement returns

    x =
        9

indicating that the value stored in the memory location named **x** has been changed to 9. The assignment statement is similar to the familiar process of saving a file. When you first save a word-processing document, you assign it a name. Subsequently, after you've made changes, you resave your file, but still assign it the same name. The first and second versions are not equal: You've just assigned a new version of your document to an existing memory location.

Order of Operations
In all mathematical calculations, it is important to understand the order in which operations are performed. MATLAB® follows the standard algebraic rules for the order of operation:

- First, perform calculations inside parentheses, working from the innermost set to the outermost.
- Next, perform exponentiation operations.
- Then, perform multiplication and division operations, working from left to right.
- Finally, perform addition and subtraction operations, working from left to right.

To better understand the importance of the order of operations, consider the calculations involved in finding the surface area of a right circular cylinder.

The surface area is the sum of the areas of the two circular bases and the area of the curved surface between them, as shown in Figure 2.5. If we let the height of the cylinder be 10 cm and the radius 5 cm, the following MATLAB® code can be used to find the surface area:

```
radius = 5;
height = 10;
surface_area = 2*pi*radius^2 + 2*pi*radius*height
```

The code returns

```
surface_area =
           471.2389.
```

Figure 2.5

Finding the surface area of a right circular cylinder involves addition, multiplication, and exponentiation.

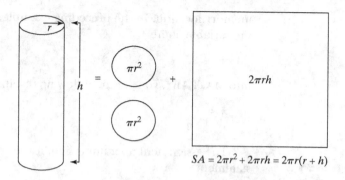

$$SA = 2\pi r^2 + 2\pi rh = 2\pi r(r + h)$$

In this case, MATLAB® first performs the exponentiation, raising the radius to the second power. It then works from left to right, calculating the first product and then the second product. Finally, it adds the two products together. You could instead formulate the expression as

```
surface_area = 2*pi*radius*(radius + height)
```

which also returns

```
surface_area =
        471.2389.
```

In this case, MATLAB® first finds the sum of the radius and height then performs the multiplications, working from left to right. If you forgot to include the parentheses, you would have

```
surface_area = 2*pi*radius*radius + height
```

in which case the program would have first calculated the product of `2*pi*radius*radius` and then added `height`—obviously resulting in the wrong answer. Note that it was necessary to include the multiplication operator before the parentheses, because MATLAB® does not assume any operators and would misinterpret the expression

```
radius(radius + height)
```

as follows. The value of radius plus height is 15 (radius = 10 and height = 5), so MATLAB® would have looked for the 15th value in an array called radius. This interpretation would have resulted in the following error statement:

```
??? Index exceeds matrix dimensions.
```

It is important to be extra careful in converting equations into MATLAB® statements. There is no penalty for adding extra parentheses, and they often make the code easier to interpret, both for the programmer and for others who may use the code in the future. Here's another common error that could be avoided by liberally using parentheses. Consider the following mathematical expression:

$$e^{\frac{-Q}{RT}}$$

In MATLAB®, the mathematical constant e is evaluated as using the function, exp, so the appropriate syntax is

```
exp(-Q/(R*T)).
```

Unfortunately, leaving out the parentheses as in

```
exp(-Q/R*T)
```

gives a very different result. Since the expression is evaluated from left to right, first Q is divided by R, then the result is multiplied by T—not at all what was intended.

Another way to make computer code more readable is to break long expressions into multiple statements. For example, consider the equation

$$f = \frac{\log(ax^2 + bx + c) - \sin(ax^2 + bx + c)}{4\pi x^2 + \cos(x-2)*(ax^2 + bx + c)}.$$

It would be very easy to make an error keying in this equation. To minimize the chance of that happening, break the equation into several pieces. For example, first assign values for x, a, b, and c (you can do it all on the same line):

```
x = 9; a = 1; b = 3; c = 5;
```

Then define a polynomial and the denominator:

```
poly = a*x^2 + b*x + c;
denom = 4*pi*x^2 + cos(x - 2)*poly;
```

Combine these components into a final equation:

```
f = (log(poly) - sin(poly))/denom
```

The result is

```
f =
      0.0044.
```

KEY IDEA
Try to minimize opportunity for error.

As mentioned, this approach minimizes your opportunity for error. Instead of keying in the polynomial three times (and risking an error each time), you need to key it in only once. Your MATLAB® code is more likely to be accurate, and it's easier for others to understand.

HINT

MATLAB® does not read "white space," so you may add spaces to your commands without changing their meaning. A long expression is easier to read if you add a space before and after plus (+) signs and minus (−) signs but not before and after multiplication (*) and division (/) signs.

PRACTICE EXERCISE 2.3

Predict the results of the following MATLAB® expressions, then check your predictions by keying the expressions into the command window. The correct answers can be found on the Pearson website.

1. $6/6 + 5$
2. $2*6^2$
3. $(3 + 5)*2$
4. $3 + 5*2$
5. $4 * 3/2 * 8$
6. $3 - 2/4 + 6^2$
7. 2^3^4
8. $2^(3^4)$
9. 3^5+4
10. $3^(5+4)$

Create and test MATLAB® syntax to evaluate the following expressions, and then check your answers with a handheld calculator.

11. $\dfrac{5 + 3}{9 - 1}$

12. $2^3 - \dfrac{4}{5 + 3}$

13. $\dfrac{5^{2+1}}{4 - 1}$

14. $4\dfrac{1}{2}*5\dfrac{2}{3}$

15. $\dfrac{5 + 6*\dfrac{7}{3} - 2^2}{\dfrac{2}{3}*\dfrac{3}{3*6}}$

EXAMPLE 2.1

SCALAR OPERATIONS

Wind tunnels (see Figure 2.6) play an important role in our study of the behavior of high-performance aircraft. In order to interpret wind tunnel data, engineers need to understand how gases behave. The basic equation describing the properties of gases

Figure 2.6
Wind tunnels are used to test aircraft designs. (Louis Bencze/Getty Images)

is the ideal gas law, a relationship studied in detail in freshman chemistry classes. The law states that

$$PV = nRT$$

where P = pressure in kPa,

V = volume in m^3,

n = number of kmoles of gas in the sample,

R = ideal gas constant, 8.314 kPa m^3/kmol K, and

T = temperature, expressed in kelvins (K).

In addition, we know that the number of kmoles of gas is equal to the mass of the gas divided by the molar mass (also known as the molecular weight) or

$$n = m/MW$$

where

m = mass in kg and

MW = molar mass in kg/kmol.

Different units can be used in the equations if the value of R is changed accordingly.

Now, suppose you know that the volume of air in the wind tunnel is 1000 m^3. Before the wind tunnel is turned on, the temperature of the air is 300 K, and the pressure is 100 kPa. The average molar mass (molecular weight) of air is approximately 29 kg/kmol. Find the mass of the air in the wind tunnel.

To solve this problem, use the following problem-solving methodology:

1. State the problem
   When you solve a problem, it is a good idea to restate it in your own words: Find the mass of air in a wind tunnel.

2. Describe the input and output

   Input

Volume	$V = 1000$ m^3
Temperature	$T = 300$ K
Pressure	$P = 100$ kPa
Molecular weight	$MW = 29$ kg/kmol
Gas constant	$R = 8.314$ kPa m^3/kmol K

   Output

Mass	$m = ?$ kg

3. Develop a hand example
   Working the problem by hand (or with a calculator) allows you to outline an algorithm, which you can translate to MATLAB® code later. You should choose simple data that make it easy to check your work. In this problem, we know two equations relating the data:

   $PV = nRT$ ideal gas law

   $n = m/MW$ relationship between mass and moles

(*continued*)

Solve the ideal gas law for n, and plug in the given values:

$$n = PV/RT$$

$$= \frac{100 \text{ kPa} \times 1000 \text{ m}^3}{8.314 \text{ kPa m}^3/\text{kmol K} \times 300\text{K}}$$

$$= 40.0930 \text{ kmol}$$

Convert moles to mass by solving the conversion equation for the mass m and plugging in the values:

$$m = n \times \text{MW} = 40.0930 \text{ kmol} \times 29 \text{ kg/mol}$$

$$m = 1162.70 \text{ kg}$$

4. Develop a MATLAB® solution
First, clear the screen and memory:

```
clear, clc
```

Now perform the following calculations in the command window:

```
P = 100
P =
       100
T = 300
T =
       300
V = 1000
V =
        1000
MW = 29
MW =
         29
R = 8.314
R =
       8.3140
n = (P*V)/(R*T)
n =
       40.0930
m = n*MW
m =
            1.1627e+003
```

There are several things you should notice about this MATLAB® solution. First, because no semicolons were used to suppress the output, the values of the variables are repeated after each assignment statement. Notice also the use of parentheses in the calculation of n. They are necessary in the denominator, but not in the numerator. However, using parentheses in both makes the code easier to read.

5. Test the solution
In this case, comparing the result with that obtained by hand is sufficient. More complicated problems solved in MATLAB® should use a variety of input data, to confirm that your solution works in a variety of cases. The MATLAB® screen used to solve this problem is shown in Figure 2.7.

Figure 2.7
MATLAB® screen used to solve the ideal gas problem.

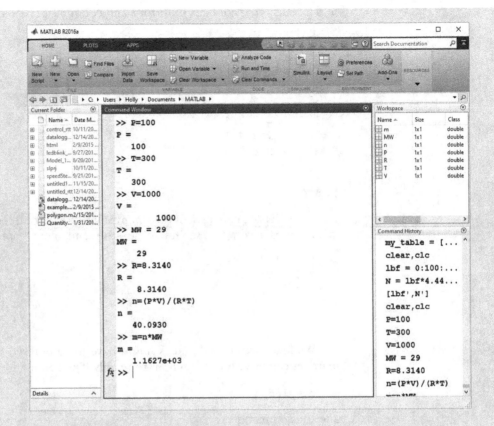

Notice that the variables defined in the command window are listed in the workspace window. Notice also that the command history lists the commands executed in the command window. If you were to scroll up in the command history window, you would see commands from previous MATLAB® sessions. All of these commands are available for you to move to the command window.

EXPLICIT LIST
A list identifying each member of a matrix

Array Operations

Using MATLAB® as a glorified calculator is fine, but its real strength is in matrix manipulations. As described previously, the simplest way to define a matrix is to use a list of numbers, called an *explicit list*. The command

    x = [1 2 3 4]

returns the row vector

    x =
        1 2 3 4.

Recall that, in defining this vector, you may list the values either with or without commas. A new row is indicated by a semicolon, so a column vector is specified as

    y = [1; 2; 3; 4]

and a matrix that contains both rows and columns is created with the statement

```
a = [1 2 3 4; 2 3 4 5; 3 4 5 6]
```

and will return

```
a =
    1 2 3 4
    2 3 4 5
    3 4 5 6.
```

HINT

It's easier to keep track of how many values you've entered into a matrix if you enter each row on a separate line—the semicolon is optional.

```
a = [1 2 3 4;
2 3 4 5;
3 4 5 6]
```

While a complicated matrix might have to be entered by hand, evenly spaced matrices can be entered much more readily. The command

```
b = 1:5
```

and the command

```
b = [1:5]
```

are equivalent statements. Both return a row matrix

```
b =
    1 2 3 4 5.
```

(The square brackets are optional.) The default increment is 1, but if you want to use a different increment, put it between the first and final values on the right side of the command. For example,

```
c = 1:2:5
```

indicates that the increment between values will be 2 and returns

```
c =
    1   3   5.
```

If you want MATLAB® to calculate the spacing between elements, you may use the linspace command. Specify the initial value, the final value, and how many total values you want. For example,

```
d = linspace(1, 10, 3)
```

returns a vector with three values, evenly spaced between 1 and 10:

```
d =
    1   5.5   10.
```

If you don't specify the number of values in the third field, the function defaults to generating 100 values, so that

```
d = linspace(1, 10);
```

creates an array with 100 values. In this example a semicolon was used to suppress the output, but by referring to the workspace window you can see that d is a 1×100 vector.

You can create logarithmically spaced vectors with the `logspace` command, which also requires three inputs. The first two values are powers of 10 representing the initial and final values in the array. The final value is the number of elements in the array. Thus,

```
e = logspace(1, 3, 3)
```

returns three values:

```
e =
   10 100 1000.
```

Notice that the first element in the vector is 10^1, and the last element in the array is 10^3.

HINT

New MATLAB® users often err when using the `logspace` command by entering the actual first and last values requested, instead of the corresponding power of 10. For example,

```
logspace (10,100,3)
```

is interpreted by MATLAB® as: Create a vector from 10^{10} to 10^{100} with three values. The result is

```
ans =
     1.0e+100 *
     0.0000 0.0000 1.0000.
```

A common multiplier (1×10^{100}) is specified for each result, but the first two values are so small in comparison to the third, that they are effectively 0.

HINT

You can include mathematical operations inside a matrix definition statement. For example, you might have **a = [0:pi/10:pi]**.

Matrices can be used in many calculations with scalars. If

```
a = [ 1 2 3 ]
```

we can add 5 to each value in the matrix with the syntax

```
b = a + 5
```

which returns

```
b =
        6    7    8.
```

This approach works well for addition and subtraction; however, multiplication and division are a little different. In matrix mathematics, the multiplication operator (*) indicates matrix multiplication. Because all MATLAB® operations can involve matrices, we need a different operator to indicate element-by-element multiplication. That operator is .* (called *dot multiplication* or *array multiplication*). For example,

```
a.*b.
```

results in element 1 of matrix a being multiplied by element 1 of matrix b,
element 2 of matrix a being multiplied by element 2 of matrix b,
element *n* of matrix a being multiplied by element *n* of matrix b.

For the particular case of our a (which is **[1 2 3]**) and our b (which is **[6 7 8]**),

```
a.*b
```

returns

```
ans =
        6    14    24
```

(Do the math to convince yourself that these are the correct answers.)

When you multiply a scalar times an array, you may use either operator (* or .*), but when you multiply two arrays together, they mean something quite different. Just using * implies a matrix multiplication, which in this case would return an error message, because a and b here do not meet the rules for multiplication in matrix algebra. The moral is, be careful to use the correct operator when you mean element-by-element multiplication.

Similar syntax holds for exponentiation (.^) and element-by-element division (./) of individual elements:

```
a.^2
a./b
```

Unfortunately, when you divide a scalar by an array you still need to use the ./ syntax, because the / means taking the matrix inverse to MATLAB®. As a general rule, unless you specifically are doing problems involving linear algebra (matrix mathematics), you should use the dot operators.

As an exercise, predict the values resulting from the preceding two expressions, then test your predictions by executing the commands in MATLAB®.

PRACTICE EXERCISE 2.4

As you perform the following calculations, recall the difference between the * and .* operators, as well as the / and ./ and the ^ and .^ operators. The correct answers can be found on the Pearson website.

1. Define the matrix *a* = [2.3 5.8 9] as a MATLAB® variable.
2. Find the sine of *a*.
3. Add 3 to every element in *a*.
4. Define the matrix *b* = [5.2 3.14 2] as a MATLAB® variable.

5. Add together each element in matrix *a* and in matrix *b*.
6. Multiply each element in *a* by the corresponding element in *b*.
7. Square each element in matrix *a*.
8. Create a matrix named *c* of evenly spaced values from 0 to 10, with an increment of 1.
9. Create a matrix named *d* of evenly spaced values from 0 to 10, with an increment of 2.
10. Use the `linspace` function to create a matrix of six evenly spaced values from 10 to 20.
11. Use the `logspace` function to create a matrix of five logarithmically spaced values between 10 and 100.

KEY IDEA

The matrix capability of MATLAB® makes it easy to do repetitive calculations.

The matrix capability of MATLAB® makes it easy to do repetitive calculations. For example, suppose you have a list of angles in degrees that you would like to convert to radians. First put the values into a matrix. For angles of 10, 15, 70, and 90, enter

```
degrees = [10 15 70 90];.
```

To change the values to radians, you must multiply by $\pi/180$:

```
radians = degrees*pi/180.
```

This command returns a matrix called `radians`, with the values in radians. (Try it!) In this case, you could use either the `*` or the `.*` operator, because the multiplication involves a single matrix (`degrees`) and two scalars (pi and 180). Thus, you could have written

```
radians = degrees.*pi/180
```

HINT

The value of π is built into MATLAB® as a floating-point number called `pi`. Because π is an irrational number, it cannot be expressed *exactly* with a floating-point representation, so the MATLAB® constant pi is really an approximation. You can see this when you find `sin(pi)`. From trigonometry, the answer should be 0. However, MATLAB® returns a very small number, 1.2246e–016. In most calculations, this won't make a difference in the final result.

Another useful matrix operator is transposition. The transpose operator changes rows to columns and vice versa. For example,

```
degrees'
```

returns

```
ans =
        10
        15
        70
        90.
```

This makes it easy to create tables. For example, to create a table that converts degrees to radians, enter

```
my_table = [degrees', radians']
```

which tells MATLAB® to create a matrix named my_table, in which column 1 is degrees and column 2 is radians:

```
my_table =
        10.0000 0.1745
        15.0000 0.2618
        70.0000 1.2217
        90.0000 1.5708
```

If you transpose a two-dimensional matrix, all the rows become columns and all the columns become rows. For example, the command

```
my_table'
```

results in

```
    10.0000    15.0000    70.0000    90.0000
     0.1745     0.2618     1.2217     1.5708.
```

Note that **my_table** is not a MATLAB® command, but merely a convenient variable name. We could have used any meaningful name, say, **conversions** or **degrees_to_radians**.

HINT

Although my_table is not a MATLAB function name, `table` is. Confirm this with the **which** command
```
which table
```
which returns the storage location of the table function file.
Do not use table as a variable name, because you will overwrite the table function. Use of the table function is covered in a later chapter.

EXAMPLE 2.2

MATRIX CALCULATIONS WITH SCALARS

Scientific data, such as data collected from wind tunnels, is usually in SI (Système International) units. However, much of the manufacturing infrastructure in the United States has been tooled in English (sometimes called American Engineering or American Standard) units. Engineers need to be fluent in both systems, and should be especially careful when sharing data with other engineers. Perhaps the most notorious example of unit confusion problems is the Mars Climate Orbiter (see Figure 2.8), which was the second flight of the Mars Surveyor Program. The spacecraft burned up in the orbit of Mars in September of 1999 because of a lookup table embedded in the craft's software. The table, probably generated

Figure 2.8
Climate Orbiter. (Courtesy of NASA/Jet Propulsion Laboratory.)

from wind-tunnel testing, used pounds force (lbf) when the program expected values in newtons (N).

In this example, we'll use MATLAB® to create a conversion table of pounds force to newtons. The table will start at 0 and go to 1000-lbf, at 100-lbf intervals. The conversion factor is

$$1 \text{ lbf} = 4.4482216 \text{ N}.$$

1. State the problem
   Create a table converting pounds force (lbf) to newtons (N).
2. Describe the input and output

   Input

   The starting value in the table is: 0 lbf
   The final value in the table is: 1000 lbf
   The increment between values is: 100 lbf
   The conversion from lbf to N is: 1 lbf = 4.4482216 N

   Output

   Table listing pounds force (lbf) and newtons (N)

3. Develop a hand example
   Since we are creating a table, it makes sense to check a number of different values. Choosing numbers for which the math is easy makes the hand example simple to complete, but still valuable as a check:

$$
\begin{aligned}
0 \quad &* \quad 4.4482216 = 0 \\
100 \quad &* \quad 4.4482216 = 444.82216 \\
1000 \quad &* \quad 4.4482216 = 4448.2216
\end{aligned}
$$

4. Develop a MATLAB® solution

```
clear, clc
lbf = [0:100:1000];
N = lbf * 4.44822;
[lbf',N']
ans =
  1.0e+003 *
```

(*continued*)

0	0
0.1000	0.4448
0.2000	0.8896
0.3000	1.3345
0.4000	1.7793
0.5000	2.2241
0.6000	2.6689
0.7000	3.1138
0.8000	3.5586
0.9000	4.0034
1.0000	4.4482

It is always a good idea to clear both the workspace and the command window before starting a new problem. Notice in the workspace window (see Figure 2.9) that lbf and **N** are 1×11 matrices, and that ans (which is where the table we created is stored) is an 11×2 matrix. The output from the first two commands was suppressed by adding a semicolon at the end of each line. It would be very easy to create a table with more entries by changing the increment to 10 or even to 1. Notice also that you'll need to multiply the results shown in the table by 1000 to get the correct answers. MATLAB® tells you that this is necessary directly above the table, where the common scale factor is shown.

5. Test the solution

Comparing the results of the MATLAB® solution with the hand solution shows that they are the same. Once we've verified that our solution works, it's easy to use the same algorithm to create other conversion tables. For instance, modify this example to create a table that converts newtons (N) to pounds force (lbf), with an increment of 10 N, from 0 N to 1000 N.

Figure 2.9
The MATLAB® workspace window shows the variables as they are created.

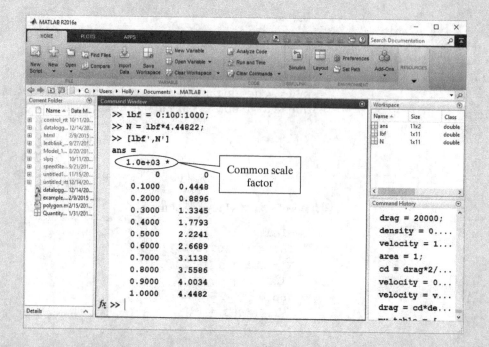

EXAMPLE 2.3

CALCULATING DRAG

One performance characteristic that can be determined in a wind tunnel is drag. The friction related to drag on the Mars Climate Observer (caused by the atmosphere of Mars) resulted in the spacecraft's burning up during course corrections. Drag is extremely important in the design of terrestrial aircraft as well (see Figure 2.10).

Drag is the force generated as an object, such as an airplane, moves through a fluid. Of course, in the case of a wind tunnel, air moves past a stationary model, but the equations are the same. Drag is a complicated force that depends on many factors. One factor is skin friction, which is a function of the surface properties of the aircraft, the properties of the moving fluid (air in this case), and the flow patterns caused by the shape of the aircraft (or, in the case of the Mars Climate Observer, by the shape of the spacecraft). Drag can be calculated with the drag equation

$$\text{drag} = C_d \frac{\rho V^2 A}{2}$$

where C_d = drag coefficient, which is determined experimentally, usually in a wind tunnel,
ρ = air density,
V = velocity of the aircraft, and
A = reference area (the surface area over which the air flows).

Although the drag coefficient is not a constant, it can be taken to be constant at low speeds (less than 200 mph). Suppose the following data were measured in a wind tunnel:

drag	20,000 N
ρ	$1 \times 10^{-6} \text{ kg/m}^3$
V	100 mph (you'll need to convert this to meters per second)
A	1 m²

Calculate the drag coefficient, and use this experimentally determined value to predict how much drag will be exerted on the aircraft at velocities from 0 mph to 200 mph.

Figure 2.10
Drag is a mechanical force generated by a solid object moving through a fluid.

Lift

Drag

Thrust

Weight

(continued)

1. State the problem
   Calculate the drag coefficient on the basis of the data collected in a wind tunnel. Use the drag coefficient to determine the drag at a variety of velocities.
2. Describe the input and output

   ### Input

Drag	20,000 N
Air density ρ	$1 \times 10^{-6}\,\text{kg/m}^3$
Velocity V	100 mph
Surface area A	$1\,\text{m}^2$

   ### Output

   Drag coefficient
   Drag at velocities from 0 to 200 mph

3. Develop a hand example
   First, find the drag coefficient from the experimental data. Notice that the velocity is in miles/h and must be changed to units consistent with the rest of the data (m/s). The importance of carrying units in engineering calculations cannot be overemphasized!

   $$C_d = \frac{\text{drag} \times 2}{\rho \times V^2 \times A}$$

   $$= \frac{(20{,}000\,\text{N} \times 2)}{1 \times 10^{-6}\,\text{kg/m}^3 \times \left(100\,\text{miles/h} \times 0.4470 \dfrac{\text{m/s}}{\text{miles/h}}\right)^2 \times 1\,\text{m}^2}$$

   $$= 2.0019 \times 10^7$$

   Since a newton is equal to a kg m/s², the drag coefficient is dimensionless. Now use the drag coefficient to find the drag at different velocities:

   $$\text{drag} = C_d \times \rho \times V^2 \times A/2$$

   Using a calculator, find the value of the drag with $V = 200$ mph:

   $$\text{drag} = \frac{2.0019 \times 10^7 \times 1 \times 10^{-6}\,\text{kg/m}^3 \times \left(200\,\text{miles/h} \times 0.4470 \dfrac{\text{m/s}}{\text{miles/h}}\right)^2 \times 1\,\text{m}^2}{2}$$

   $$\text{drag} = 80{,}000\,\text{N}$$

4. Develop a MATLAB® solution

   ```
   drag = 20000;
   density = 0.000001;
   velocity = 100*0.4470;
   area = 1;
   cd = drag*2/(density*velocity^2*area)
   cd =
     2.0019e+007
   velocity = 0:20:200;
   velocity = velocity*0.4470;
   ```

   Define the variables, and change V to SI units.

   Calculate the coefficient of drag.

   Redefine V as a matrix. Change it to SI units and calculate the drag.

```
drag = cd*density*velocity.^2*area/2;
my_table = [velocity', drag']
my_table =
1.0e+004 *
     0            0
     0.0009    0.0800
     0.0018    0.3200
     0.0027    0.7200
     0.0036    1.2800
     0.0045    2.0000
     0.0054    2.8800
     0.0063    3.9200
     0.0072    5.1200
     0.0080    6.4800
     0.0089    8.0000
```

Notice that the equation for drag, or

```
drag = cd * density * velocity.^2 * area/2;
```

uses the .^ operator, because we intend that each value in the matrix velocity be squared, not that the entire matrix velocity be multiplied by itself.
Using just the exponentiation operator (^) would result in an error message. We
could have used the .* operator as well in places where * was used, but since all
the other quantities are scalars it doesn't matter. Unfortunately, it is possible to
compose problems in which using the wrong operator does not give us an error
message, but does give us a wrong answer. This makes step 5 in our problem-
solving methodology especially important.

Figure 2.11
The command history
window creates a record of
previous commands.

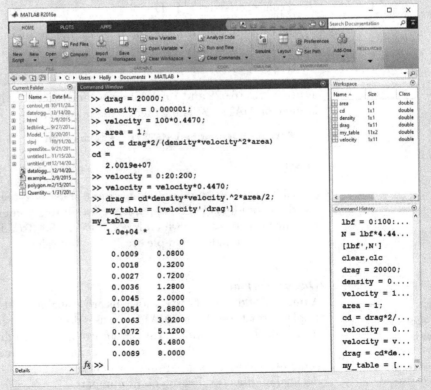

(continued)

5. Test the solution

Comparing the hand solution with the MATLAB® solution (see Figure 2.11), we see that they give the same results. Once we have confirmed that our algorithm works with sample data, we can substitute new data and be confident that the results will be correct. Ideally, the results should also be compared with experimental data, to confirm that the equations we are using accurately model the real physical process.

SCIENTIFIC NOTATION
A number represented as a value between one and ten times ten to an appropriate power

2.3.3 Number Display

Scientific Notation

Although you can enter any number in decimal notation, that isn't always the best way to represent very large or very small numbers. For example, a number that is used frequently in chemistry is Avogadro's constant, whose value, to four significant digits, is 602,200,000,000,000,000,000,000. Similarly, the diameter of an iron atom is approximately 140 picometers, which is 0.000000000140 m. Scientific notation expresses a value as a number between 1 and 10, multiplied by a power of 10 (the exponent). Thus, Avogadro's number becomes 6.022×10^{23}, and the diameter of an iron atom, 1.4×10^{-10} m. In MATLAB®, values in scientific notation are designated with an **e** between the decimal number and the exponent. (Your calculator probably uses similar notation.) For example, you might have

```
Avogadro's_constant = 6.022e23;
Iron_diameter = 140e-12; or
Iron_diameter = 1.4e-10.
```

It is important to omit blanks between the decimal number and the exponent. For instance, MATLAB® will interpret

```
6.022 e23
```

as two values (6.022 and 10^{23}). Since putting two values in an assignment statement is an error, MATLAB® will generate the message:

```
Error: Unexpected MATLAB® expression.
```

HINT

Although it is a common convention to use e to identify a power of 10, students (and teachers) sometimes confuse this nomenclature with the mathematical constant e, which is equal to 2.7183. To raise e to a power, use the `exp` function, for example `exp(3)` is equivalent to e^3.

Display Format

KEY IDEA
MATLAB® does not differentiate between integers and floating-point numbers, unless special functions are invoked.

A number of different display formats are available in MATLAB®. No matter which display format you choose, MATLAB® uses double-precision floating-point numbers in its calculations, which results in approximately 16 decimal digits of precision. Changing the display format does not change the accuracy of the results. Unlike some other computer programs, by default MATLAB® handles both integers and decimal numbers as floating-point numbers.

KEY IDEA
No matter what display format is selected, calculations are performed using double-precision floating-point numbers.

When elements of a matrix are displayed in MATLAB®, integers are always printed without a decimal point. However, values with decimal fractions are printed in the default short format that shows four digits after the decimal point. Thus,

```
A = 5
```

returns

```
A =
     5
```

but

```
A = 5.1
```

returns

```
A =
     5.1000
```

and

```
A = 51.1
```

returns

```
A =
     51.1000.
```

MATLAB® allows you to specify other formats that show additional digits. For example, to specify that you want values to be displayed in a decimal format with 15 digits after the decimal point, use the command

```
format long
```

which changes all subsequent displays. Thus, with `format long` specified,

```
A
```

now returns

```
A =
     51.100000000000001.
```

Notice that the final digit in this case is 1, which represents a round-off error. Two decimal digits are displayed when the format is specified as `format bank`:

```
A =
     51.10
```

The bank format displays only real numbers, so it's not appropriate when complex numbers need to be represented. Thus, the command

```
A = 5+3i
```

returns the following using bank format

```
A =
     5.00.
```

Using `format long` the same command returns

```
A =
     5.000000000000000 + 3.000000000000000i
```

You can return the format to four decimal digits with the command

format short.

To check the results, recall the value of **A**:

```
A
A =
      5.0000 + 3.0000i
```

When numbers become too large or too small for MATLAB® to display in the default format, it automatically expresses them in scientific notation. For example, if you enter Avogadro's constant into MATLAB® in decimal notation as

```
a = 602000000000000000000000
```

the program returns

```
a =
      6.0200e+023
```

You can force MATLAB® to display all numbers in scientific notation with format short e (with four decimal digits) or format long e (with 15 decimal digits). For instance,

```
format short e
x = 10.356789
```

returns

```
x =
      1.0357e+001.
```

Another pair of formats that are often useful to engineers and scientists, format short eng and format long eng, are similar to scientific notation but require the power of 10 to be a multiple of three. This corresponds to common naming conventions. For example:

$$1 \text{ millimeter} = 1 \times 10^{-3} \text{ meters}$$
$$1 \text{ micrometer} = 1 \times 10^{-6} \text{ meters}$$
$$1 \text{ nanometer} = 1 \times 10^{-9} \text{ meters}$$
$$1 \text{ picometer} = 1 \times 10^{-12} \text{ meters}$$

Consider the following example. First, change to engineering format and then enter a value for *y*.

```
format short eng
y = 12000
```

which gives the result

```
y =
      12.0000e+003.
```

When a matrix of values is sent to the screen, and if the elements become very large or very small, a common scale factor is often applied to the entire matrix. This scale factor is printed along with the scaled values. For example, when the command window is returned to

format short

the results from Example 2.3 are displayed as follows:

```
table =
1.0e+005 *
                    0              0
               0.0002         0.0400
               0.0004         0.1602
               0.0006         0.3603
               0.0008         0.6406     etc . . .
```

Two other formats that you may occasionally find useful are `format +` and `format rat`. When a matrix is displayed in `format +`, the only characters printed are plus and minus signs. If a value is positive, a plus sign will be displayed; if a value is negative, a minus sign will be displayed. If a value is zero, nothing will be displayed. This format allows us to view a large matrix in terms of its signs:

```
format +
B = [1, -5, 0, 12; 10005, 24, -10,4]
B =
        +- +
        ++-+
```

RATIONAL NUMBER
A number that can be represented as a fraction

The `format rat` command displays numbers as rational numbers (i.e., as fractions). Thus,

```
format rat
x = 0:0.1:0.5
```

returns

```
x =
    0    1/10    1/5    3/10    2/5    1/2.
```

KEY IDEA
The `format shortg` or `format longg` are the most popular formats used by engineers.

If you're not sure which format is the best for your application, you may select `format short g` or `format long g` (`format shortg` or `format longg` is an alternate syntax). This format selects the best of fixed-point or floating-point representations. Many people find this to be the most generally useful of the format styles, since it eliminates the use of the common multiplier.

The `format` command also allows you to control how tightly information is spaced in the command window. The default (`format loose`) inserts a line feed between user-supplied expressions and the results returned by the computer. The `format compact` command removes those line feeds. The examples in this text use the compact format to save space. Table 2.2 shows how the values of π and of 123.456 are displayed in each format.

If none of these predefined numeric display formats is right for you, you can control individual lines of output with the `fprintf` function, described in a later chapter.

2.4 SAVING YOUR WORK

Working in the command window is similar to performing calculations on your scientific calculator. When you turn off the calculator or when you exit the program, your work is gone. It *is* possible to save the *values* of the variables you defined in the command window and that are listed in the workspace window, but while doing

Table 2.2 Numeric Display Formats

MATLAB® Command	Display	Example
format short	4 decimal digits	**3.1416**
format long	14 decimal digits	**3.14159265358979**
format short e	4 decimal digits scientific notation	**3.1416e+000** **1.2346e+002**
format long e	14 decimal digits scientific notation	**3.141592653589793e+000** **1.234567890000000e+002**
format bank	2 decimal digits, only real values are displayed	**3.14**
format short eng	4 decimal digits engineering notation	**3.1416e+000** **123.4568e+000**
format long eng	14 decimal digits engineering notation	**3.141592653589793e+000** **123.456789000000e+000**
format +	+, −, blank	**+**
format rat	fractional form	**355/113**
format short g	MATLAB® selects the best format	**3.1416** **123.46**
format long g	MATLAB® selects the best format	**3.14159265358979** **123.456789**

so is useful, it is more likely that you will want to save the list of commands that generated your results. The `diary` command allows you to do just that. Also, we will show you how to save and retrieve variables (the results of the assignments you made and the calculations you performed) to MAT-files or to DAT-files. Finally, we'll introduce script M-files, which are created in the edit window and stored as M-files. Scripts allow you to save a list of commands and to execute them later. You will find scripts especially useful for solving homework problems. When you create a program in MATLAB®, it is stored as a script.

2.4.1 Diary

The diary function allows you to record a MATLAB® command window session in a file and retrieve it for later review. Both the MATLAB® commands and the results are stored—including all your mistakes. To activate the diary function simply type

    diary

or

    diary on

at the command prompt. To end a recording session, type `diary` again, or `diary off`. A file named *diary* should appear in the current folder. You can retrieve the file by double-clicking on the file name in the current folder window. An editor window will open with the recorded commands and results. You can also open the file in any text editor, such as Notepad. Subsequent sessions are added to the end of the file. If you prefer to store the diary session in a different file, specify the filename

    diary <filename>

or

```
diary('filename').
```

In this text, we'll use angle brackets ($<\ >$) to indicate user-defined names. Thus, to save a diary session in a file named **My_diary_file**, type

```
diary My_diary_file
```

or

```
diary('My_diary_file').
```

2.4.2 Saving Variables

To preserve the values stored in the variables you created in the command window (check the workspace window on the left-hand side of the MATLAB® screen for the list of variables), you must save the contents of the workspace window to a file. The default format is a binary file called a MAT-file. To save the workspace (remember, this is just the variables, not the list of commands in the command window) to a file, type

```
save <file_name>
```

at the prompt. Recall that, although `save` is a MATLAB® command, **file_name** is a user-defined file name. It can be any name you choose, as long as it conforms to the naming conventions for variables in MATLAB®. Actually, you don't even need to supply a file name. If you don't, MATLAB® names the file **matlab.mat**. You could also choose

```
Save Workspace
```

from the toolstrip, which will then prompt you to enter a file name for your data. To restore a workspace, type

```
load <file_name>.
```

Again, `load` is a MATLAB® command, but **file_name** is the user-defined file name. If you just type `load`, MATLAB® will look for the default **matlab.mat** file.

The file you save will be stored in the current folder.

For example, type

```
clear, clc.
```

This command will clear both the workspace and the command window. Verify that the workspace is empty by checking the workspace window or by typing

```
whos.
```

Now define several variables—for example,

```
a = 5;
b = [1, 2, 3];
c = [1, 2; 3, 4];
```

Check the workspace window once again to confirm that the variables have been stored. Now, save the workspace to a file called **my_example_file**:

```
save my_example_file
```

Confirm that a new file has been stored in the current folder. If you prefer to save the file to another directory (for instance, onto a flash drive), browse (see Figure 2.2) to the directory of your choice. Remember that in a public computer lab, the current folder is probably purged after each user logs off the system.

Now, clear the workspace and command window by typing

```
clear, clc.
```

The workspace window should be empty. You can recover the missing variables and their values by loading the file (**my_example_file.mat**) back into the workspace:

```
load my_example_file
```

The file you want to load must be in the current folder, or MATLAB® won't be able to find it. In the command window, type

```
a
```

which returns

```
a =
     5.
```

Similarly you can retrieve any of the variables now listed in the workspace window.

MATLAB® can also store individual matrices or lists of matrices into a file in the current folder with the command

```
save <file_name> <variable_list>
```

where **file_name** is the user-defined file name designating the location in memory at which you wish to store the information, and **variable_list** is the list of variables to be stored in the file. For example,

```
save my_new_file a b
```

would save just the variables a and b into **my_new_file.mat**.

ASCII
binary data storage format

If your saved data will be used by a program other than MATLAB® (such as C or C++), the .mat format is not appropriate, because .mat files are unique to MATLAB®. The ASCII format is standard between computer platforms, and is more appropriate if you need to share files. MATLAB® allows you to save files as ASCII files by modifying the save command to

```
save <file_name> <variable_list> -ascii.
```

The command -ascii tells MATLAB® to store the data in a standard eight-digit text format. ASCII files should be saved into a .dat file or .txt file instead of a .mat file; be sure to add the extension to your file name:

KEY IDEA
When you save the workspace, you save only the variables and their values; you do not save the commands you've executed.

```
save my_new_file.dat a b -ascii
```

If you don't add .dat, MATLAB® will default to .mat.
If more precision is needed, the data can be stored in a 16-digit text format:

```
save file_name variable_list -ascii -double
```

Figure 2.12
Double-clicking the file name in the command directory launches the Import Wizard.

You can retrieve the data from the current folder with the load command:

```
load <file_name>
```

For example, to create the matrix z and save it to the file **data_2.dat** in eight-digit text format, use the following commands:

```
z = [5 3 5; 6 2 3];
save data_2.dat z -ascii
```

Together, these commands cause each row of the matrix z to be written to a separate line in the data file. You can view the **data_2.dat** file by double-clicking the file name in the current folder window (see Figure 2.12). If your file contains a single array, the easiest way to retrieve data from an ASCII .dat file is to enter the **load** command followed by the file name. This causes the information to be read into a matrix with the same name as the data file. This won't work if your file contains multiple variables. However, it is quite easy to use MATLAB®'s interactive Import Wizard to load the data. When you double-click a data file name in the current folder to view the contents of the file, the Import Wizard will automatically launch. Just follow the directions to load the data into the workspace, with the same name as the data file. You can use this same technique to import data from other programs, including Excel spreadsheets, or you can select Import Data from the toolstrip.

2.4.3 Scripts

Using the command window for calculations is an easy and powerful tool. However, once you close the MATLAB® program, all of your calculations are gone. Fortunately, MATLAB® contains a powerful programming language. As a programmer, you can create and save code in files called scripts and stored as M-files. These files can be reused anytime you wish to repeat your calculations. An M-file is an ASCII text file similar to a C or FORTRAN source-code file. It can be created and edited with the MATLAB® editor/debugger (the edit window discussed in Section 2.2.7), or you can use another text editor of your choice. To open the editing window, select

```
New Script
```

from the MATLAB® toolstrip. The MATLAB® edit window is shown in Figure 2.13. Many programmers prefer to dock the editing window onto the MATLAB® desktop,

Figure 2.13
The MATLAB® edit window, also called the editor/debugger.

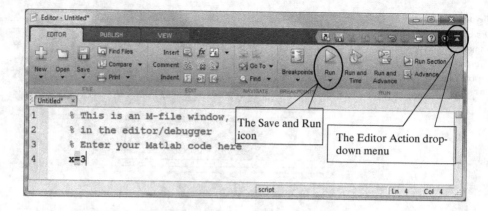

using the show window actions drop-down menu from the upper right-hand corner of the window (select dock editor). This allows you to see both the contents of the script and the results displayed when the program is executed. The results are displayed in the command window.

If you choose a different text editor, make sure that the files you save are ASCII files. Notepad is an example of a text editor that defaults to an ASCII file structure. Other word processors, such as WordPerfect or Word, will require you to specify the ASCII structure when you save the file. These programs default to proprietary file structures that are not ASCII compliant, and may yield some unexpected results if you try to use code written in them without specifying that the files be saved in ASCII format.

When you save a script, it is stored in the current folder. You'll need to name your file with a valid MATLAB® variable name—that is, a name starting with a letter and containing only letters, numbers, and the underscore (_). Spaces are not allowed (see Section 2.3.1).

SCRIPT
A list of MATLAB® commands stored in a separate file, also called an M-file

KEY IDEA
The two types of M-files are scripts and functions.

There are two types of M-files, called *scripts* and *functions*. A script M-file is simply a list of MATLAB® statements that are saved in a file with a .m file extension. The script can use any variables that have been defined in the workspace, and any variables created in the script are added to the workspace when the script executes. You can execute a script created in the MATLAB® edit window by selecting the **Save and Run** icon from the menu bar, as shown in Figure 2.13. (The **Save and Run** icon changed appearance with MATLAB® 7.5. Previous versions of the program used an icon similar to an exclamation point.) You can also execute a script by typing a file name, or by using the run command from the command window as shown in Table 2.3. No matter how you do it, you can only run a MATLAB program if it is in the current folder.

You can find out what M-files and MAT files are in the current folder by typing

`what`

into the command window. You can also browse through the current folder by looking in the current folder window.

Using scripts allows you to work on a project and to save the list of commands for future use. Because you will be using these files in the future, it is a good idea to sprinkle them liberally with comments. The comment operator in MATLAB® is the percentage sign, as in

`% This is a comment.`

MATLAB® will not execute any code on a commented line.

Table 2.3 Approaches to Executing a Script from the Command Window

MATLAB® Command	Comments
myscript	Type the file name, for example **myscript**. The .m file extension is assumed.
run myscript	Use the run command with the file name.
run('myscript')	Use the functional form of the run command.

You can also add comments after a command, but on the same line:

```
a = 5     %The variable a is defined as 5
```

Here is an example of MATLAB® code that could be entered into a script and used to solve Example 2.3:

```
clear, clc
% A Script to find Drag
% First define the variables
drag = 20000;                    %Define drag in Newtons
density = 0.000001;              %Define air density in kg/m^3
velocity = 100*0.4470;          %Define velocity in m/s
area = 1;                        %Define area in m^2
% Calculate coefficient of drag
cd = drag *2/(density*velocity^2*area)
% Find the drag for a variety of velocities
velocity = 0:20:200;             %Redefine velocity
velocity = velocity*0.4470       %Change velocity to m/s
drag = cd*density*velocity.^2*area/2;    %Calculate drag
table = [velocity',drag']        %Create a table of results
```

This code can be run either from the script (by clicking the **Save and Run** icon) or from the command window (by typing in the file name). The results will appear in the command window in either case, and the variables will be stored in the workspace. The advantage of an script is that you can save your program to run again later.

HINT

You can execute a portion of a script by highlighting a section and then right-clicking and selecting **Evaluate Section**. You can also comment or "uncomment" whole sections of code from this menu; doing so is useful when you are creating programs while you are still debugging your work.

Example 2.4 uses a script to find the velocity and acceleration that a spacecraft might reach in leaving the solar system.

EXAMPLE 2.4

CREATING A SCRIPT TO CALCULATE THE ACCELERATION OF A SPACECRAFT

In the absence of drag, the propulsion power requirements for a spacecraft are determined fairly simply. Recall from basic physical science that

$$F = ma$$

In other words, force (F) is equal to mass (m) times acceleration (a). Work (W) is force times distance (d), and since power (P) is work per unit time, power becomes force times velocity (v):

$$W = Fd$$

$$P = \frac{W}{t} = F \times \frac{d}{t} = F \times v = m \times a \times v$$

This means that the power requirements for the spacecraft depend on its mass, how fast it's going, and how quickly it needs to speed up or slow down. If no power is applied, the spacecraft just keeps traveling at its current velocity. As long as we don't want to do anything quickly, course corrections can be made with very little power. Of course, most of the power requirements for spacecraft are not related to navigation. Power is required for communication, for housekeeping, and for science experiments and observations.

The *Voyager 1* and *Voyager 2* spacecraft explored the outer solar system during the last quarter of the 20th century (see Figure 2.14). *Voyager 1* encountered both Jupiter and Saturn; *Voyager 2* not only encountered Jupiter and Saturn, but continued on to Uranus and Neptune. The *Voyager* program was enormously successful, and the *Voyager* spacecraft continue to gather information as they leave the solar system. The power generators (low-level nuclear reactors) on each spacecraft are expected to function until at least 2020. The power source is a sample of plutonium-238, which, as it decays, generates heat that is used to produce electricity. At the launch of each spacecraft, its generator produced about 470 watts of power. Because the plutonium

Figure 2.14
The *Voyager 1* and *Voyager 2* spacecraft were launched in 1977 and have since left the solar system. (NASA Headquarters)

is decaying, the power production had decreased to about 335 watts in 1997, almost 20 years after launch. This power is used to operate the science package, but if it were diverted to propulsion, how much acceleration would it produce in the spacecraft? *Voyager 1* is currently traveling at a velocity of 3.50 AU/year (an AU is an astronomical unit), and *Voyager 2* is traveling at 3.15 AU/year. Each spacecraft weighs 721.9 kg.

1. State the problem
   Find the acceleration that is possible with the power output from the spacecraft power generators.
2. Describe the input and output

   Input
   Mass = 721.9 kg
   Power = 335 watts = 335 J/s
   Velocity = 3.50 AU/year (*Voyager* 1)
   Velocity = 3.15 AU/year (*Voyager* 2)

   Output
   Acceleration of each spacecraft, in m/s/s

3. Develop a hand example
   We know that

   $$P = m \times a \times v$$

   which can be rearranged to give

   $$a = \frac{p}{m \times v}.$$

   The hardest part of this calculation will be keeping the units straight. First let's change the velocity to m/s. For *Voyager 1*,

   $$v = 3.50\frac{\text{AU}}{\text{year}} \times \frac{150 \times 10^9 \text{m}}{\text{AU}} \times \frac{\text{year}}{365 \text{ days}} \times \frac{\text{day}}{24 \text{ h}} \times \frac{\text{h}}{3600 \text{ s}} = 16.650 \text{ m/s}$$

   Then, we calculate the acceleration:

   $$a = \frac{335 \text{ J/s} \times 1 \text{ kg} \times \text{m}^2/\text{s}^2 \text{J}}{721.9 \text{ kg} \times 16.650 \text{ m/s}} = 2.7 \times 10^{-5} \text{ m/s}^2$$

4. Develop a MATLAB® solution

```
clear, clc
%Example 2.4
%Find the possible acceleration of the Voyager 1
%and Voyager 2 Spacecraft using the on board power
%generator
format shortg
mass=721.9;              %mass in kg
power=335;               %power in watts
velocity=[3.5 3.15];     %velocity in AU/year
%Change the velocity to m/sec
velocity=velocity*150e9/365/24/3600
%Calculate the acceleration
acceleration=power./(mass.*velocity)
```

(continued)

Figure 2.15

The results of a script execution are reported in the command window. The variables created are reflected in the workspace and the script is listed in the current folder window. The commands issued in the script are not mirrored in the command history.

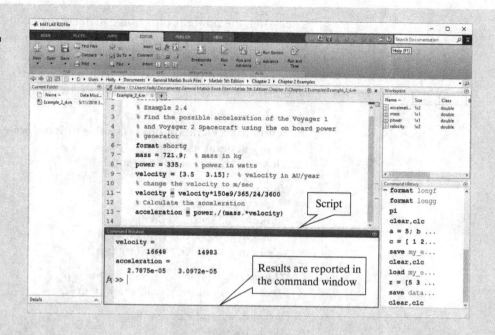

To evaluate the program, click the **Save and Run** icon. The results are printed in the command window, as shown in Figure 2.15.

5. Test the solution

Compare the MATLAB® results with the hand example results. Notice that the velocity and acceleration calculated from the hand example and the MATLAB® solution for *Voyager 1* match. The acceleration seems quite small, but applied over periods of weeks or months such an acceleration can achieve significant velocity changes. For example, a constant acceleration of 2.8×10^{-5} m/s² results in a velocity change of about 72 m/s over the space of a month:

$$2.8 \times 10^{-5} \text{ m/s}^2 \times 3600 \text{ s/h}$$
$$\times 24 \text{ h/day} \times 30 \text{ days/month} = 72.3 \text{ m/s}$$

Now that you have a MATLAB® program that works, you can use it as the starting point for other, more complicated calculations.

2.4.4 Section Mode

Section mode, also called cell mode is a utility that allows the user to divide scripts into sections, or cells, that can be executed one at a time. This feature is particularly useful as you develop MATLAB® programs.

KEY IDEA

Section mode allows you to execute portions of the code incrementally.

To divide your M-file program into sections, create section dividers by using a double percentage sign followed by a space. If you want to name the section, just add a name on the same line as the section divider:

`%% Section Name`

It's important to include the space after the double percentage sign (%%). If you don't, the line is recognized as a comment, not a section divider.

Figure 2.16
Section mode allows the user to execute one cell, or section, at a time.

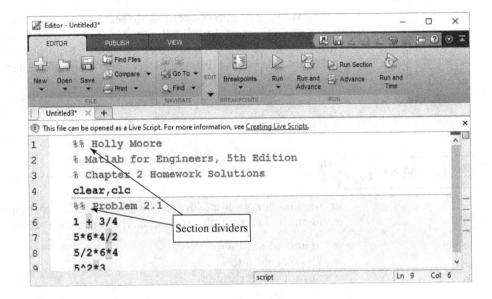

Figure 2.17
The Navigate drop-down menu lists all the sections in the M-file.

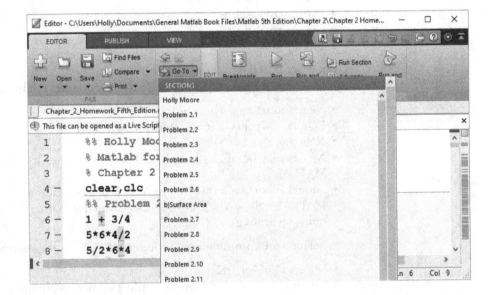

Once the section dividers are in place, if you position the cursor anywhere inside the section, the entire section turns pale yellow. For example, in Figure 2.16, the first four lines of the M-file program make up the first section. Now we can use the run icons on the editing tab of the toolstrip to evaluate a single section, evaluate the current section and move on to the next section, or evaluate the entire file. The Navigate menu lists all the sections in the M-file and allows you to jump to a particular section or function (functions are covered in another chapter), as shown in Figure 2.17.

Figure 2.16 shows the first few lines of a script written to solve some homework problems. By dividing the program into sections, it was possible to work on each problem separately.

Dividing a homework script into sections offers a big advantage to the person who must evaluate it. By using the `Run and Advance` function, the grader can step through the program one problem at a time. Even more important, the programmer can divide a complicated project into manageable sections and evaluate these sections independently.

SUMMARY

In this chapter, we introduced the basic MATLAB® structure. The MATLAB® environment includes multiple windows, three of which are open in the default view:

- Command window
- Workspace window
- Current folder window

In addition, the environment includes the following:

- Command history window
- Document window
- Graphics window
- Edit window

open as needed during a MATLAB® session.

Variables defined in MATLAB® follow common computer naming conventions:

- Names must start with a letter.
- Letters, numbers, and the underscore are the only characters allowed.
- Names are case sensitive.
- Names may be of any length, although only the first 63 characters are used by MATLAB®.
- Some keywords are reserved by MATLAB® and cannot be used as variable names.
- MATLAB® allows the user to reassign function names as variable names, although doing so is not good practice.

The basic computational unit in MATLAB® is the matrix. Matrices may be:

- Scalars (1×1 matrix)
- Vectors ($1 \times n$ or $n \times 1$ matrix, either a row or a column)
- Two-dimensional arrays ($m \times n$ or $n \times m$)
- Multidimensional arrays

Matrices often store numeric information, although they can store other kinds of information as well. Data can be entered into a matrix manually or can be retrieved from stored data files. When entered manually, a matrix is enclosed in square brackets, elements in a row are separated by either commas or spaces, and a new row is indicated by a semicolon:

```
a = [1 2 3 4; 5 6 7 8]
```

Evenly spaced matrices can be generated with the colon operator. Thus, the command

```
b = 0:2:10
```

creates a matrix starting at 0, ending at 10, and with an increment of 2. The `linspace` and `logspace` functions can be used to generate a matrix of specified length from given starting and ending values, spaced either linearly or logarithmically. The `help` function or the MATLAB® Help menu can be used to determine the appropriate syntax for these and other functions.

MATLAB® follows the standard algebraic order of operations.

MATLAB® supports both standard (decimal) and scientific notation. It also supports a number of different display options. No matter how values are displayed, they are stored as double-precision floating-point numbers.

MATLAB® variables can be saved or imported from either .mat or .dat files. The .mat format is proprietary to MATLAB® and is used because it stores data more efficiently than other file formats. The .dat format employs the standard ASCII format, and is used when data created in MATLAB® will be shared with other programs.

Collections of MATLAB® commands can be saved in script M-files. This is the best way to save the list of commands used to solve a problem so that they can be reused at a later time. Section mode allows the programmer to group code into sections and to run each section individually. It is especially convenient when one script is used to solve multiple problems.

MATLAB® SUMMARY

The following MATLAB® summary lists all the special characters, commands, and functions that were defined in this chapter:

Special Characters	
[ ]	forms matrices
( )	used in statements to group operations;
	used with a matrix name to identify specific elements
,	separates subscripts or matrix elements
;	separates rows in a matrix definition;
	suppresses output when used in commands
:	used to generate matrices;
	indicates all rows or all columns
+	assignment operator assigns a value to a memory location;
	not the same as an equality
%	indicates a comment
%%	section divider
+	scalar and array addition
−	scalar and array subtraction
*	scalar multiplication and multiplication in matrix algebra

Special Characters

.*	array multiplication (dot multiply or dot star)
/	scalar division and division in matrix algebra
./	array division (dot divide or dot slash)
^	scalar exponentiation and matrix exponentiation in matrix algebra
.^	array exponentiation (dot power or dot caret)

Commands and Functions

ans	default variable name for results of MATLAB® calculations
ascii	indicates that data should be saved in standard ASCII format
clc	clears command window
clear	clears workspace
diary	creates a copy of all the commands issued in the workspace window and most of the results
exit	terminates MATLAB®
format +	sets format to plus and minus signs only
format compact	sets format to compact form
format long	sets format to 14 decimal places
format long e	sets format to scientific notation with 14 decimal places
format long eng	sets format to engineering notation with 14 decimal places
format long g	allows MATLAB® to select the best format (either fixed point or floating point), using 14 decimal digits
format loose	sets format to the default, noncompact form
format short	sets format to the default, 4 decimal places
format short e	sets format to scientific notation with 4 decimal places
format short eng	sets format to engineering notation with 4 decimal places
format short g	allows MATLAB® to select the best format (either fixed point or floating point), using 4 decimal digits
format rat	sets format to rational (fractional) display
help	invokes help utility
linspace	linearly spaced vector function
load	loads matrices from a file
logspace	logarithmically spaced vector function
namelengthmax	Finds the maximum variable name length
pi	numeric approximation of the value of π
quit	terminates MATLAB®
save	saves variables in a file
who	lists variables in memory
whos	lists variables and their sizes

KEY TERMS

arguments
array
array editor
array operators
ASCII
assignment
section mode
command history
command window

current folder
document window
dot operators
edit window
function
graphics window
M-file
matrix
operator

prompt
scalar
scientific notation
script
toolstrip
transpose
vector
workspace

PROBLEMS

You can either solve these problems in the command window, using MATLAB® as an electronic calculator, or you can create a script of the solutions. If you are solving these problems as a homework assignment or if you want to keep a record of your work, the best strategy is to use a script, divided into sections with the section divider %%.

Getting Started

2.1 Predict the outcome of the following MATLAB® calculations:

$$1 + 3/4$$
$$5*6*4/2$$
$$5/2*6*4$$
$$5\wedge2*3$$
$$5\wedge(2*3)$$
$$1 + 3 + 5/5 + 3 + 1$$
$$(1 + 3 + 5)(5 + 3 + 1)$$

Check your results by entering the calculations into the command window.

Using Variables

2.2 Identify which name in each of the following pairs is a legitimate MATLAB® variable name:

fred	fred!
book_1	book-1
2ndplace	Second_Place
#1	No_1
vel_5	vel.5
tan	while

Test your answers by using `isvarname`—for example,

```
isvarname fred
```

Remember, isvarname returns a 1 if the name is valid, and a 0 if it is not. Although it is possible to reassign a function name as a variable name, doing so is not a good idea. Use which to check whether the preceding names are function names—for example,

which sin.

In what case would MATLAB® tell you that sin is a variable name, not a function name?

Scalar Operations and Order of Operations

2.3 Create MATLAB® code to perform the following calculations:

$$5^2$$

$$\frac{5+3}{5 \cdot 6}$$

$$\sqrt{4+6^3} \quad (\textit{Hint: A square root is the same thing as a 1/2 power.})$$

$$9\frac{6}{12} + 7 \cdot 5^{3+2}$$

$$1 + 5 \cdot 3/6^2 + 2^{2-4}/ \cdot 1/5.5$$

Check your code by entering it into MATLAB® and performing the calculations on your scientific calculator.

2.4 (a) The area of a circle is πr^2. Define r as 5, then find the area of a circle, using MATLAB®.

Figure P2.4(a)

(b) The surface area of a sphere is $4\pi r^2$. Find the surface area of a sphere with a radius of 10 ft.

(c) The volume of a sphere is $4/3\pi r^2$. Find the volume of a sphere with a radius of 2 ft.

2.5 (a) The area of a square is the edge length squared ($A = edge^2$). Define the edge length as 5, then find the area of a square, using MATLAB®.

(b) The surface area of a cube is 6 times the edge length squared ($SA = 6 \times edge^2$). Find the surface area of a cube with edge length 10.

(c) The volume of a cube is the edge length cubed ($V = edge^3$). Find the volume of a cube with edge length 12.

Figure P2.5(a–c)

2.6 Consider the barbell shown in Figure P2.6.

(a) Find the volume of the figure, if the radius of each sphere is 10 cm, the length of the bar connecting them is 15 cm, and the diameter of the bar is 1 cm. Assume that the bar is a simple cylinder.

(b) Find the surface area of the figure.

Figure P2.6
The geometry of a barbell can be modeled as two spheres and a cylindrical rod.

2.7 The ideal gas law was introduced in Example 2.1. It describes the relationship between pressure (P), temperature (T), volume (V), and the number of moles of gas (n).

$$PV = nRT$$

The additional symbol, R, represents the ideal gas constant. The ideal gas law is a good approximation of the behavior of gases when the pressure is low and the temperature is high. (What constitutes low pressure and high temperature varies with different gases.) In 1873, Johannes Diderik van der Waals, (see Figure P2.7) proposed a modified version of the ideal gas law that better models the behavior of real gases over a wider range of temperature and pressure.

$$\left(P + \frac{n^2 a}{V^2}\right)(V - nb) = nRT$$

In this equation, the additional variables a and b represent values characteristic of individual gases.

Use both the ideal gas law and van der Waals' equation to calculate the temperature of water vapor (steam), given the data in table P2.7.

Table P2.7 Steam Data

Pressure, P	220 bar
Moles, n	2 mol
Volume, V	1 L
a	5.536 L²bar/mol² *
b	0.03049 L/mol *
Ideal gas constant, R	0.08314472 L bar/K mol

Source: Weast, R. C. (Ed.), *Handbook of Chemistry and Physics* (53rd Edn.), Cleveland: Chemical Rubber Co., 1972.

Figure P2.7

Johannes Diderik van der Waals. (Bygone Collection/Alamy)

Figure P2.8(a)

Figure P2.8(b)

Array Operations

2.8 **(a)** The volume of a cylinder is $\pi r^2 h$. Define r as 3 and h as the matrix

    h = [1, 5, 12].

Find the volume of the cylinders (see Figure P2.8(a)).

(b) The area of a triangle is 1/2 the length of the base of the triangle, times the height of the triangle. Define the base as the matrix

    b = [2, 4, 6]

and the height h as 12, and find the area of the triangles (see Figure P2.8(b)).

(c) The volume of any right prism is the area of the base of the prism, times the vertical dimension of the prism. The base of the prism can be any shape—for example, a circle, a rectangle, or a triangle.

Find the volume of the prisms created from the triangles of part (b). Assume that the vertical dimension of these prisms is 6 (see Figure P2.8(c)).

base is   base is a   base is a
a circle   rectangle   triangle

Figure P2.8(c)

2.9 The response of circuits containing resistors, inductors, and capacitors depends upon the relative values of the resistors and the way they are connected. An important intermediate quantity used in describing the response of such circuits is s. Depending on the values of R, L, and C, the values of s will be either both real values, a pair of complex values, or a duplicated value.

Figure P2.9
Series circuit.

The equation that identifies the response of a particular series circuit (Figure P2.9) is

$$S = -\frac{R}{2L} \pm \sqrt{\left(\frac{R}{2L}\right)^2 - \frac{1}{LC}}.$$

(a) Determine the values of s for a resistance of 800 Ω.
(b) Create a vector of values for R ranging from 100 to 1000 Ω and evaluate s. Refine your values of R until you find the approximate size of resistor that yields a pure real value of s. Describe the effect on s as R increases in value.

Hint:
$1 \ \mu F = 1e - 6F$
$1 \ mH = 1e - 3H$

2.10 The equation that identifies the response parameter, s, of the parallel circuit shown in Figure P2.10 is

$$S = -\frac{1}{2RC} \pm \sqrt{\left(\frac{1}{2RC}\right)^2 - \frac{1}{LC}}.$$

(a) Determine the values of s for a resistance of 200 Ω.
(b) Create a vector of values for R ranging from 100 to 1000 Ω and evaluate s. Refine your values of R until you find the size of resistor that yields a pure real value of s. Describe the effect on s as R decreases.

Figure P2.10
Parallel circuit.

2.11 Burning one gallon of gasoline in your car produces 19.4 pounds of CO_2. Calculate the amount of CO_2 emitted during a year for the following vehicles, assuming they all travel 12,000 miles per year. The reported fuel-efficiency numbers shown in table P2.11 were extracted from the U.S. Department of Energy website, www.fueleconomy.gov, and reflect the combined city and highway estimates.

Table P2.11 Fuel Efficiency

2016	Smart Car FortwoEV	107 mpg
2016	Honda Civic	35 mpg
2016	Honda Fit	35 mpg
2016	Chevrolet Malibu (Hybrid)	46 mpg
2016	Toyota Prius (Hybrid)	56 mpg
2016	Toyota Yaris	32 mpg

2.12 **(a)** Create an evenly spaced vector of values from 1 to 20 in increments of 1.

(b) Create a vector of values from 0 to 2π in increments of $\pi/10$.

(c) Create a vector containing 15 values, evenly spaced between 4 and 20. (*Hint:* Use the `linspace` command. If you can't remember the syntax, type `help linspace`.)

(d) Create a vector containing 10 values, spaced logarithmically between 10 and 1000. (*Hint:* Use the `logspace` command.)

2.13 **(a)** Create a table of conversions from feet to meters. Start the feet column at 0, increment it by 1, and end it at 10 feet. (Look up the conversion factor in a textbook or online.)

(b) Create a table of conversions from radians to degrees. Start the radians column at 0 and increment by 0.1π radian, up to π radians. (Look up the conversion factor in a textbook or online.)

(c) Create a table of conversions from mi/h to ft/s. Start the mi/h column at 0 and end it at 100 mi/h. Print 15 values in your table. (Look up the conversion factor in a textbook or online.)

(d) The acidity of solutions is generally measured in terms of pH. The pH of a solution is defined as $-\log_{10}$ of the concentration of hydronium ions. Create a table of conversions from concentration of hydronium ion to pH, spaced logarithmically from 0.001 to 0.1 mol/liter with 10 values. Assuming that you have named the concentration of hydronium ions `H_conc`, the syntax for calculating the negative of the logarithm of the concentration (and thus the pH) is

```
pH = -log10(H_conc).
```

2.14 The general equation for the distance that a freely falling body has traveled (neglecting air friction) is

$$d = \frac{1}{2}gt^2.$$

Assume that $g = 9.8$ m/s^2. Generate a table of time versus distance traveled for values of time from 0 to 100 seconds. Choose a suitable increment for your time vector. (*Hint:* Be careful to use the correct operators; t^2 is an array operation!)

2.15 In direct current applications, electrical power is calculated using Joule's law as

$$P = VI$$

where

P is power in watts,

V is the potential difference, measured in volts,

I is the electrical current, measured in amperes, and

Joule's law can be combined with Ohm's law

$$V = IR$$

to give

$$P = I^2 R$$

where R is resistance measured in ohms.

The resistance of a conductor of uniform cross section (a wire or rod for example) is

$$R = \rho \frac{l}{A}$$

where

ρ is the electrical resistivity measured in ohm-meters,

l is the length of the wire, and

A is the cross-sectional area of the wire.

This results in the equation for power

$$P = I^2 \rho \frac{l}{A}.$$

Electrical resistivity is a material property that has been tabulated for many materials. For example,

Material	Resistivity, ohm-meters (measured at 20°C)
Silver	1.59×10^{-8}
Copper	1.68×10^{-8}
Gold	2.44×10^{-8}
Aluminum	2.82×10^{-8}
Iron	1.0×10^{-7}

Calculate the power that is dissipated through a wire with the following dimensions for each of the materials listed.

diameter   0.001 m

length   2.00 m

Assume the wire carries a current of 120 amps.

2.16 Repeat the previous problem for 10 wire lengths, from 1 m to 1 km. Use logarithmic spacing.

2.17 Newton's law of universal gravitation tells us that the force exerted by one particle on another is

$$F = G \frac{m_1 m_2}{r^2}$$

where the universal gravitational constant G is found experimentally to be

$$G = 6.673 \times 10^{-11} \text{ N m}^2/\text{kg}^2$$

The mass of each particle is m_1 and m_2, respectively, and r is the distance between the two particles. Use Newton's law of universal gravitation to find the force exerted by the earth on the moon, assuming that

the mass of the earth is approximately 6×10^{24} kg,
the mass of the moon is approximately 7.4×10^{22} kg, and
the earth and the moon are an average of 3.9×10^{8} m apart.

2.18 We know that the earth and the moon are not always the same distance apart. Based on the equation in the previous problem, find the force the moon exerts on the earth for 10 distances between 3.8×10^{8} m and 4.0×10^{8} m. Be careful to use the correct operator when you do the division.

2.19 Recall from Problem 2.7 that the ideal gas law is

$$PV = nRT$$

and that the Van der Waals modification of the ideal gas law is

$$\left(P + \frac{n^2 a}{V^2}\right)(V - nb) = nRT.$$

Using the data from Problem 2.7, find the value of temperature (T), for
(a) Ten values of pressure from 0 bar to 400 bar for volume of 1 L.
(b) Ten values of volume from 0.1 L to 10 L for a pressure of 220 bar.

Number Display

2.20 Create a matrix **a** equal to $[-1/3, 0, 1/3, 2/3]$, and use each of the built-in format options to display the results:

```
format short (which is the default)
format long
format bank
format short e
format long e
format short eng
format long eng
format short g
format long g
format +
format rat
```

Saving Your Work in Files

2.21 • Create a matrix called **D_to_R** composed of two columns, one representing degrees, and the other representing the corresponding value in radians. Any value set will do for this exercise.
• Save the matrix to a file called **degrees.dat**.
• Once the file is saved, clear your workspace then load the data from the file back into MATLAB®.

2.22 Create a script M-file and use it to do the homework problems you've been assigned from this chapter. Your file should include appropriate comments to identify each problem and to describe your calculation process. Don't forget to include your name, the date, and any other information your instructor requests. Divide the script into convenient sections, using section dividers.

3

Built-In MATLAB® Functions

Objectives

After reading this chapter, you should be able to:

- Use a variety of common mathematical functions.
- Understand and use trigonometric functions in MATLAB®.
- Compute and use statistical and data analysis functions.

- Generate uniform and Gaussian random-number matrices.
- Understand the computational limits of MATLAB®.
- Recognize and be able to use the special values and functions built into MATLAB®.

INTRODUCTION

The vast majority of engineering computations require quite complicated mathematical functions, including logarithms, trigonometric functions, and statistical analysis functions. MATLAB® has an extensive library of built-in functions to allow you to perform these calculations easily.

KEY IDEA
Most of the MATLAB® function names are the same as those used in other computer programs.

3.1 USING BUILT-IN FUNCTIONS

Many of the names for MATLAB®'s built-in functions are the same as those defined not only in the C programming language, but in Fortran and Java as well. For example, to take the square root of the variable x, we type

```
b = sqrt(x).
```

A big advantage of MATLAB® is that function arguments can generally be either scalars or matrices. In our example, if x is a scalar, a scalar result is returned. Thus, the statement

```
x = 9;
b = sqrt(x)
```

returns a scalar:

```
b =
       3
```

However, the square-root function, `sqrt`, can also accept matrices as input. In this case, the square root of each element is calculated, so

```
x = [4, 9, 16];
b = sqrt(x)
```

returns

```
b =
    2   3   4.
```

All functions can be thought of as having three components: a name, an input, and an output. In the preceding example, the name of the function is `sqrt`, the required input (also called the *argument*) goes inside the parentheses and can be a scalar or a matrix, and the output is a calculated value or values. In this example, the output was assigned the variable name `b`.

ARGUMENT
Input to a function

Some functions require multiple inputs. For example, the remainder function, `rem`, requires two inputs: a dividend and a divisor. We represent this as `rem(x, y)`, so

```
rem(10,3)
```

calculates the remainder of 10 divided by 3:

```
ans =
         1
```

The `size` function is an example of a function that returns two outputs, which are stored in a single array. It determines the number of rows and columns in a matrix. Thus,

```
d = [1, 2, 3; 4, 5, 6];
f = size(d)
```

returns the 1×2 result matrix

```
f =
    2       3.
```

You can also assign variable names to each of the answers by representing the left-hand side of the assignment statement as a matrix. For example,

```
[rows,cols] = size(d)
```

gives

```
rows =
          2
cols =
          3.
```

A useful feature of the more recent versions of MATLAB® is the adaptive help capability. As you type a function name, a screen tip appears showing the correct function format. It also includes a link to the function's help page.

NESTING
Using one function as the input to another

You can create more complicated expressions by nesting functions. For instance,

```
g = sqrt(sin(x))
```

finds the square root of the sine of whatever values are stored in the matrix named x. If x is assigned a value of 2,

```
x = 2;
```

the result is

```
g =
      0.9536.
```

Nesting functions can result in some complicated MATLAB® code. Be sure to include the arguments for each function inside their own set of parentheses. Often, your code will be easier to read if you break nested expressions into two separate statements. Thus,

```
a = sin(x);
g = sqrt(a)
```

gives the same result as `g = sqrt(sin(x))` and is easier to follow.

HINT

You can probably *guess* the name and syntax for many MATLAB® functions. However, check to make sure that the function of interest is working the way you assume it is, before you do any important calculations.

3.2 USING THE HELP FEATURE

MATLAB® includes extensive help tools, which are especially useful in understanding how to use functions. There are two ways to get help from within MATLAB®: a command-line help function `help`, which is fairly limited; and an HTML-based set of documentation accessed with the `doc` function. You can also open the HTML-based documentation by selecting **Help** from the toolstrip or by using the **F1** function key. You should use both help options, since they provide different information and insights into how to use a specific function.

To use the command-line help function, type `help` in the command window:

```
help
```

KEY IDEA
Use the help function to help you use MATLAB®'s built-in functions.

A list of help topics will appear:

```
HELP topics:

MATLAB\general    - General-purpose commands
MATLAB\ops        - Operators and special characters
MATLAB\lang       - Programming language constructs
MATLAB\elmat      - Elementary matrices and matrix
                    manipulation
MATLAB\elfun      - Elementary math functions
MATLAB\specfun    - Specialized math functions
```

and so on

To get help on a particular topic, type `help <topic>`. (Angle brackets, < and >, identify where you should type your input; they are not included in your actual MATLAB® statement.)

For example, to get help on the `tangent` function, type

help tan.

The following should be displayed:

```
tan             Tangent of argument in radians.
  tan(X) is the tangent of the elements of X.
See also atan, atan2, tand, atan2d.
```

To use the windowed help screen, select **Help → Documentation** from the toolstrip. A windowed version of the help list will appear, which includes access to documentation for all of the MATLAB® products you have installed on your computer (see Figure 3.1). You can then navigate to the appropriate topic. To access this version of the help utility directly from the command window, type `doc <topic>`. Thus, to access the windowed help for tangent, type

doc tan.

The contents of the two methods for getting help on a function are different. If your question isn't immediately answered by whichever method you try first, it's often useful to try the other technique.

You will find browsing through the windowed help utility extremely useful. First, select MATLAB® from the Help opening window, which opens the interactive MATLAB® documentation. On the left is the table of contents, which can either be expanded or minimized as needed. The main screen includes links to a list of topics, organized by category. You can use these links to find out what MATLAB® functions are available to solve many problems. For example, you might want to round a number you've calculated. To use the MATLAB® help window to determine whether an appropriate MATLAB® function is available, expand the `Mathematics` link and select `Elementary Math`, which lists rounding as a topic under the heading "Arithmetic" (see Figure 3.2). Selecting Arithmetic generates a function list, including a whole category devoted to rounding functions, with a brief description of their use. For example, `round` rounds to the nearest decimal or integer, depending on the input. (see Figure 3.3).

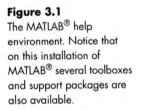

Figure 3.1
The MATLAB® help environment. Notice that on this installation of MATLAB® several toolboxes and support packages are also available.

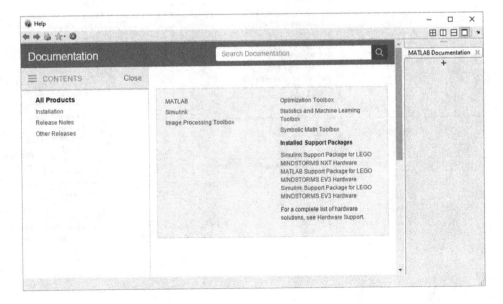

Figure 3.2
The MATLAB® help window. Mathematics and Elementary Math have been selected.

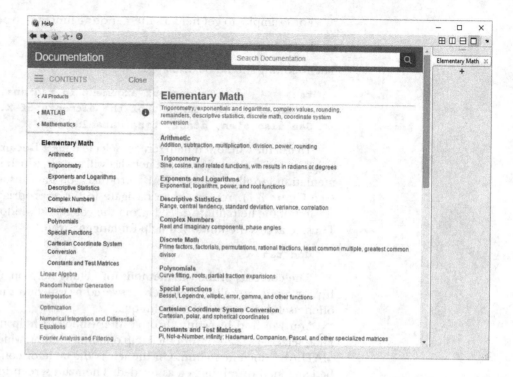

Figure 3.3
The Arithmetic help window.

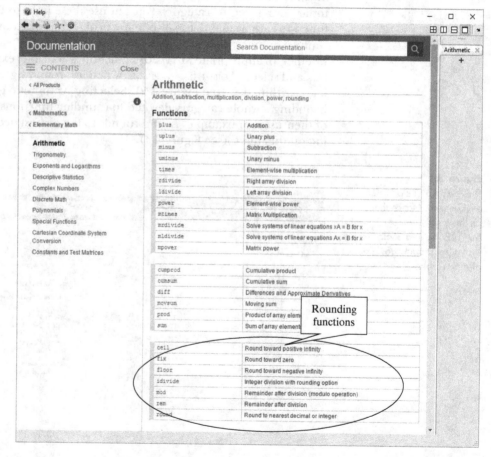

PRACTICE EXERCISE 3.1

1. Use the `help` command in the command window to find the appropriate syntax for the following functions:
   a. `cos`
   b. `sqrt`
   c. `exp`
2. Use the windowed help function from the menu bar to learn about the functions in Exercise 1.
3. Access the windowed help information for the functions in Exercise 1 using the `doc` function from the command window.

KEY IDEA

Most functions accept scalars, vectors, or matrices as input.

3.3 ELEMENTARY MATH FUNCTIONS

Elementary math functions include logarithms, exponentials, absolute value, rounding functions, and functions used in discrete mathematics.

3.3.1 Common Computations

The functions listed in Table 3.1 accept either a scalar or a matrix of x values.

HINT

As a rule, the function `log` in all computer languages means the `natural logarithm`. Although not the standard in mathematics textbooks, it *is* the standard in computer programming. Not knowing this distinction is a common source of errors, especially for new users. If you want logarithms to the base 10, you'll need to use the `log10` function. A `log2` function is also included in MATLAB®, but logarithms to any other base will need to be computed; there is no general logarithm function that allows the user to input the base.

PRACTICE EXERCISE 3.2

Consult Table 3.1 for the appropriate function to solve the following problems. The correct answers can be found on the Pearson website.

1. Create a vector **x** from -2 to $+2$ with an increment of 1. Your vector should be

$$\mathbf{x} = [-2, -1, 0, 1, 2].$$

   a. Find the absolute value of each member of the vector.
   b. Find the square root of each member of the vector.
2. Find the square root of both -3 and $+3$.
   a. Use the `sqrt` function.
   b. Use the `nthroot` function. (You should get an error statement for -3.)

  c. Raise -3 and $+3$ to the $1/2$ power (Don't forget parentheses around -3). How do the results vary?

3. Create a vector **x** from -9 to 12 with an increment of 3.
  a. Find the result of **x** divided by 2.
  b. Find the remainder of **x** divided by 2.

4. Using the vector from Exercise 3, find e^x.

5. Using the vector from Exercise 3:
  a. Find $\ln(\mathbf{x})$ (the natural logarithm of **x**).
  b. Find $\log_{10}(\mathbf{x})$ (the common logarithm of **x**). Explain your results.

6. Use the `sign` function to determine which of the elements in vector **x** are positive.

7. Change the `format` to `rat`, and display the value of the **x** vector divided by 2.

(Don't forget to change the format back to `format short` or `format shortg` when you are done with this exercise set.)

HINT

The mathematical notation and MATLAB® syntax for raising e to a power are not the same. To raise e to the third power, the mathematical notation would be e^3. However, the MATLAB® syntax is `exp(3)`. Students also sometimes confuse the syntax for scientific notation with exponentials. The number 5e3 should be interpreted as 5×10^3.

Table 3.1 Common Math Functions

`abs(x)`	Finds the absolute value of **x**.	`abs(-3)` `ans = 3`
`sqrt(x)`	Finds the square root of **x**.	`sqrt(85)` `ans = 9.2195`

`nthroot(x,n)`	Finds the real nth root of **x**. This function will not return complex results. Thus,
	  (−2)^(1/3)
	does not return the same result, yet both answers are legitimate third roots of -2.
		`nthroot(-2,3)`
		`ans = -1.2599`
		
		`(-2)^(1/3)`
		`ans = 0.6300 - 1.0911 i`

`sign(x)`	Returns a value of [&|minus|~futurabk~1~normal~&] if **x** is less than zero, a value of 0 if **x** equals zero, and a value of +1 if **x** is greater than zero.	`sign(-8)` `ans = -1`
`rem(x,y)`	Computes the remainder of **x/y**.	`rem(25,4)` `ans = 1`
`exp(x)`	Computes the value of e^x, where e is the base for natural logarithms, approximately 2.7183.	`exp(10)` `ans = 2.2026e + 004`
`log(x)`	Computes ln(**x**), the natural logarithm of **x** (to the base e).	`log(10)` `ans = 2.3026`
`log10(x)`	Computes $\log_{10}$(**x**), the common logarithm of **x** (to the base 10).	`log10(10)` `ans = 1`

| EXAMPLE 3.1 |

USING THE CLAUSIUS–CLAPEYRON EQUATION

Meteorologists study the atmosphere in an attempt to understand and ultimately predict the weather (see Figure 3.4). Weather prediction is a complicated process, even with the best data. Meteorologists study chemistry, physics, thermodynamics, and geography, in addition to specialized courses about the atmosphere.

One equation used by meteorologists is the Clausius–Clapeyron equation, which is usually introduced in chemistry classes and examined in more detail in advanced thermodynamics classes. Rudolf Clausius and Emile Clapeyron were physicists responsible for the early development of thermodynamic principles during the mid-1800s (see Figure 3.5(a) and 3.5(b)).

In meteorology, the Clausius–Clapeyron equation is employed to determine the relationship between saturation water-vapor pressure and the atmospheric temperature. The saturation water-vapor pressure can be used to calculate relative humidity, an important component of weather prediction, when the actual partial pressure of water in the air is known.

The Clausius–Clapeyron equation is

$$\ln\left(\frac{P^0}{6.11}\right) = \left(\frac{\Delta H_v}{R_{\text{air}}}\right) \times \left(\frac{1}{273} - \frac{1}{T}\right).$$

Figure 3.4
View of the earth's weather from space. (NASA Headquarters)

Figure 3.5(a)
Rudolf Clausius. (bilwissedition Ltd. & Co. KG/Alamy)

Figure 3.5(b)
Emile Clapeyron. (SPL/Science Source)

(a)

(b)

(continued)

where

P^0 = saturation water-vapor pressure, in mbar, at temperature T,
ΔH_v = latent heat of vaporization for water, 2.453×10^6 J/kg,
R_{air} = gas constant for moist air, 461 J/kg, and
T = temperature in kelvins (K).

It is rare that temperatures on the surface of the earth are lower than $-60°F$ or higher than 120°F. Use the Clausius–Clapeyron equation to find the saturation vapor pressure for temperatures in this range. Present your results as a table of Fahrenheit temperatures and saturation vapor pressures.

1. State the problem
   Find the saturation vapor pressure at temperatures from $-60°F$ to 120°F, using the Clausius–Clapeyron equation.
2. Describe the input and output

   Input

   $$\Delta H_v = 2.453 \times 10^6 \text{ J/kg}$$
   $$R_{air} = 461 \text{ J/kg}$$
   $$T = -60°F \text{ to } 120°F$$

   As the number of temperature values was not specified, we'll choose to recalculate every 10°F.

   Output

   Saturation vapor pressures.

3. Develop a hand example
   The Clausius–Clapeyron equation requires that all the variables have consistent units. This means that temperature (T) needs to be in kelvins. To change degrees Fahrenheit to kelvins, we use the conversion equation

   $$T_k = \frac{(T_f + 459.6)}{1.8}.$$

   (There are many places to find unit conversions. The Internet is one source, as are science and engineering textbooks.)
   Now we need to solve the Clausius–Clapeyron equation for the saturation vapor pressure P^0. We have

   $$\ln\left(\frac{P^0}{6.11}\right) = \left(\frac{\Delta H_v}{R_{air}}\right) \times \left(\frac{1}{273} - \frac{1}{T}\right)$$

   $$P^0 = 6.11 \times e^{\left(\left(\frac{\Delta H_v}{R_{air}}\right) \times \left(\frac{1}{273} - \frac{1}{T}\right)\right)}.$$

   Next, we solve for one temperature—for example, $T = 0°F$. As the equation requires temperature in kelvins, we must perform the unit conversion to obtain

   $$T = \frac{(0 + 459.6)}{1.8} = 255.3333 \text{ K}.$$

   Finally, we substitute values to get

   $$P^0 = 6.11 \times e^{\left(\left(\frac{2.453 \times 10^6}{461}\right) \times \left(\frac{1}{273} - \frac{1}{255.3333}\right)\right)} = 1.5836 \text{ mbar}.$$

4. **Develop a MATLAB® solution**

Create the MATLAB® solution in an M-file, and then run it in the command environment:

```
%Example 3.1
%Using the Clausius–Clapeyron Equation, find the
%saturation vapor pressure for water at different
%temperatures

TempF= [-60:10:120];        %Define temp matrix in F
TempK=(TempF + 459.6)/1.8;  %Convert temp to K
Delta_ H=2.45e6;            %Define latent heat of
                            %vaporization

R_air = 461;                %Define ideal gas constant for air
%Calculate the vapor pressures
Vapor_Pressure=6.11*exp((Delta_H/R_air)*(1/273 - 1./TempK));
%Display the results in a table
my_results = [TempF',Vapor_Pressure']
```

When you create a MATLAB® program, it is a good idea to comment liberally (lines beginning with %). This makes your program easier for others to understand, and may make it easier for you to "debug." Notice that most of the lines of code end with a semicolon, which suppresses the output. Therefore, the only information that displays in the command window is the table `my_results`:

```
my_results =
  -60.0000      0.0698
  -50.0000      0.1252
  -40.0000      0.2184
  ...
  120.0000      118.1931
```

5. **Test the solution**

Compare the MATLAB® solution when $T = 0°F$ with the hand solution:

Hand solution: $P^0 = 1.5888$ mbar
MATLAB® solution: $P^0 = 1.5888$ mbar

The Clausius–Clapeyron equation can be used for more than just humidity problems. By changing the values of ΔH and R, you could generalize the program to deal with any condensing vapor.

3.3.2 Rounding Functions

MATLAB® contains functions for a number of different rounding techniques (see Table 3.2). You are probably most familiar with rounding to the closest integer; however, you may want to round either up or down, depending on the situation.

For example, suppose you want to buy apples at the grocery store. The apples cost \$0.52 apiece. You have \$5.00. How many apples can you buy? Mathematically,

$$\frac{\$5.00}{\$0.52/\text{apple}} = 9.6154 \text{ apples.}$$

Table 3.2 Rounding Functions

`round(x)`	Rounds **x** to the nearest integer.	`round(8.6)` `ans = 9`
`round(x,N)`	Rounds **x** to a specified decimal digit	`round(8.6436, 3)` `ans = 8.644`

`fix(x)`	Rounds (or truncates) **x** to the nearest integer toward zero. Notice that 8.6 truncates to 8, not 9, with this function.	`fix(8.6)`
		`ans = 8`
		`fix(-8.6)`
		`ans = -8`

`floor(x)`	Rounds **x** to the nearest integer toward negative infinity.	`floor(-8.6)` `ans = -9`
`ceil(x)`	Rounds **x** to the nearest integer toward positive infinity.	`ceil(-8.6)` `ans = -8`

But clearly, you can't buy part of an apple, and the grocery store won't let you round to the nearest number of apples. Instead, you need to round down. The MATLAB® function to accomplish this is `fix`. Thus,

```
fix(5/0.52)
```

returns the maximum number of apples you can buy:

```
ans =
    9.
```

3.3.3 Discrete Mathematics

Discrete mathematics is the mathematics of whole numbers. MATLAB® includes functions to factor numbers, find common denominators and multiples, calculate factorials, and explore prime numbers (see Table 3.3). All of these functions require integer scalars as input. In addition, MATLAB® includes the `rats` function, which expresses a floating-point number as a rational number—that is, a fraction.

A factorial is the product of all the positive integers from 1 to a given value. Thus 3 factorial (indicated in mathematics textbooks as 3!) is $3 \times 2 \times 1 = 6$. Many problems involving probability can be solved with factorials. For example, the number of ways that five cards can be arranged is $5 \times 4 \times 3 \times 2 \times 1 = 5! = 120$. When you select the first card, you have five choices; when you select the second card, you have only four choices remaining, then three, two, and one. This approach is called combinatorial mathematics, or combinatorics. To calculate a factorial in MATLAB® use the factorial function. Thus,

```
factorial(5)
ans =
    120
```

gives the same result as

```
5*4*3*2*1
ans =
    120.
```

The value of a factorial quickly becomes very large. 10 factorial is 3,628,800. MATLAB® can handle up to 170! Anything larger gives `Inf` for an answer, because the maximum value for a real number that can be expressed in MATLAB® is exceeded.

Table 3.3 Functions Used in Discrete Mathematics

`factor(x)`	Finds the prime factors of **x**.	`factor(12)` `ans = 2 2 3`
`gcd(x,y)`	Finds the greatest common denominator of **x** and **y**.	`gcd(10,15)` `ans = 5`

`lcm(x,y)`	Finds the least common multiple of **x** and **y**.	`lcm(2,5)`
		`ans = 10`
		`lcm(2,10)`
		`ans = 10`

`rats(x)`	Represents **x** as a fraction.	`rats(1.5)` `ans = 3/2`
`factorial(x)`	Finds the value of **x** factorial (**x**!). A factorial is the product of all the integers less than **x**. For example, $6! = 6 \times 5 \times 4 \times 3 \times 2 \times 1 = 720$	`factorial(6)` `ans = 720`
`nchoosek(n,k)`	Finds the number of possible combinations of k items from a group of n items. For example, use this function to determine the number of possible subgroups of 3 chosen from a group of 10.	`nchoosek(10,3)` `ans = 120`
`primes(x)`	Finds all the prime numbers less than **x**.	`primes(10)` `ans = 2 3 5 7`

`isprime(x)`	Checks to see if **x** is a prime number. If it is, the function returns 1; if not, it returns 0.	`isprime(7)`
		`ans = 1`
		`isprime(10)`
		`ans = 0`

```
factorial(170)
        ans =
        7.2574e+306
factorial(171)
        ans =
                Inf
```

Factorials are used to calculate the number of permutations and combinations of possible outcomes. A permutation is the number of subgroups that can be formed when sampling from a larger group, *when the order matters.* Consider the following problem. How many different teams of two people can you form from a group of four? Assume that the order matters, since for this problem the first person chosen is the group leader. If we represent each person as a letter, the possibilities are as follows:

AB	BA	CA	DA
AC	BC	CB	DB
AD	BD	CD	DC

For the first member of the team, there are four choices, and for the second, there are three choices, so the number of possible teams is $4 \times 3 = 12$. We could also express this as 4!/2!. More generally, if you have a large group to choose from, call the group size n, and the size of the subgroup (team) m. Then the possible number of permutations is

$$\frac{n!}{(n-m)!}.$$

If there are 100 people to choose from, the number of teams of 2 (where order matters) is

$$\frac{100!}{(100-2)!} = 9900.$$

But, what if the order doesn't matter? In this case, team AB is the same as team BA, and we refer to all the possibilities as combinations instead of permutations. The possible number of combinations is

$$\frac{n!}{(n-m)! \times m!}.$$

Although you could use MATLAB®'s factorial function to calculate the number of combinations, the nchoosek function will do it for you, and it offers some advantages when using larger numbers. If we want to know the number of possible teams of 2, chosen from a pool of 100 (100 choose 2),

```
nchoosek(100,2)
ans =
    4950.
```

The nchoosek function allows us to calculate the number of combinations even if the pool size is greater than 170, which would not be possible using the factorial approach.

```
nchoosek(200,2)
ans =
    19900
        factorial(200)/(factorial(198)*factorial(2))
        ans =
            NaN
```

HINT

Although the exclamation point (!) is used in mathematics to indicate taking a factorial, it is not a MATLAB® operator. Use the factorial function instead.

PRACTICE EXERCISE 3.3

The correct answers can be found on the Pearson website.

1. Factor the number 322.
2. Find the greatest common denominator of 322 and 6.
3. Is 322 a prime number?
4. How many primes occur between 0 and 322?
5. Approximate π as a rational number.
6. Find 10! (10 factorial).
7. Find the number of possible groups containing 3 people from a group of 20, when order does not matter (20 choose 3).

3.4 TRIGONOMETRIC FUNCTIONS

MATLAB® includes a complete set of the standard trigonometric functions and the hyperbolic trigonometric functions. As is standard in most computer languages and in common mathematics usage, most of these functions assume that angles are expressed in radians. To convert radians to degrees or degrees to radians, we need to take advantage of the fact that π radians equals 180 degrees:

$$\text{degrees} = \text{radians}\left(\frac{180}{\pi}\right) \text{ and radians} = \text{degrees}\left(\frac{\pi}{180}\right)$$

KEY IDEA

Most trig functions require input in radians.

The MATLAB® code to perform these conversions is

```
degrees = radians * 180/pi;
radians = degrees * pi/180;
```

With the revised 2015b edition, MATLAB® also includes functions to convert from degrees to radians (deg2rad) or radians to degrees (rad2deg). For example, to convert pi radians to degrees, use

```
rad2deg(pi)
ans =
      180.
```

Similarly to convert 90 degrees to radians use

```
deg2rad(90)
ans =
      1.5708.
```

To carry out these calculations, we need the value of π, so a constant, pi, is built into MATLAB®. However, since π cannot be expressed exactly as a floating-point number, the constant pi in MATLAB® is only an approximation of the mathematical quantity π. Usually this is not important; however, you may notice some surprising results. For example, for

```
sin(pi)
ans =
      1.2246e-016
```

when you expect an answer of zero.

MATLAB® also includes a set of trigonometric functions that accept the angle in degrees so that you need not do the conversion to radians. These include sind, cosd, and tand.

You may access the help function from the toolstrip for a complete list of trigonometric functions available in MATLAB®. Table 3.4 shows some of the more common ones.

HINT

Math texts often use the notation $\sin^{-1}(x)$ to indicate an inverse sine function, also called an arcsine. Students are often confused by this notation and try to create parallel MATLAB® code. Note, however, that

```
a = sin^-1(x)
```

is *not* a valid MATLAB® statement but instead should be

```
a = asin(x).
```

Table 3.4 Some of the Available Trigonometric Functions

`deg2rad`	Converts degrees to radians.	`deg2rad(90)` `ans = 1.5708`
`rad2deg`	Converts radians to degrees.	`rad2deg(pi)` `ans = 180`
`sin(x)`	Finds the sine of **x** when **x** is expressed in radians.	`sin(0)` `ans = 0`
`cos(x)`	Finds the cosine of **x** when **x** is expressed in radians.	`cos(pi)` `ans = -1`

`tan(x)`	Finds the tangent of **x** when **x** is expressed in radians.	`tan(pi)`
		`ans = -1.2246`
		`e-016`

`asin(x)`	Finds the arcsine, or inverse sine, of **x**, where **x** must be between −1 and 1. The function returns an angle in radians between $\pi/2$ and $-\pi/2$.	`asin(-1)` `ans = -1.5708`
`sinh(x)`	Finds the hyperbolic sine of **x** when **x** is expressed in radians.	`sinh(pi)` `ans = 11.5487`
`asinh(x)`	Finds the inverse hyperbolic sin of **x**.	`asinh(1)` `ans = 0.8814`
`sind(x)`	Finds the sin of **x** when **x** is expressed in degrees.	`sind(90)` `ans = 1`
`asind(x)`	Finds the inverse sin of **x** and reports the result in degrees.	`asind(1)` `ans = 90`

PRACTICE EXERCISE 3.4

Calculate the following (remember that mathematical notation is not necessarily the same as MATLAB® notation). The correct answers can be found on the Pearson website.

1. $\sin(2\theta)$ for $\theta = 3\pi$.
2. $\cos(\theta)$ for $0 \le \theta \le 2\pi$; let θ change in steps of 0.2π.
3. $\sin^{-1}(1)$.
4. $\cos^{-1}(x)$ for $-1 \le x \le 1$; let x change in steps of 0.2.
5. Find the cosine of 45°.
   a. Convert the angle from degrees to radians, and then use the **cos** function.
   b. Use the **cosd** function.
6. Find the angle whose sine is 0.5. Is your answer in degrees or radians?
7. Find the cosecant of 60. You may have to use the help function to find the appropriate syntax.

EXAMPLE 3.2

USING TRIGONOMETRIC FUNCTIONS

A basic calculation in engineering is finding the resulting force on an object that is being pushed or pulled in multiple directions. Adding up forces is the primary calculation performed in both statics and dynamics classes. Consider a balloon that is acted upon by the forces shown in Figure 3.6.

To find the net force acting on the balloon, we need to add up the force due to gravity, the force due to buoyancy, and the force due to the wind. One approach is to

Gravity

Wind

Buoyancy

Figure 3.6
Force balance on a
balloon.

find the force in the x direction and the force in the y direction for each individual force, and then to recombine them into a final result.

The forces in the x and y directions can be found by trigonometry:

F = total force
F_x = force in the x direction
F_y = force in the y direction

We know from trigonometry that the sine is the opposite side over the hypotenuse, so

$$\sin(\theta) = \frac{F_y}{F}$$

and therefore,

$$F_y = F\sin(\theta).$$

Similarly, since the cosine is the adjacent side over the hypotenuse,

$$F_x = F\cos(\theta).$$

We can add up all the forces in the x direction and all the forces in the y direction, and use these totals to find the resulting force:

$$F_{x\,\text{total}} = \sum F_{xi} \quad F_{y\,\text{total}} = \sum F_{yi}$$

To find the magnitude and angle for F_{total}, we use trigonometry again. The tangent is the opposite side over the adjacent side. Therefore,

$$\tan(\theta) = \frac{F_{y\,\text{total}}}{F_{x\,\text{total}}}.$$

We use an inverse tangent to write

$$\theta = \tan^{-1}\left(\frac{F_{y\,\text{total}}}{F_{x\,\text{total}}}\right).$$

(The inverse tangent is also called the *arctangent*, which you may see on your scientific calculator as atan.)

Once we know θ, we can find F_{total}, using either the sine or the cosine. We have

$$F_{x\,\text{total}} = F_{\text{total}}\cos(\theta).$$

Rearranging terms gives

$$F_{\text{total}} = \frac{F_{x\,\text{total}}}{\cos(\theta)}.$$

Now consider again the balloon shown in Figure 3.6. Assume that the force due to gravity on this particular balloon is 100 N, pointed downward. Assume further that the buoyant force is 200 N, pointed upward. Finally, assume that the wind is pushing on the balloon with a force of 50 N, at an angle of 30° from the horizontal.

Find the resulting force on the balloon.

1. State the problem
   Find the resulting force on a balloon. Consider the forces due to gravity, buoyancy, and the wind.

(continued)

2. Describe the input and output
Input

Force	Magnitude	Direction
Gravity	100 N	−90
Buoyancy	200 N	+90
Wind	50 N	+30

Output

We'll need to find both the magnitude and the direction of the resulting force.
3. Develop a hand example
First, find the *x* and *y* components of each force and sum the components:

Force	Horizontal Component	Vertical Component
Gravity	$F_x = F\cos(\theta)$ $F_x = 100\cos(-90°) = 0$ N	$F_y = F\sin(\theta)$ $F_y = 100\sin(-90°) = -100$ N
Buoyancy	$F_x = F\cos(\theta)$ $F_x = 200\cos(+90°) = 0$ N	$F_y = F\sin(\theta) =$ $F_y = 200\sin(+90°) = +200$ N
Wind	$F_x = F\cos(\theta)$ $F_x = 50\cos(+30°) = 43.301$ N	$F_y = F\sin(\theta)$ $F_y = 50\sin(+30°) = +25$ N
Sum	$F_{x\,total} = 0 + 0 + 43.301$ $= 43.301$ N	$F_{y\,total} = -100 + 200 + 25$ $= 125$ N

Find the resulting angle:

$$\theta = \tan^{-1}\left(\frac{F_{y\,total}}{F_{x\,total}}\right)$$

$$\theta = \tan^{-1}\frac{125}{43.301} = 70.89°$$

Find the magnitude of the total force:

$$F_{total} = \frac{F_{x\,total}}{\cos(\theta)}$$

$$F_{total} = \frac{43.301}{\cos(70.89°)} = 132.29 \text{ N}$$

4. Develop a MATLAB® solution
One solution is

```
%Example 3_2
clear, clc
%Define the input
Force =[100, 200, 50];
theta = [-90, + 90, + 30];
%convert angles to radians
theta = theta*pi/180;
%Find the x components
ForceX = Force.*cos(theta);
%Sum the x components
ForceX_total = sum(ForceX);
```

```
%Find and sum the y components in the same step
ForceY_total = sum(Force.*sin(theta));
%Find the resulting angle in radians
result_angle = atan(ForceY_total/ForceX_total);
%Find the resulting angle in degrees
result_degrees = result_angle*180/pi
%Find the magnitude of the resulting force
Force_total = ForceX_total/cos(result_angle)
```

which returns

```
result_degrees = 70.8934
Force_total = 132.2876
```

Notice that the values for the force and the angle were entered into an array. This makes the solution more general. Notice also that the angles were converted to radians. In the program listing, the output from all but the final calculations was suppressed. However, while developing the program, we left off the semicolons so that we could observe the intermediate results.

5. Test the solution

Compare the MATLAB® solution with the hand solution. Now that you know it works, you can use the program to find the resultant of multiple forces. Just add the additional information to the definitions of the force vector *Force* and the angle vector *theta*. Note that we assumed a two-dimensional world in this example, but it would be easy to extend our solution to forces in all three dimensions.

3.5 DATA ANALYSIS FUNCTIONS

Analyzing data statistically in MATLAB® is particularly easy, partly because whole data sets can be represented by a single matrix, and partly because of the large number of built-in data analysis functions.

3.5.1 Maximum and Minimum

Table 3.5 lists functions that find the minimum and maximum in a data set, and the element at which those values occur.

Table 3.5 Maxima and Minima

`max(x)`	Finds the largest value in a **vector x**. For example, if $x = [1\ 5\ 3]$, the maximum value is 5.	`x = [1, 5, 3];`
		`max(x)`
		`ans = 5`

	Creates a row vector containing the maximum element from each column "of a **matrix x**. For example, if $x = \begin{bmatrix} 1 & 5 & 3 \\ 2 & 4 & 6 \end{bmatrix}$, then the maximum value in column 1 is 2, the maximum value in column 2 is 5, and the maximum value in column 3 is 6.	`x = [1, 5, 3; 2, 4, 6];`
		`max(x)`
		`ans = 2    5    6`

(continued)

Table 3.5 Maxima and Minima (Continued)

[a,b] = max(x)	Finds both the largest value in a **vector x** and its location in vector **x**. For x = [1 5 3] the maximum value is named **a** and is equal to 5. The location of the maximum value is element 2 and is named **b**.	x = [1, 5, 3]; [a,b] = max(x) a = 5 b = 2
	Creates a row vector containing the maximum element from each column of a matrix **x** and returns a row vector with the location of the maximum in each column of matrix **x**. For example, if $= \begin{bmatrix} 1 & 5 & 3 \\ 2 & 4 & 6 \end{bmatrix}$, then the maximum value in column 1 is 2, the maximum value in column 2 is 5, and the maximum value in column 3 is 6. These maxima occur in row 2, row 1, and row 2, respectively.	x = [1, 5, 3; 2, 4, 6]; [a,b] = max(x) a = 2 5 6 b = 2 1 2

max(x,y)	Creates a matrix the same size as **x** and **y**. (Both **x** and **y** must have the same number of rows and columns.) Each element in the resulting matrix contains the maximum value from the corresponding positions in **x** and **y**. For example, if $x = \begin{bmatrix} 1 & 5 & 3 \\ 2 & 4 & 6 \end{bmatrix}$ and $y = \begin{bmatrix} 10 & 2 & 4 \\ 1 & 8 & 7 \end{bmatrix}$, then the resulting matrix will be $x = \begin{bmatrix} 10 & 5 & 4 \\ 2 & 8 & 7 \end{bmatrix}$.	x = [1, 5, 3; 2, 4, 6];
		y = [10,2,4; 1, 8, 7];
		max(x,y)
		ans = 10 5 4
		    2 8 7

min(x)	The syntax for the min function is the same as that for the max function, except that minimums are returned.	

All of the functions in this section work on the *columns* in two-dimensional matrices. MATLAB® is column dominant—in other words, if there is a choice to make, MATLAB® will choose columns first over rows. If your data analysis requires you to evaluate data in rows, the easiest approach is to transpose the data matrix. (In other words, the rows must become columns and the columns must become rows.) The transpose operator is a single quote ('). For example, if you want to find the maximum value in each *row* of the matrix

$$x = \begin{bmatrix} 1 & 5 & 3 \\ 2 & 4 & 6 \end{bmatrix}$$

use the command

```
max(x')
```

which returns

```
ans=
    5 6.
```

Another approach to solving this same problem is to specify the dimension to be analyzed. Since MATLAB is column dominant, columns are specified as dimension 1 and rows are specified as dimension 2. The dimension must be entered in the third input field in the max function. Since most commonly the second field is not used, this requires a place-holder. Thus, to find the maximum in each row of the x matrix,

```
max(x,[],2)
```

returns

```
ans =
```
$$5$$
$$6.$$

HINT

A common mistake when finding the maximum or minimum value in a data set is to name the result max or min. This overwrites the function, and the function is no longer available for calculations. For example,

```
max = max(x)
```

results in a variable named max for the answer. This is allowable MATLAB® code, but is not wise. Trying to use the max function later in the program will result in an error. For example,

```
another_max = max(y)
```

will return

```
??? Index exceeds matrix dimensions
```

PRACTICE EXERCISE 3.5

The correct answers can be found on the Pearson website. Consider the following matrix:

$$x = \begin{bmatrix} 4 & 90 & 85 & 75 \\ 2 & 55 & 65 & 75 \\ 3 & 78 & 82 & 79 \\ 1 & 84 & 92 & 93 \end{bmatrix}$$

1. What is the maximum value in each column?
2. In which row does that maximum occur?
3. What is the maximum value in each row? (You'll have to transpose the matrix to answer this question or specify the dimension number.)
4. In which column does the maximum occur?
5. What is the maximum value in the entire table?

MEAN
The average of all the values in the data set

MEDIAN
The middle value in a data set

3.5.2 Mean and Median

There are several ways to find the "average" value in a data set. In statistics, the *mean* of a group of values is probably what most of us would call the average. The mean is the sum of all the values, divided by the total number of values. Another kind of average is the *median*, or the middle value. There are an equal number of values both larger and smaller than the median. The *mode* is the value that appears most often in a data set. MATLAB® provides functions for finding the mean, median, and the mode, as shown in Table 3.6. Recall that all of these functions are column dominant, and will return an answer for each column in a two-dimensional matrix. As is true with the max and min functions, you can specify the dimension of interest to determine these function values based on rows. The dimension is specified in the second field, unlike the max and min functions where it is specified in the third field.

Table 3.6 Averages

`mean(x)`	Computes the mean value (or average value) of a **vector x**. For example, if $x = [1\ 5\ 3]$, the mean value is 3.	`x = [1, 5, 3];`
		`mean(x)`
		`ans = 3.0000`

	Returns a row vector containing the mean value from each column of a **matrix x**. For example, if $x = \begin{bmatrix} 1 & 5 & 3 \\ 2 & 4 & 6 \end{bmatrix}$, then the mean value of column 1 is 1.5, the mean value of column 2 is 4.5, and the mean value of column 3 is 4.5.	`x = [1, 5, 3; 2, 4, 6];`
		`mean(x)`
		`ans = 1.5    4.5    4.5`

`median(x)`	Finds the median of the elements of a **vector x**. For example, if $x = [1\ 5\ 3]$, the median value is 3.	`x = [1, 5, 3];`
		`median(x)`
		`ans = 3`

	Returns a row vector containing the median value from each column of a **matrix x**. For example, if $x = \begin{bmatrix} 1 & 5 & 3 \\ 2 & 4 & 6 \\ 3 & 8 & 4 \end{bmatrix}$, then the median value from column 1 is 2, the median value from column 2 is 5, and the median value from column 3 is 4.	`x = [1, 5, 3;`
		`2, 4, 6;`
		`3, 8, 4];`
		`median(x)`
		`ans = 2    5    4`

`mode(x)`	Finds the value that occurs most often in an array. Thus, for the array $x = [1, 2, 3, 3]$ the mode is 3.	`x = [1, 2, 3, 3]`
		`mode(x)`
		`ans = 3`

PRACTICE EXERCISE 3.6

The correct answers can be found on the Pearson website. Consider the following matrix:

$$x = \begin{bmatrix} 4 & 90 & 85 & 75 \\ 2 & 55 & 65 & 75 \\ 3 & 78 & 82 & 79 \\ 1 & 84 & 92 & 93 \end{bmatrix}$$

1. What is the mean value in each column?
2. What is the median for each column?
3. What is the mean value in each row?
4. What is the median for each row?
5. What is returned when you request the mode?
6. What is the mean for the entire matrix?

3.5.3 Sums and Products

Often it is useful to add up (sum) all of the elements in a matrix, or to multiply all of the elements together. MATLAB® provides a number of functions to calculate both sums and products, as shown in Table 3.7.

In addition to simply adding up all the elements, which returns a single value for each column in the array, the cumsum function (cumulative sum) adds all of

Table 3.7 Sums and Products

sum(x)	Sums the elements in **vector x**. For example, if $x = [1\ 5\ 3]$, the sum is 9.	```x = [1, 5, 3];```
		 ```sum(x)```
		 ```ans = 9```

	Computes a row vector containing the sum of the elements in each column of a **matrix x**. For example, if $x = \begin{bmatrix} 1 & 5 & 3 \\ 2 & 4 & 6 \end{bmatrix}$, then the sum of column 1 is 3, the sum of column 2 is 9, and the sum of column 3 is 9.	```x = [1, 5, 3; 2, 4, 6];```
		 ```sum(x)```
		 ```ans = 3 9 9```

prod(x)	Computes the product of the elements of a **vector x**. For example, if $x = [1\ 5\ 3]$, the product is 15.	```x = [1, 5, 3];```
		 ```prod(x)```
		 ```ans = 15```

	Computes a row vector containing the product of the elements in each column of a **matrix x**. For example, if $x = \begin{bmatrix} 1 & 5 & 3 \\ 2 & 4 & 6 \end{bmatrix}$, then the product of column 1 is 2, the product of column 2 is 20, and the product of column 3 is 18.	```x = [1, 5, 3; 2, 4, 6];```
		 ```prod(x)```
		 ```ans = 2 20 18```

cumsum(x)	Computes a vector of the same size as, and containing cumulative sums of the elements of, a **vector x**. For example, if $x = [1\ 5\ 3]$, the resulting vector is $x = [169]$.	```x = [1, 5, 3];```
		 ```cumsum(x)```
		 ```ans = 1 6 9```

	Computes a matrix containing the cumulative sum of the elements in each column of a **matrix x**. For example, if $x = \begin{bmatrix} 1 & 5 & 3 \\ 2 & 4 & 6 \end{bmatrix}$, the resulting matrix is $x = \begin{bmatrix} 1 & 5 & 3 \\ 3 & 9 & 9 \end{bmatrix}$.	```x = [1, 5, 3; 2, 4, 6];```
		 ```cumsum(x)```
		 ```ans = 1 5 3```
		 ``` 3 9 9```

cumprod(x)	Computes a vector of the same size as, and containing cumulative products of the elements of, a **vector x**. For example, if $x = [1\ 5\ 3]$, the resulting vector is $x = [1\ 5\ 15]$.	```x = [1, 5, 3];```
		 ```cumprod(x)```
		 ```ans = 1 5 15```

	Computes a matrix containing the cumulative product of the elements in each column of a **matrix x**. For example, if $x = \begin{bmatrix} 1 & 5 & 3 \\ 2 & 4 & 6 \end{bmatrix}$, the resulting matrix is $x = \begin{bmatrix} 1 & 5 & 3 \\ 2 & 20 & 18 \end{bmatrix}$.	```x = [1, 5, 3; 2, 4, 6];```
		 ```cumprod(x)```
		 ```ans = 1 5 3```
		 ``` 2 20 18```

the previous elements in an array and creates a new array of these intermediate totals. This is useful when dealing with the sequences of numbers in a series. Consider the harmonic series

$$\sum_{k=1}^{n} \frac{1}{k}$$

which is equivalent to

$$\frac{1}{1} + \frac{1}{2} + \frac{1}{3} + \frac{1}{4} + \cdots + \frac{1}{n}.$$

We could use MATLAB® to create a sequence representing the first five values in the sequence as follows

```
k = 1:5;
sequence = 1./k
```

which gives us

```
sequence =
   1.0000    0.5000    0.3333    0.2500    0.2000.
```

We could view the series as a sequence of fractions by changing the format to rational with the following code

```
format rat
sequence =
      1      1/2      1/3      1/4      1/5.
```

Now we could use the cumsum function to find the value of the entire series for values of n from 1 to 5

```
format short
series = cumsum(sequence)
series =
   1.0000    1.5000    1.8333    2.0833    2.2833.
```

Similarly, the cumprod function finds the cumulative product of a sequence of numbers stored in an array.

3.5.4 Sorting Values

Table 3.8 lists several commands to sort data in a matrix into ascending or descending order. For example, if we define an array **x**

$$x = [1\ 6\ 3\ 9\ 4]$$

we can use the sort function to rearrange the values.

```
sort(x)
ans =
   1    3    4    6    9
```

The default is ascending order, but adding the string 'descend' to the second field will force the function to list the values in descending order.

```
sort(x, 'descend')
ans =
   9    6    4    3    1
```

You can also use the sort command to rearrange entire matrices. This function is consistent with other MATLAB® functions, and sorts based on columns. Each column will be sorted independently. Thus,

$$x = [1\ 3;\ 10\ 2;\ 3\ 1;\ 82\ 4;\ 5\ 5]$$

Table 3.8 Sorting Functions

Function	Description	Example
sort(x)	Sorts the elements of a vector **x** in ascending order. For example, if $x = [1\ 5\ 3]$, the resulting vector is $x = [1\ 3\ 5]$.	x = [1,5,3]; sort(x) ans = 1 3 5
	Sorts the elements in each column of a matrix **x** in ascending order. For example, if $x = \begin{bmatrix} 1 & 5 & 3 \\ 2 & 4 & 6 \end{bmatrix}$, the resulting matrix is $x = \begin{bmatrix} 1 & 5 & 3 \\ 2 & 4 & 6 \end{bmatrix}$.	x = [1,5,3; 2,4,6]; sort(x) ans = 1 4 3 2 5 6
sort(x,'descend')	Sorts the elements in each column in descending order.	x = [1,5,3; 2,4,6]; sort(x,'descend') ans = 2 5 6 1 4 3

sortrows(x)	Sorts the rows in a matrix in ascending order on the basis of the values in the first column, and keeps each row intact. For example, if $x = \begin{bmatrix} 1 & 5 & 3 \\ 2 & 4 & 6 \\ 3 & 8 & 4 \end{bmatrix}$, then using the sortrows command will move the middle row into the top position. The first column defaults to the basis for sorting.	x = [3,1,3; 1,9,3;
		4, 3, 6]
		sortrows(x)
		ans = 1 9 3
		    3 1 2
		    4 3 6

sortrows(x,n)	Sorts the rows in a matrix on the basis of the values in column n. If n is negative, the values are sorted in descending order. If n is not specified, the default column used as the basis for sorting is column 1.	sortrows(x,2)
		ans = 3 1 2
		    4 3 6
		    1 9 3

gives the following:

```
x =
     1    3
    10    2
     3    1
    82    4
     5    5.
```

When we sort the array

    sort(x)

each column is sorted in ascending order.

```
ans =
     1    1
     3    2
     5    3
    10    4
    82    5
```

The sortrows function allows you to sort entire rows, based on the value in a specified column. Thus,

    sortrows(x,1)

sorts based on the first column, but maintains the relationship between values in columns one and two.

```
ans =
    1    3
    3    1
    5    5
   10    2
   82    4
```

Similarly, you can sort based on values in the second column.

```
sortrows(x,2)
ans =
    3    1
   10    2
    1    3
    2    4
    5    5
```

These functions are particularly useful in analyzing data. Consider the results of the Men's 2014 Olympic 1000 meter speed skating event shown in Table 3.9.

Table 3.9 2014 Olympic Speed Skating Times

Skater Number	Time (min)
1	68.89
2	68.74
3	68.86
4	68.39
5	68.43

The skaters were given a random number for this illustration, but once the race is over we'd like to sort the table in ascending order, based on the times in the second column.

```
skating_results = [1    68.89
                   2    68.74
                   3    68.86
                   4    68.39
                   5    68.43]

sortrows(skating_results,2)
ans =

    4    68.39
    5    68.43
    2    68.74
    3    68.86
    1    68.89
```

As you may remember, the winning time was posted by Stefan Groothuis of the Netherlands, who in our example, is skater number 4.

The `sortrows` function can also sort in descending order, but it uses a different syntax from the `sort` function. To sort in descending order, place a minus sign in front of the column number used for sorting. Thus,

`sortrows(skating_results, -2)`

sorts the array in descending order, based on the second column. The result of this command is

```
ans =
     1      68.89
     3      68.86
     2      68.74
     5      68.43
     4      68.39.
```

3.5.5 Determining Matrix Size

MATLAB® offers three functions (see Table 3.10) that allow us to determine how big a matrix is: `size`, `length`, and `numel`. The `size` function returns the number of rows and columns in a matrix. The `length` function returns the larger of the matrix dimensions. The `numel` function returns the total number of elements in a matrix. For example, if

```
x = [1 2 3; 4 5 6];
size(x);
```

MATLAB® returns the following result:

```
ans =
     2      3
```

This tells us that the **x** array has two rows and three columns. However, if we use the `length` function

```
length(x)
```

the result is

```
ans =
     3
```

Table 3.10 Size Functions

`size(x)`	Determines the number of rows and columns in matrix **x**. (If **x** is a multidimensional array, `size` determines how many dimensions exist and how big they are.)	`x = [1,5,3; 2,4,6];`
		`size(x)`
		`ans = 2 3`

`[a,b] = size(x)`	Determines the number of rows and columns in matrix **x** and assigns the number of rows to **a** and the number of columns to **b**.	`[a,b] =`
		`size(x)`
		`a = 2`
		`b = 3`

`length(x)`	Determines the largest dimension of a matrix **x**.	`x = [1,5,3; 2,4,6];`
		`length(x)`
		`ans = 3`

`numel(x)`	Determines the total number of elements in a matrix **x**.	`x = [1,5,3; 2,4,6];`
		`numel(x)`
		`ans = 6`

because the largest of the array dimensions is 3.

Finally, if we use the `numel` function

    numel(x)

the result is

    ans =
        6.

The `length` function is particularly useful when used with a loop structure, since it can easily determine how many times to execute the loop—based on the dimensions of an array.

PRACTICE EXERCISE 3.7

The correct answers can be found on the Pearson website. Consider the following matrix:

$$x = \begin{bmatrix} 4 & 90 & 85 & 75 \\ 2 & 55 & 65 & 75 \\ 3 & 78 & 82 & 79 \\ 1 & 84 & 92 & 93 \end{bmatrix}$$

1. Use the `size` function to determine the number of rows and columns in this matrix.
2. Use the `sort` function to sort each column in ascending order.
3. Use the `sort` function to sort each column in descending order.
4. Use the `sortrows` function to sort the matrix so that the first column is in ascending order, but each row still retains its original data. Your matrix should look like this:

$$x = \begin{bmatrix} 1 & 84 & 92 & 93 \\ 2 & 55 & 65 & 75 \\ 3 & 78 & 82 & 79 \\ 4 & 90 & 85 & 75 \end{bmatrix}$$

5. Use the `sortrows` function to sort the matrix from Exercise 4 in descending order, based on the third column.

EXAMPLE 3.3

WEATHER DATA

The National Weather Service collects massive amounts of weather data every day (see Figure 3.7). Those data are available to all of us on the agency's online service at http://www.ncdc.noaa.gov/. Analyzing large amounts of data can be confusing, so it's a good idea to start with a small data set, develop an approach that works, then apply it to the larger data set that we are interested in.

Figure 3.7
Satellite photo of a
hurricane. (NASA
Headquarters)

We have extracted precipitation information from the National Weather Service for one location for all of 1999 and stored it in a file called **Weather_Data.xlsx.** (The .xlsx indicates that the data are in an Excel spreadsheet.) Each row represents a month, so there are 12 rows, and each column represents the day of the month (1 to 31), so there are 31 columns. As not every month has the same number of days, data are missing for some locations in the last several columns. The precipitation information is presented in hundredths of an inch. For example, on February 1, there was 0.61 inch of precipitation, and on April 1, 2.60 inches. A sample of the data is displayed in Table 3.11, with labels added for clarity; however, *the data in the file contain only numbers.*

Use the data in the file to find the following:

a. The total precipitation in each month.
b. The total precipitation for the year.
c. The month and day on which the maximum precipitation during the year was recorded.

1. State the problem
   Using the data in the file **Weather_Data.xlsx**, find the total monthly precipitation, the total precipitation for the year, and the day on which it rained the most.
2. Describe the input and output
   Input The input for this example is included in a data file called **Weather_Data. xlsx** and consists of a two-dimensional matrix. Each row represents a month, and each column represents a day.

   Output The output should be the total precipitation for each month, the total precipitation for the year, and the day on which the precipitation was a maximum. We have decided to present precipitation in inches, since no other units were specified in the statement of the problem.
3. Develop a hand example
   For the hand example, deal only with a small subset of the data. The information included in Table 3.11 is enough. The total for January, days 1 to 4, is

$$\text{total\_1} = (0 + 0 + 272 + 0)/100 = 2.72 \text{ inches}$$

Table 3.11 Precipitation Data from Asheville, North Carolina

1999	Day1	Day2	Day3	Day4	...	Day28	Day29	Day30	Day31
January	0	0	272	0		0	0	33	33
February	61	103	0	2		62			
March	2	0	17	27		0	5	8	0
April	260	1	0	0		13	86	0	
May	47	0	0	0		0	0	0	0
June	0	0	30	42		14	14	8	
July	0	0	0	0		5	0	0	0
August	0	45	0	0		0	0	0	0
September	0	0	0	0		138	58	10	
October	0	0	0	14		0	0	0	1
November	1	163	5	0		0	0	0	
December	0	0	0	0		0	0	0	0

(*continued*)

The total for February, days 1 to 4, is

$$total\_2 = (61 + 103 + 0 + 2)/100 = 1.66 \text{ inches}$$

Now add the months together to get the combined total. If our sample "year" is just January and February, then

$$total = total\_1 + total\_2 = 2.72 + 1.66 = 4.38 \text{ inches}$$

To find the day on which the maximum precipitation occurred, first find the maximum in the table, and then determine which row and which column it is in.

Working through a hand example allows you to formulate the steps required to solve the problem in MATLAB®.

4. Develop a MATLAB® solution

First, we'll need to save the data file into MATLAB® as a matrix. Because the file is an Excel spreadsheet, the easiest approach is to import the data interactively. Double-click on the file in the current folder window to open the file in MATLAB. Select **Numeric Matrix** as the import type, and Replace Blanks with NaN, then select **Import**.

The variable name `weatherdata` will appear in the workspace window (see Figure 3.8). Because not every month has 31 days, there were a number of blanks in the spreadsheet. The value NaN was inserted into those fields by MATLAB, based on our choices when we imported the file. You can double-click the variable name, `weatherdata`, in the workspace window, to view the resulting matrix (see Figure 3.9).

Now write the script to solve the problem:

```
clc
%Example 3.3 - Weather Data
%In this example we will find the total precipitation
%for each month, and for the entire year, using a data file
%We will also find the month and day on which the
%precipitation was the maximum
%Find the sum of each row, which is the sum for each month
monthly_total=sum (weatherdata,2,'omitnan')/100
```

Figure 3.8
The MATLAB® allows the user to import data interactively.

Figure 3.9
The MATLAB® array editor. You can edit the array in this window and change any values if needed.

```
%Find the annual total
yearly_total = sum(monthly_total)
%Find the annual maximum and the day on which it occurs
[max_precip,month]=max(max(weatherdata,[],2,'omitnan'))
%Find the annual maximum and the month in which it occurs
[max_precip,day] = max(max(weatherdata,[],1,'omitnan'))
```

Notice that the code did not start with our usual `clear`, `clc` commands, because that would clear the workspace, effectively deleting the `weatherdata` variable.

To find the monthly total we needed to add up the values on each row. We could have transposed the matrix and just used sum directly,

$$\text{monthly\_total} = \text{sum}(\text{weatherdata}', '\text{omitnan}')/100$$

but instead we chose to specify rows in the second field with the number 2. With either approach, we needed to tell MATLAB® to ignore the NaN (not a number) entries.

Now we can add up all the monthly totals to get the total for the year. An alternative syntax is

$$\text{yearly\_total} = \text{sum}(\text{sum}(\text{weatherdata}, '\text{omitnan}'))/100$$

Finding the maximum daily precipitation is easy; what makes this example hard is determining the day and month on which the maximum occurred. The command

$$[\text{max\_precip, month}] = \text{max}(\text{max}(\text{weatherdata},[\ ], 2, '\text{omitnan}'))$$

is easier to understand if we break it up into two commands. First,

$$[\text{a,b}] = \text{max}(\text{weatherdata},[\ ], 2, '\text{omitnan}')$$

(continued)

returns a matrix of maxima for each row, which in this case is the maximum for each month. This value is assigned to the variable name *a*. The variable *b* becomes a matrix of index numbers that represent the row in each column at which the maximum occurred. The result, then, is

```
a =
    Columns 1 through 9
    272    135    78    260    115    240    157    158    138
    Columns 10 through 12
    156    255    97
b =
    Columns 1 through 9
      3     18    27      1      6     25     12     24     28
    Columns 10 through 12
      5     26    14
```

Now when we execute the `max` command the second time, we determine the maximum precipitation for the entire data set, which is the maximum value in matrix *a*. Also, from matrix *a*, we find the index number for that maximum:

```
[c,d] = max(a)
c =
    272
d =
    1
```

These results tell us that the maximum precipitation occurred in row 1 of the a matrix, which means that it occurred in the first month.

Similarly, specifying columns in the third field with the number one

[max_precip,day] = max(weatherdata,[ ], 1, 'omitnan')

and finding the maximum twice allows us to find the day of the month on which the maximum occurred.

There are several things you should notice about the MATLAB® screen shown in Figure 3.10. All of the variables created when the script was executed are now available to the command window. This makes it easy to perform additional calculations in the command window after the program has completed running. For example, notice that we forgot to change the `max_precip` value to inches from hundredths of an inch. Adding the command

max_precip = max_precip/100

would correct that oversight. Notice also that the **Weather_Data.xlsx** file is still in the current folder. Finally, notice that the command history window reflects only commands issued from the command window; it does not show commands executed from a script.

5. Test the solution

Open the **Weather_Data.xlsx** file, and confirm that the maximum precipitation occurred on January 3. Once you've confirmed that your program works, you can use it to analyze other data. The National Weather Service maintains similar records for all of its recording stations.

Figure 3.10
Results from the precipitation calculations.

STANDARD DEVIATION

A measure of the spread of values in a data set

3.5.6 Variance and Standard Deviation

The standard deviation and variance are measures of how much elements in a data set vary with respect to each other. Every student knows that the average score on a test is important, but you also need to know the high and low scores to get an idea of how well you did. Test scores, like many kinds of data that are important in engineering, are often distributed in a bell-shaped curve. In a normal (Gaussian) distribution of a large amount of data, approximately 68% of the data falls within one standard deviation (sigma) of the mean ($\pm$ one sigma). If you extend the range to a two-sigma variation ($\pm$ two sigma), approximately 95% of the data should fall inside these bounds, and if you go out to three sigma, over 99% of the data should fall in this range (see Figure 3.11). Usually, measures such as the standard deviation and variance are meaningful only with large data sets.

Consider the data graphed in Figure 3.12. Both sets of data have the same average (mean) value of 50. However, it is easy to see that the first data set has more variation than the second.

The mathematical definition of variance is

$$\text{variance} = \sigma^2 = \frac{\sum\limits_{k=1}^{N}(x_k - \mu)^2}{N-1}.$$

In this equation, the symbol μ represents the mean of the values x_k in the data set. Thus, the term $x_k - \mu$ is simply the difference between the actual value and the average value. The terms are squared and added together:

$$\sum_{k=1}^{N}(x_k - \mu)^2$$

Finally, we divide the summation term by the number of values in the data set (N), minus 1.

The standard deviation (σ), which is used more often than the variance, is the square root of the variance.

34.13%　　34.13%

13.59%　　13.59%

02.15%　　02.15%

-3 -2 -1 0 1 2 3
Standard Deviations

Figure 3.11
Normal distribution.

Figure 3.12
Test scores from two different tests.

The MATLAB® function used to find the standard deviation is std. When we applied this function on the large data set shown in Figure 3.12, we obtained the following output:

```
std(scores1)
ans =
    20.3653
std(scores2)
ans =
    9.8753
```

In other words, approximately 68% of the data in the first data set fall between the average, 50, and ±20.3653. Similarly 68% of the data in the second data set fall between the same average, 50, and ±9.8753.

The variance is found in a similar manner with the var function:

```
var(scores1)
ans =
  414.7454
var(scores2)
ans =
   97.5209
```

The syntax for calculating both standard deviation and variance is shown in Table 3.12.

Table 3.12 Statistical Functions

std(x)	Computes the standard deviation of the values in a vector **x**. For example, if $x = [1\ 5\ 3]$, the standard deviation is 2. However, standard deviations are not usually calculated for small samples of data.		`x = [1,5,3];`
			`std(x)`
			`ans = 2`

	Returns a row vector containing the standard deviation calculated for each column of a matrix **x**. For example, if $x = \begin{bmatrix} 1 & 5 & 3 \\ 2 & 4 & 6 \end{bmatrix}$, the standard deviation in column 1 is 0.7071, the standard deviation in column 2 is 0.7071, and standard deviation in column 3 is 2.1213. Again, standard deviations are not usually calculated for small samples of data.		`x = [1,5,3;2,4,6];`
			`std (x)`
			`ans =`
			`0.7071   0.7071`
			`2.1213`

var (x)	Calculates the variance of the data in **x**. For example, if $x = [1\ 5\ 3]$, the variance is 4. However, variance is not usually calculated for small samples of data. Notice that the standard deviation in this example is the square root of the variance.		`var(x)` `ans = 4`

PRACTICE EXERCISE 3.8

The correct answers can be found on the Pearson website. Consider the following matrix:

$$x = \begin{bmatrix} 4 & 90 & 85 & 75 \\ 2 & 55 & 65 & 75 \\ 3 & 78 & 82 & 79 \\ 1 & 84 & 92 & 93 \end{bmatrix}$$

1. Find the standard deviation for each column.
2. Find the variance for each column.
3. Calculate the square root of the variance you found for each column.
4. How do the results from Exercise 3 compare against the standard deviation you found in Exercise 1?

EXAMPLE 3.4

CLIMATOLOGICAL DATA

Climatologists examine weather data over long periods of time, trying to find a pattern. Weather data have been kept reliably in the United States since the 1850s; however, most reporting stations have been in place only since the 1930s and 1940s (see Figure 3.13). Climatologists perform statistical calculations on the data they collect. Although the data in **Weather_Data.xlsx** represent just one location for one year, we can use them to practice statistical calculations. Find the mean daily precipitation for each month and the mean daily precipitation for the year, and then find the standard deviation for each month and for the year.

(continued)

Figure 3.13
The National Weather Service is an agency of the United States government, and is part of NOAA (lafoto/ Shutterstock).

1. State the problem
   Find the mean daily precipitation for each month and for the year, on the basis of the data in **Weather_Data.xlsx**. Also, find the standard deviation of the data during each month and during the entire year.
2. Describe the input and output
   Input Use the **Weather_Data.xlsx** file as input to the problem.

   Output find:
   The mean daily precipitation for each month.
   The mean daily precipitation for the year.
   The standard deviation of the daily precipitation data for each month.
   The standard deviation of the daily precipitation data for the year.
3. Develop a hand example
   Use just the data for the first 4 days of the month:
   January average = $(0 + 0 + 272 + 0)/4 = 68$ hundredths of an inch of precipitation, or 0.68 inch.
   The standard deviation is found from the following equation:

$$\sigma = \sqrt{\frac{\sum_{k=1}^{N}(x_k - \mu)^2}{N-1}}$$

   Using just the first 4 days of January, first calculate the sum of the squares of the difference between the mean and the actual value:

$$(0 - 68)^2 + (0 - 68)^2 + (272 - 68)^2 + (0 - 68)^2 = 55{,}488$$

   Divide by the number of data points minus 1:

$$55{,}488/(4 - 1) = 18{,}496$$

   Finally, take the square root, to give 136 hundredths of an inch of precipitation, or 1.36 inches.
4. Develop a MATLAB® solution
   First we need to load the **Weather_ Data.xlsx** file making sure the blank values are replaced with NaN (not a number). Although we could do that as described in Example 3.3, there is an easier way: The data from Example 3.3 could be

saved to a file, so that they are available to use later. If we want to save the entire workspace, just type

```
save <filename>
```

where `filename` is a user-defined file name. If you just want to save one variable, type

```
save <filename> <variable_name>
```

which saves a single variable or a list of variables to a file. All we need to save is the variable `weatherdata`, so the following command is sufficient:

```
save weatherdata weatherdata
```

This command saves the matrix `weatherdata` into the **weatherdata.mat** file. Check the current folder window to make sure that **weatherdata.mat** has been stored (see Figure 3.14).

Now the script we create to solve this example can load the data automatically:

```
%% Example 3.4 Climatological Data
%In this example, we find the mean daily
%precipitation for each month
%and the mean daily precipitation for the year
%We also find the standard deviation of the data
clear, clc
%Changing the format to shortg often makes the output
%easier to read
format shortg
%By saving the variable weatherdata from the last example,
%it is available to use in this problem
```

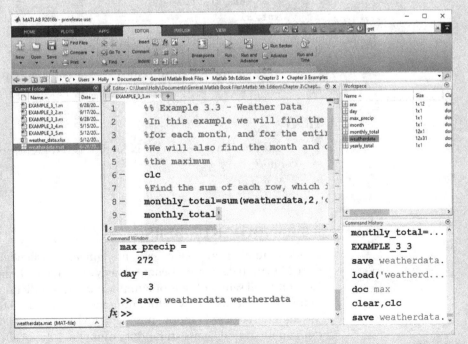

Figure 3.14
The current folder records the name of the saved file.

(continued)

```
load weatherdata
Average_daily_precip_monthly = mean(weatherdata','omitnan')
Average_daily_precip_yearly =mean(weatherdata(:),'omitnan')
%Now calculate the standard deviation
Monthly_Stdeviation = std(weatherdata','omitnan')
Yearly_Stdeviation = std(weatherdata(:),'omitnan')
```

The results are shown in the command window. Notice that we included the command `omitnan` to tell the functions not to include the array values listed as NaN (not a number) in the calculation. The weatherdata array was also transposed because we desired the standard deviation of the row, not the column.

Some new syntax was introduced in this example. The command

```
weatherdata(:)
```

converts the two-dimensional matrix **weatherdata** into a one-dimensional matrix, thus making it possible to find the mean and the standard deviation of the entire array.

5. Test the solution

First, check the results to make sure they make sense. Although calculating the mean daily rainfall for one month by hand would serve as an excellent check, it would be tedious. You can use MATLAB® to help you by calculating the mean without using a predefined function. The command window is a convenient place to perform these calculations:

```
load weatherdata
sum(weatherdata(:,1))      %Find the sum of all the rows in
                           %column one of matrix weather_data
ans =
    848.00
ans/31
ans =
    27.35
```

Compare these results with those for January (month 1).

HINT

Use the colon operator to change a two-dimensional matrix into a single column:
```
A = X (:)
```

3.6 RANDOM NUMBERS

Random numbers are often used in engineering calculations to simulate measured data. Measured data rarely behave exactly as predicted by mathematical models, so we can add small values of random numbers to our predictions to make a model behave more like a real system. Random numbers are also used to model games of chance. Two different types of random numbers can be generated in MATLAB®: uniform random numbers and Gaussian random numbers (often called a normal distribution).

3.6.1 Uniform Random Numbers

Uniform random numbers are generated with the rand function. These numbers are evenly distributed between 0 and 1. (Consult the help function for more details.) Table 3.13 lists several MATLAB® commands for generating random numbers.

We can create a set of random numbers over other ranges by modifying the numbers created by the rand function. For example, to create a set of 100 evenly distributed numbers between 0 and 5, first create a set over the default range with the command

```
r = rand(100,1);
```

This results in a 100×1 matrix of values. Now we just need to multiply by 5 to expand the range to 0 to 5:

```
r = r * 5;
```

If we want to change the range to 5 to 10, we can add 5 to every value in the array:

```
r = r + 5;
```

The result will be random numbers varying from 5 to 10. We can generalize these results with the equation

$$x = (\text{max} - \text{min}) \cdot \text{random\_number\_set} + \text{min}$$

3.6.2 Gaussian Random Numbers

Gaussian random numbers have the normal distribution shown in Figure 3.11. There is no absolute upper or lower bound to a data set of this type; we are just less and less likely to find data, the farther away from the mean we get. Gaussian random-number sets are described by specifying their average (mean) and the standard deviation of the data set.

MATLAB® generates Gaussian values with a mean of 0 and a variance of 1.0, using the randn function. For example,

Table 3.13 Random-Number Generators

rand(n)	Returns an $n \times n$ matrix. Each value in the matrix is a random number between 0 and 1.	rand(2) ans = 0.9501 0.2311	0.6068 0.4860
rand(m,n)	Returns an $m \times n$ matrix. Each value in the matrix is a random number between 0 and 1.	rand(3,2) ans = 0.8913 0.7621 0.4565	0.0185 0.8214 0.4447
randn(n)	Returns an $n \times n$ matrix. Each value in the matrix is a Gaussian (or normal) random number with a mean of 0 and a variance of 1.	randn(2) ans = −0.4326 −1.6656	0.1253 0.2877
randn(m,n)	Returns an $m \times n$ matrix. Each value in the matrix is a Gaussian (or normal) random number with a mean of 0 and a variance of 1.	randn(3,2) ans = −1.1465 1.1909 1.1892	−0.0376 0.3273 0.1746

```
randn(3)
```

returns a 3 × 3 matrix:

```
ans =
  -0.4326    0.2877    1.1892
  -1.6656   -1.1465   -0.0376
   0.1253    1.1909    0.3273
```

If we need a data set with a different average or a different standard deviation, we start with the default set of random numbers, and then modify it. Since the default standard deviation is 1, we must *multiply* by the required standard deviation for the new data set. Since the default mean is 0, we'll need to *add* the new mean:

$$x = standard\_deviation \cdot random\_data\_set + mean$$

For example, to create a sequence of 500 Gaussian random variables with a standard deviation of 2.5 and a mean of 3, type

```
x = randn(1,500)*2.5 + 3;
```

Notice that both `rand` and `randn` can accept either one or two input values. If only one is specified, the result is a square matrix. If two values are specified, they represent the number of rows and the number of columns in the resulting matrix.

PRACTICE EXERCISE 3.9

The correct answers can be found on the Pearson website.

1. Create a 3 × 3 matrix of evenly distributed random numbers.
2. Create a 3 × 3 matrix of normally distributed random numbers.
3. Create a 100 × 5 matrix of evenly distributed random numbers. Be sure to suppress the output.
4. Find the maximum, the standard deviation, the variance, and the mean for each column in the matrix that you created in Exercise 3.
5. Create a 100 × 5 matrix of normally distributed random numbers. Be sure to suppress the output.
6. Find the maximum, the standard deviation, the variance, and the mean for each column in the matrix you created in Exercise 5.
7. Explain why your results for Exercises 4 and 6 are different.

EXAMPLE 3.5

NOISE

Random numbers can be used to simulate the noise we hear as static on the radio. By adding this noise to data files that store music, we can study the effect of static on recordings.

MATLAB® has the ability to play music files by means of the `sound` function. To demonstrate this function, it also has a built-in music file with a short segment of

Handel's *Messiah* (see Figure 3.15). In this example, we will use the `randn` function to create noise, then we'll add the noise to the music clip.

Music is stored in MATLAB® as an array with values from −1 to 1. To convert this array into music, the `sound` function requires a sample frequency. The **handel.mat** file contains both an array representing the music and the value of the sample frequency. To hear the *Messiah,* you must first load the file, using the command

load handel.

Notice that two new variables—y and Fs—were added to the workspace window when the `handel` file was loaded. To play the clip, type

sound(y, Fs).

Experiment with different values of Fs to hear the effect of different sample frequencies on the music. For example, multiply Fs by 1.5 and observe the result. (Clearly, the sound must be engaged on your computer, or you won't be able to hear the playback.)

1. State the problem
   Add a noise component to the recording of Handel's *Messiah* included with MATLAB®.
2. Describe the input and output

   Input   MATLAB® data file of Handel's *Messiah,* stored as the built-in file **handel.mat**

   Output   An array representing the *Messiah,* with static added
   A graph of the first 200 elements of the data file

3. Develop a hand example
   As the data in the music file vary between −1 and +1, we should add noise values of a smaller order of magnitude. First, we'll try values centered on 0 and with a standard deviation of 0.1.
4. Develop a MATLAB® solution

```
%Example 3.5
%Noise
load handel          %Load the music data file
sound(y,Fs)          %Play the music data file
pause                %Pause to listen to the music
%Be sure to hit enter to continue after playing the music
%Add random noise
noise=randn (length(y), 1) *0.10
sound(y+noise, Fs)
```

Figure 3.15
Utah Symphony Orchestra.
(Chris Fredriksson/Alamy
Stock Photo)

(*continued*)

This program allows you to play the recording of the *Messiah,* both with and without the added noise. You can adjust the multiplier on the noise line to observe the effect of changing the magnitude of the added static. For example,

```
noise=randn (length(y),1)*0.20
```

5. Test the solution
   In addition to playing back the music both with and without the added noise, we could plot the results. Because the file is quite large (73,113 elements), we'll just plot the first 200 points:

```
%Plot the first 200 data points in each file
t=1:length(y);
noisy = y + noise;
plot(t(1,1:200),y(1:200,1),t(1,1:200),noisy(1:200,1),':')
title('Handel''s Messiah')
xlabel('Element Number in Music Array')
ylabel('Frequency')
```

These commands tell MATLAB® to plot the index number of the data on the *x*-axis, and the value stored in the music arrays on the *y*-axis. Plotting is introduced in more detail in a later chapter.

In Figure 3.16, the solid line represents the original data, and the dotted line the data to which we've added noise. As expected, the noisy data have a bigger range and don't always follow the same pattern as the original.

Figure 3.16
Handel's *Messiah*. The solid line represents the original data, and the dotted line is the data to which we've added noise.

VARIANCE
The standard deviation
squared

3.7 COMPLEX NUMBERS

MATLAB® includes several functions used primarily with complex numbers. Complex numbers consist of two parts: a real component and an imaginary component. For example,

$$5 + 3i$$

COMPLEX NUMBER
A number with both real
and imaginary components

is a complex number. The real component is 5, and the imaginary component is 3. Complex numbers can be entered into MATLAB® in two ways: as an addition problem, such as

```
A = 5 + 3i or A = 5 + 3*i or A = 5 + 3*j
```

or with the complex function, as in

```
A = complex (5,3)
```

which returns

```
A =
   5.0000 + 3.0000i.
```

KEY IDEA
MATLAB® supports the
use of both *i* and *j* for
imaginary numbers.

As is standard in MATLAB®, the input to the complex function can be either two scalars or two arrays of values. Thus, if **x** and **y** are defined as

```
x = 1:3;
y = [-1,5,12];
```

then the complex function can be used to define an array of complex numbers as follows:

```
complex (x, y)
ans =
   1.0000 - 1.0000i 2.0000 + 5.0000i 3.0000 + 12.0000i
```

The real and imag functions can be used to separate the real and imaginary components of complex numbers. For example, for A = 5 + 3*i, we have

```
real(A)
ans =
        5
imag(A)
ans =
        3.
```

The isreal function can be used to determine whether a variable is storing a complex number. It returns a 1 if the variable is real, and a 0 if it is complex. As A is a complex number, we get

```
isreal(A)
ans =
        0.
```

Thus, the isreal function is false and returns a value of 0.

The complex conjugate of a complex number consists of the same real component, but an imaginary component of the opposite sign. The `conj` function returns the complex conjugate:

```
conj(A)
ans =
      5.0000 - 3.0000i
```

The transpose operator also returns the complex conjugate of an array, in addition to converting rows to columns and columns to rows. Thus, we have

```
A'
ans =
      5.0000 - 3.0000i.
```

Of course, in this example A is a scalar. We can create a complex array B by using A and performing both addition and multiplication operations:

```
B = [A, A+1, A*3]
B =
      5.0000 + 3.0000i 6.0000 + 3.0000i 15.0000 + 9.0000i
```

The transpose of B is

```
B'
ans =
       5.0000 - 3.0000i
       6.0000 - 3.0000i
      15.0000 - 9.0000i
```

POLAR COORDINATES
A technique for describing a location using an angle and a distance

Complex numbers are often thought of as describing a position on an x–y plane. The real part of the number corresponds to the x-value, and the imaginary component corresponds to the y-value, as shown in Figure 3.17(a). Another way to think about this point is to describe it with polar coordinates—that is, with a radius and an angle (see Figure 3.17(b)).

MATLAB® includes functions to convert complex numbers from Cartesian to polar form.

Figure 3.17
(a) Complex number represented in a Cartesian coordinate system.
(b) A complex number can also be described with polar coordinates.

(a) Complex number plotted on x–y coordinates   (b) Complex number plotted on x–y coordinates

When the absolute-value function is used with a complex number, it calculates the radius, using the Pythagorean theorem:

```
abs(A)
ans =
      5.8310
```

$$\text{radius} = \sqrt{(\text{real component})^2 + (\text{imaginary component})^2}$$

Since, in this example, the real component is 5, and the imaginary component is 3,

$$\text{radius} = \sqrt{5^2 + 3^2} = 5.8310.$$

We could also calculate the radius in MATLAB®, using the `real` and `imag` functions described earlier:

```
sqrt(real(A).^2 + imag(A).^2)
ans =
      5.8310
```

Similarly, the angle is found with the angle function:

```
angle(A)
ans =
      0.5404
```

The result is expressed in radians. Both functions, `abs` and `angle`, will accept scalars or arrays as input. Recall that B is a 1×3 array of complex numbers:

```
B =
    5.0000 + 3.0000i 6.0000 + 3.0000i 15.0000 + 9.0000i
```

The `abs` function returns the radius if the number is represented in polar coordinates:

```
abs(B)
ans =
      5.8310 6.7082 17.4929
```

The angle from the horizontal can be found with the `angle` function:

```
angle(B)
ans =
      0.5404 0.4636 0.5404
```

The MATLAB® functions commonly used with complex numbers are summarized in Table 3.14.

Table 3.14 Functions Used with Complex Numbers

abs(x)	Computes the absolute value of a complex number, using the Pythagorean theorem. This is equivalent to the radius if the complex number is represented in polar coordinates.	`x = 3 + 4i;`
		`abs(x)`
		`ans =`
		`      5`

angle(x)	For example, if $x = 3 + 4i$, the absolute value is $\sqrt{3^2 + 4^2} = 5$. Computes the angle from the horizontal in radians when a complex number is represented in polar coordinates.	`x = 3 + 4i;`
		`angle(x)`
		`ans =`
		`      0.9273`

`complex(x,y)`	Generates a complex number with a real component *x* and an imaginary component *y*.	`x = 3;`
		`y = 4;`
		`complex(x,y)`
		`ans =`
		`    3.0000 +`
		`    4.0000i`

`real(x)`	Extracts the real component from a complex number.	`x = 3 + 4i;`
		`real(x)`
		`ans =`
		`    3`

`imag(x)`	Extracts the imaginary component from a complex number.	`x = 3 + 4i;`
		`imag(x)`
		`ans =`
		`    4`

`isreal(x)`	Determines whether the values in an array are real. If they are real, the function returns a 1; if they are complex, it returns a 0.	`x = 3 = 4i;`
		`isreal(x)`
		`ans =`
		`    0`

`conj(x)`	Generates the complex conjugate of a complex number.	`x = 3 + 4i;`
		`conj(x)`
		`ans =`
		`    3.0000 -`
		`    4.0000i`

PRACTICE EXERCISE 3.10

The correct answers can be found on the Pearson website.

1. Create the following complex numbers:
   a. $A = 1 + i$
   b. $B = 2 - 3i$
   c. $C = 8 + 2i$
2. Create a vector D of complex numbers whose real components are 2, 4, and 6 and whose imaginary components are -3, 8, and -16.
3. Find the magnitude (absolute value) of each of the vectors you created in Exercises 1 and 2.
4. Find the angle from the horizontal of each of the complex numbers you created in Exercises 1 and 2.
5. Find the complex conjugate of vector D.
6. Use the transpose operator to find the complex conjugate of vector D.
7. Multiply A by its complex conjugate, and then take the square root of your answer. How does this value compare against the magnitude (absolute value) of A?

KEY IDEA
There is a limit to how small or how large a number can be handled by computer programs.

3.8 COMPUTATIONAL LIMITATIONS

The variables stored in a computer can assume a wide range of values. On the majority of computers, the range extends from about 10^{-308} to 10^{308}, which should be enough to accommodate most computations. MATLAB® includes functions to identify the largest real numbers and the largest integers the program can process (see Table 3.15).

Table 3.15 Computational Limits

`realmax`	Returns the largest possible floating-point number used in MATLAB®.	`realmax`
		`ans =`
		   `1.7977e + 308`

`realmin`	Returns the smallest possible floating-point number used in MATLAB®.	`realmin`
		`ans =`
		   `2.2251e - 308`

`intmax`	Returns the largest possible integer number used in MATLAB®.	`intmax`
		`ans =`
		   `2147483647`

`intmin`	Returns the smallest possible integer number used in MATLAB®.	`intmin`
		`ans =`
		   `-2147483648`

The value of `realmax` corresponds roughly to 2^{1024}, since computers actually perform their calculations in binary (base-2) arithmetic. Of course, it is possible to formulate a problem in which the result of an expression is larger or smaller than the permitted maximum. For example, suppose that we execute the following commands:

```
x = 2.5e200;
y = 1.0e200;
z = x*y
```

MATLAB® responds with

```
z =
    Inf
```

OVERFLOW
A calculational result that is too large for the computer program to handle

because the answer (2.5e400) is outside the allowable range. This error is called *exponent overflow*, because the exponent of the result of an arithmetic operation is too large to store in the computer's memory.

Exponent underflow is a similar error, caused by the exponent of the result of an arithmetic operation being too *small* to store in the computer's memory. Using the same allowable range, we obtain an exponent underflow with the following commands:

UNDERFLOW
A calculational result that is too small for the computer program to distinguish from zero

```
x = 2.5e-200;
y = 1.0e200
z = x/y
```

Together, these commands return

```
z = 0.
```

The result of an exponent underflow is zero.

We also know that division by zero is an invalid operation. If an expression results in a division by zero, the result of the division is infinity:

KEY IDEA
Careful planning can help you avoid calculational overflow or underflow.

```
z = y/0
z =
        Inf
```

In performing calculations with very large or very small numbers, it may be possible to reorder the calculations to avoid an underflow or an overflow. Suppose, for example, that you would like to perform the following string of multiplications:

$$(2.5 \times 10^{200}) \times (2 \times 10^{200}) \times (1 \times 10^{-100})$$

The answer is 5×10^{300}, within the bounds allowed by MATLAB®. However, consider what happens when we enter the problem into MATLAB®:

```
2.5e200*2e200*1e-100
ans =
        Inf
```

Because MATLAB® executes the problem from left to right, the first multiplication yields a value outside the allowable range (5×10^{400}), resulting in an answer of infinity. However, by rearranging the problem to

```
2.5e200*1e-100*2e200
ans =
        5.0000e+300
```

we avoid the overflow and find the correct answer.

3.9 SPECIAL VALUES AND MISCELLANEOUS FUNCTIONS

Most, but not all, functions require an input argument. Although used as if they were scalar constants, the commands listed in Table 3.16 are functions that do *not* require any input.

MATLAB® allows you to redefine these functions as variable names; however, doing so can have unexpected consequences. For example, the following MATLAB® code is allowed, even though it is not wise:

```
pi = 12.8;
```

From this point on, whenever the variable pi is called, the new value will be used. Similarly, you can redefine **any** function as a variable name, such as

```
sin = 10;
```

To restore sin to its job as a trigonometric function (or to restore the default value of pi), you must clear the workspace with

```
clear
```

or you may clear each independently with

```
clear sin
clear pi
```

Now check to see the result by issuing the command for π.

```
pi
```

This command returns

```
pi =
3.1416.
```

Table 3.16 Special Functions

pi	Mathematical constant [&|pi|~futurabkmath~.~normal~&]	pi ans = 3.1416
I	Imaginary number.	i ans = 0 + 1.0000i
J	Imaginary number.	j ans = 0 + 1.0000i
Inf	Infinity, which often occurs during a calculational overflow or when a number is divided by zero.	5/0 Warning: Divide by zero. ans = Inf
NaN	Not a number. Occurs when a calculation is undefined.	0/0 Warning: Divide by zero. ans = NaN inf/inf ans = NaN

Clock	Current time.
	Returns a six-member array [year month day hour minute second].
	When the **clock** function was called on July 19, 2008, at 5:19 P.M. and 30.0 seconds, MATLAB® returned the output shown at the right.
	
	The **fix** and **clock** functions together result in a format that is easier to read.
	The fix function rounds toward zero. A similar result could be obtained by setting **format bank** or **format shortg.**
		clock
		ans =
		   1.0e + 003*
		2.0080 0.0070 0.0190
		0.0170 0.0190 0.0300
		fix(clock)
		ans =
		   2008 7 19
		   17 19 30

Date	Current date. Similar to the **clock** function. However, it returns the date in a "string format."	date ans = 19-Jul-2008
Eps	The distance between 1 and the next-larger double-precision floating-point number.	eps ans = 2.2204e-016

HINT

The function i is the most common of these functions to be unintentionally renamed by MATLAB® users.

The NaN function stands for "not a number." It is returned when a user attempts a calculation where the result is undefined—for example, 0/0. It can also be useful as a placeholder in an array.

PRACTICE EXERCISE 3.11

The correct answers can be found on the Pearson website.

1. Use the clock function to add the time and date to your work sheet.
2. Use the date function to add the date to your work sheet.
3. Convert the following calculations to MATLAB® code and explain your results:
   a. 322! (Remember that, to a mathematician, the symbol ! means factorial.)
   b. $5*10^{500}$
   c. $1/5*10^{500}$
   d. 0/0

SUMMARY

In this chapter, we explored a number of predefined MATLAB® functions, including the following:

- General mathematical functions, such as
  - exponential functions
  - logarithmic functions
  - roots
- Rounding functions
- Functions used in discrete mathematics, such as
  - factoring functions
  - prime-number functions
- Trigonometric functions, including
  - standard trigonometric functions
  - inverse trigonometric functions
  - hyperbolic trigonometric functions
  - trigonometric functions that use degrees instead of radians
- Data analysis functions, such as
  - maxima and minima
  - averages (mean and median)
  - sums and products
  - sorting
  - standard deviation and variance
- Random-number generation for both
  - uniform distributions
  - Gaussian (normal) distributions
- Functions used with complex numbers

We explored the computational limits inherent in MATLAB® and introduced special values, such as pi, that are built into the program.

MATLAB® SUMMARY

The following MATLAB® summary lists and briefly describes all of the special characters, commands, and functions that were defined in this chapter:

Special Characters and Functions	
eps	smallest difference recognized
i	imaginary number
clock	returns the time
date	returns the date
Inf	infinity
intmax	returns the largest possible integer number used in MATLAB®
intmin	returns the smallest possible integer number used in MATLAB®
j	imaginary number
NaN	not a number
pi	mathematical constant π
realmax	returns the largest possible floating-point number used in MATLAB®
realmin	returns the smallest possible floating-point number used in MATLAB®

Commands and Functions

abs	computes the absolute value of a real number or the magnitude of a complex number
angle	computes the angle when complex numbers are represented in polar coordinates
asin	computes the inverse sine (arcsine)
asind	computes the inverse sine and reports the result in degrees
ceil	rounds to the nearest integer toward positive infinity
complex	creates a complex number
conj	creates the complex conjugate of a complex number
cos	computes the cosine
cumprod	computes a cumulative product of the values in an array
cumsum	computes a cumulative sum of the values in an array
deg2rad	converts degrees to radians
erf	calculates the error function
exp	computes the value of e^x
factor	finds the prime factors
factorial	calculates the factorial
fix	rounds to the nearest integer toward zero
floor	rounds to the nearest integer toward minus infinity
gcd	finds the greatest common denominator
help	opens the help function
helpwin	opens the windowed help function
imag	extracts the imaginary component of a complex number
isprime	determines whether a value is prime
isreal	determines whether a value is real or complex
lcm	finds the least common multiple
length	determines the largest dimension of an array
log	computes the natural logarithm or the logarithm to the base e ($\log_e$)
log10	computes the common logarithm or the logarithm to the base 10 ($\log_{10}$)
log2	computes the logarithm to the base 2 ($\log_2$)
max	finds the maximum value in an array and determines which element stores the maximum value
mean	computes the average of the elements in an array
median	finds the median of the elements in an array
min	finds the minimum value in an array and determines which element stores the minimum value
mode	finds the most common number in an array
nchoosek	finds the number of possible combinations when a subgroup of k values is chosen from a group of n values
nthroot	find the real nth root of the input matrix
numel	determines the total number of elements in an array
primes	finds the prime numbers less than the input value
prod	multiplies the values in an array
rad2deg	converts radians to degrees
rand	calculates evenly distributed random numbers
randn	calculates normally distributed (Gaussian) random numbers
rats	converts the input to a rational representation (i.e., a fraction)
real	extracts the real component of a complex number
rem	calculates the remainder in a division problem
round	rounds to the nearest integer
sign	determines the sign (positive or negative)
sin	computes the sine, using radians as input
sind	computes the sine, using angles in degrees as input
sinh	computes the hyperbolic sine
size	determines the number of rows and columns in an array
sort	sorts the elements of a vector
sortrows	sorts the rows of a vector on the basis of the values in the first column
sound	plays back music files
sqrt	calculates the square root of a number

(continued)

Commands and Functions	
std	determines the standard deviation
sum	sums the values in an array
tan	computes the tangent, using radians as input
var	computes the variance

KEY TERMS

argument	mean	seed
average	median	standard deviation
complex number	nesting	underflow
discrete mathematics	normal random	uniform random
function	variation	number
function input	overflow	variance
Gaussian random	rational numbers	
variation	real numbers	

PROBLEMS

Elementary Math Functions

3.1 Find the cube root of -5, both by using the `nthroot` function and by raising -5 to the $1/3$ power. Explain the difference in your answers. Prove that both results are indeed correct answers by cubing them and showing that they equal -5.

3.2 MATLAB® contains functions to calculate the natural logarithm (`log`), the logarithm to the base 10 (`log10`), and the logarithm to the base 2 (`log2`). However, if you want to find a logarithm to another base—for example, base b—you'll have to do the math yourself with the formula

$$\log_b(x) = \frac{\log_e(x)}{\log_e(b)}.$$

What is the $\log_b$ of 10 when b is defined from 1 to 10 in increments of 1?

3.3 Populations tend to expand exponentially, that is,

$$P = P_0 e^{rt}$$

where

P = current population,
P_0 = original population,
r = continuous growth rate, expressed as a fraction, and
t = time.

If you originally have 100 rabbits that breed at a continuous growth rate of 90% ($r = 0.9$) per year, find how many rabbits you will have at the end of 10 years.

3.4 Chemical reaction rates are proportional to a rate constant k that changes with temperature according to the Arrhenius equation

$$k = k_0 e^{-Q/RT}.$$

For a certain reaction,

$$Q = 8000 \text{ cal/mol}$$
$$R = 1.987 \text{ cal/mol K}$$
$$k_0 = 1200 \text{ min}^{-1}$$

Find the values of k for temperatures from 100 K to 500 K, in increments of 50. Create a table of your results.

3.5 Consider the air-conditioning requirements of the large home shown in Figure P3.5.

The interior of the house is warmed by waste heat from lighting and electrical appliances, by heat leaking in from the outdoors, and by heat generated by the people in the home. An air-conditioner must be able to remove all this thermal energy in order to keep the inside temperature from rising. Suppose there are 20 light bulbs emitting 100 J/s of energy each, and four appliances emitting 500 J/s each. Suppose also that heat leaks in from the outside at a rate of 3000 J/s.

(a) How much heat must the air-conditioner be able to remove from the home per second?

(b) One particular air-conditioning unit can handle 2000 J/s. How many of these units are needed to keep the home at a constant temperature?

3.6 (a) If you have four people, how many different ways can you arrange them in a line?

(b) If you have 10 different tiles, how many different ways can you arrange them?

3.7 (a) If you have 12 people, how many different committees of two people each can you create? Remember that a committee of Bob and Alice is the same as a committee of Alice and Bob.

(b) How many different soccer teams of 11 players can you form from a class of 30 students? (Combinations—order does not matter.)

(c) Since each player on a soccer team is assigned a particular role, order *does* matter. Recalculate the possible number of different soccer teams that can be formed when order is taken into account.

3.8 There are 52 different cards in a deck. How many different hands of 5 cards each are possible? Remember, every hand can be arranged 120 (5!) different ways.

Figure P3.5
Air-conditioning must remove heat from a number of sources.

3.9 Very large prime numbers are used in cryptography. How many prime numbers are there between 10,000 and 20,000? (These aren't big enough primes to be useful in ciphers.) (*Hint:* Use the `primes` function and the `length` command.)

Trigonometric Functions

3.10 Sometimes it is convenient to have a table of sine, cosine, and tangent values instead of using a calculator. Create an array of all three of these trigonometric functions for angles from 0 to 2π, with a spacing of 0.1 radian. Your array should contain a column for the angle and columns for the sine, cosine, and tangent.

3.11 The displacement of the oscillating spring shown in Figure P3.11 can be described by

$$x = A \cos(\omega t)$$

where
x = displacement at time t,
A = maximum displacement,
ω = angular frequency, which depends on the spring constant and the mass attached to the spring, and
T = time.
Find the displacement x for times from 0 to 10 seconds when the maximum displacement A is 4 cm, and the angular frequency is 0.6 radian/second. Present your results in a table of displacement and time values.

Figure P3.11
An oscillating spring.

3.12 The acceleration of the spring described in the preceding exercise is

$$a = -A\omega^2 \cos(\omega t).$$

Find the acceleration for times from 0 to 10 seconds, using the constant values from the preceding problem. Create a table that includes the time, the displacement from corresponding values in the previous exercise, and the acceleration.

3.13 You can use trigonometry to find the height of a building, as shown in Figure P3.13. Suppose you measure the angle between the line of sight and the horizontal line connecting the measuring point and the building. You can calculate the height of the building with the following formulas:

$$\tan(\theta) = h/d$$
$$h = d \tan(\theta)$$

Assume that the distance to the building along the ground is 120 m, and the angle measured along the line of sight is 30° ± 3°. Find the maximum and minimum heights the building can be.

Figure P3.13
You can determine the height of a building with trigonometry.

3.14 Consider the building from the previous exercise.

(a) If it is 200 feet tall and you are 20 feet away, at what angle from the ground will you have to tilt your head to see the top of the building? (For simplicity assume that your head is even with the ground.)

(b) How far is it from your head to the top of the building?

(c) Challenge: Repeat parts (a) and (b) assuming your head is NOT even with the ground, but is 6 feet above ground level.

Data Analysis Functions

3.15 Consider the the data in Table P3.15, which represents temperature readings in a reactor:

Table P3.15 Reactor Temperature Readings

Thermocouple 1	Thermocouple 2	Thermocouple 3
84.3	90.0	86.7
86.4	89.5	87.6
85.2	88.6	88.3
87.1	88.9	85.3
83.5	88.9	80.3
84.8	90.4	82.4
85.0	89.3	83.4
85.3	89.5	85.4
85.3	88.9	86.3
85.2	89.1	85.3
82.3	89.5	89.0
84.7	89.4	87.3
83.6	89.8	87.2

Your instructor may provide you with a file named **thermocouple.dat**, or you may need to enter the data yourself. Use MATLAB® to find

(a) The maximum temperature measured by each thermocouple.
(b) The minimum temperature measured by each thermocouple.

3.16 The range of an object shot at an angle θ with respect to the x-axis and an initial velocity v_0 (see Figure P3.16) is given by

Figure P3.16
The range depends on the launch angle and the launch velocity.

$$\text{Range} = \frac{v_0^2}{g} \sin(2\theta)$$

for $0 \leq \theta \leq \pi/2$ and neglecting air resistance. Use $g = 9.81 \text{ m/s}^2$ and an initial velocity v_0 of 100 m/s. Show that the maximum range is obtained at approximately $\theta = \pi/4$ by computing the range in increments of $\pi/100$ between $0 \leq \theta\pi/2$. You won't be able to find the exact angle that results in the maximum range, because your calculations are at evenly spaced angles of $\pi/100$ radian.

3.17 The vector

$G = [68, 83, 61, 70, 75, 82, 57, 5, 76, 85, 62, 71, 96, 78, 76, 68, 72, 75, 83, 93]$

represents the distribution of final grades in a dynamics course. Compute the mean, median, mode, and standard deviation of G. Which better represents the "most typical grade," the mean, median or mode? Why? Use MATLAB® to determine the number of grades in the array (don't just count them) and to sort them into ascending order.

3.18 Generate 10,000 Gaussian random numbers with a mean of 80 and standard deviation of 23.5. (You'll want to suppress the output so that you don't overwhelm the command window with data.) Use the mean function to confirm that your array actually has a mean of 80. Use the `std` function to confirm that your standard deviation is actually 23.5.

3.19 Use the `date` function to add the current date to your homework.

Random Numbers

3.20 Many games require the player to roll two dice. The number on each die can vary from 1 to 6.

(a) Use the `randi` function to create a simulation of one roll of one die.

(b) Use your results from part (a) to create a simulation of the value rolled with a second die.

(c) Add your two results to create a value representing the total rolled during each turn.

(d) Use your program to determine the values rolled in a favorite board game, or use the game shown in Figure P3.20.

3.21 Suppose you are designing a container to ship sensitive medical materials between hospitals. The container needs to keep the contents within a specified temperature range. You have created a model predicting how the container responds to the exterior temperature, and you now need to run a simulation.

(a) Create a normal distribution (Gaussian distribution) of temperatures with a mean of 70°F and a standard deviation of 2°, corresponding to a 2-hour duration. You'll need a temperature for each time value from 0 to 120 minutes, at 0.5 minute intervals. (That's 241 values.)

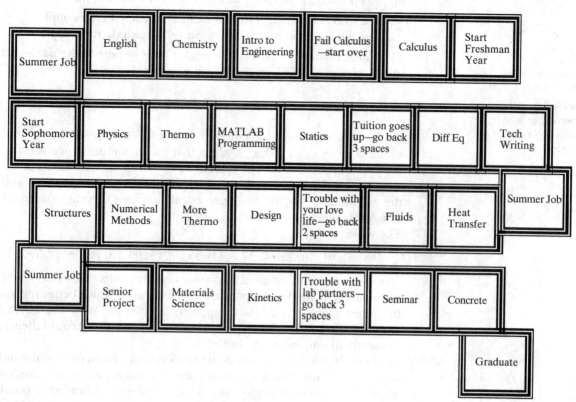

Figure P3.20
The college game.

(b) Plot the data on an *x–y* plot. Don't worry about labels. Recall that the MATLAB® function for plotting is plot(x,y).

(c) Find the maximum temperature, the minimum temperature, and the times at which they occur.

Complex Numbers

3.22 Consider the circuit shown in Figure P3.22, which includes the following:
- A sinusoidally varying voltage source, *V*.
- An inductor, with an inductance, *L*.
- A capacitor, with a capacitance, *C*.
- A resistor, with a resistance, *R*.

We can find the current, *I*, in the circuit by using Ohm's law (generalized for alternating currents),

$$V = IZ_T$$

where Z_T is the total impedance in the circuit. (Impedance is the AC corollary to resistance.)

Assume that the impedance for each component is as follows:

$$Z_L = 0 + 5j \text{ ohms}$$
$$Z_C = 0 - 15j \text{ ohms}$$
$$R = Z_R = 5 + 0j \text{ ohms}$$
$$Z_T = Z_C + Z_L + R$$

and that the applied voltage is

$$V = 10 + 0j \text{ volts.}$$

(Electrical engineers usually use *j* instead of *i* for imaginary numbers.)

Find the current, *I*, in the circuit. You should expect a complex number as a result. Enter the complex values of impedance into your calculations using the complex function.

3.23 Impedance is related to the inductance, *L*, and the capacitance, *C* by the following equations:

$$Z_C = \frac{1}{\omega c j}$$
$$Z_L = \omega L j$$

Figure P3.22
A simple circuit illustrating a sinusoidally varying voltage source, *V*.

For a circuit similar to the one shown in Figure P3.22 assume the following:

$$C = 1 \ \mu F \text{ (microfarads).}$$
$$L = 200 \text{ mH (millihenries).}$$
$$R = 5 \text{ ohms.}$$
$$f = 15 \text{ kHz (kilohertz).}$$
$$\omega = 2\pi f.$$
$$V = 10 \text{ volts.}$$

(a) Find the impedance for the capacitor (Z_C) and for the inductor (Z_L).

(b) Find the total impedance

$$Z_T = Z_C + Z_L + R$$

(c) Find the current by solving Ohm's law for I:

$$V = IZ_T$$

(d) Electrical engineers often describe complex parameters using polar coordinates, that is, the parameter has both an angle and a magnitude. (Imagine plotting a point on the complex plane, where the x-axis represents the real part of the number, and the y-axis represents the imaginary part of the number.) Use the abs function to find the magnitude of the current found in part (c), and use the angle function to find the corresponding angle.

3.24 Consider Table P3.24. The data was downloaded from the NOAA National Centers for Environmental Information website, and represents information collected at the Denver airport during 2015. It may be available to you as an Excel data file called **Denver_Climate_Data_2015.xlsx**. Import the data file to MATLAB and save each column as a vector.

EMXP:	Extreme maximum daily precipitation
MMNT:	Monthly mean minimum temperature
EMXT:	Extreme maximum daily temperature
MXSD:	Maximum snow depth
MMXT:	Monthly Mean maximum temperature
TPCP:	Total precipitation
EMNT:	Extreme minimum daily temperature
MNTM:	Monthly mean temperature
TSNW:	Total snow fall
Source:	

(a) Find the total precipitation for 2015, using the TPCP column.
(b) Find the average monthly mean minimum temperature for 2015, using the MMXT column.
(c) Find the maximum snow depth for 2015 using the MXSD column.
(d) Find the maximum total snow fall, using the TSNW column.

3.25 Consult the NOAA National Centers for Environmental Information website and download climate data for a location of your choice. (Airport names are usually good choices, for example, DEN for Denver, Colorado.) Specify temperature data in your request. Use the data file to determine the maximum and minimum temperatures during the previous year.

Table P3.24 Monthly Climate Data for Denver, Colorado, 2015

DATE	EMXP	MXSD	TPCP	TSNW	EMXT	EMNT	MMXT	MMNT	MNTM
20150101	0.12	0	0.37	7.2	75	−9.8	46.8	21.2	34
20150201	0.37	1	1.25	22.4	73.9	−5.8	46.6	21.2	34
20150301	0.34	0	0.79	2.9	81	2.1	58.8	31.3	45.1
20150401	1.22	0	2.65	5.3	79	27.1	62.1	35.4	48.7
20150501	1.08	0	3.76	4	84.9	27.1	63.3	42.8	53.1
20150601	0.99	0	2.54	0	93.9	51.1	82.9	56.1	69.4
20150701	0.33	0	1.07	0	97	52	87.6	57.9	72.7
20150801	0.68	0	1.18	0	98.1	43	89.8	58.3	74.1
20150901	0.07	0	0.11	0	91.9	44.1	85.3	53.6	69.4
20151001	0.79	0	1.76	0	87.1	28.2	70.2	42.8	56.5
20151101	0.5	0	2.13	11.2	75	3.2	51.3	25.7	38.5
20151201	0.32	1	0.71	11.3	69.1	0.1	41	18.1	29.5

4

Manipulating MATLAB® Matrices

Objectives

After reading this chapter, you should be able to:
- Manipulate matrices.
- Extract data from matrices.

- Solve problems with two matrix variables of different sizes using meshgrid.
- Create and use special matrices.

4.1 MANIPULATING MATRICES

As you solve more and more complicated problems with MATLAB®, you'll find that you will need to combine small matrices into larger matrices, extract information from large matrices, create very large matrices, and use matrices with special properties.

4.1.1 Defining Matrices

In MATLAB®, you can define a matrix by typing in a list of numbers enclosed in square brackets. You can separate the numbers by spaces or by commas, at your discretion. (You can even combine the two techniques in the same matrix definition.) To indicate a new row, you can use a semicolon. For example,

```
A = [3.5];
B = [1.5, 3.1]; or B = [1.5 3.1];
C = [-1, 0, 0; 1, 1, 0; 0, 0, 2];
```

You can also define a matrix by listing each row on a separate line, as in the following set of MATLAB® commands:

```
C =    [-1,  0, 0;
         1,  1, 0;
         1, -1, 0;
         0,  0, 2]
```

You don't even need to enter the semicolon to indicate a new row. MATLAB® interprets

```
C =      [-1,   0, 0
          1,   1, 0
          1,  -1, 0
          0,   0, 2]
```

as a 4×3 matrix. You could also enter a column matrix in this manner:

```
A = [
     1
     2
     3 ]
```

ELLIPSIS

A set of three periods used to indicate that a row is continued on the next line

If there are too many numbers in a row to fit on one line, you can continue the statement on the next line, but a comma and an ellipsis (…) are required at the end of the line, indicating that the row is to be continued. You can also use the ellipsis to continue other long assignment statements in MATLAB®.

If we want to define matrix F with 10 values, we can use either of the following statements:

```
F = [1, 52, 64, 197, 42, -42, 55, 82, 22, 109]; or
F = [1, 52, 64, 197, 42, -42, ...
           55, 82, 22, 109];
```

MATLAB® also allows you to define a matrix in terms of another matrix that has already been defined. For example, the statements

```
B = [1.5, 3.1];
S = [3.0, B]
```

return

```
S =
        3.0   1.5   3.1.
```

Similarly,

```
T = [ 1, 2, 3; S]
```

returns

```
T =
        1    2     3
        3    1.5   3.1.
```

INDEX

A number used to identify elements in an array

We can change values in a matrix, or include additional values, by using an index number to specify a particular element. This process is called *indexing into an array*. Thus, the command

```
S(2) = -1.0;
```

changes the second value in the matrix S from 1.5 to -1. If we type the matrix name

```
S
```

into the command window, then MATLAB® returns

```
S =
        3.0   -1.0   3.1.
```

Similarly, we can also extend a matrix by defining new elements. If we execute the command

    S(4) = 5.5;

we extend the matrix **S** to four elements instead of three. If we define element

    S(8) = 9.5;

matrix **S** will have eight values, and the values of S(5), S(6), and S(7) will be set to 0. Thus,

    S

returns

    S =
            3.0   -1.0   3.1   5.5   0   0   0   9.5.

4.1.2 Using the Colon Operator

The colon operator is very powerful in defining new matrices and modifying the existing ones. First, we can use it to define an evenly spaced matrix. For example,

    H = 1:8

returns

    H =
            1   2   3   4   5   6   7   8.

The default spacing is 1. However, when colons are used to separate three numbers, the middle value becomes the spacing. Thus,

    time = 0.0 : 0.5 : 2.0

returns

    time =
            0   0.5000   1.0000   1.5000   2.0000.

The colon operator can also be used to extract data from matrices, a feature that is very useful in data analysis. When a colon is used in a matrix reference in place of a specific index number, the colon represents the entire row or column.

Suppose we define M as

    M = [1 2 3 4 5;
         2 3 4 5 6;
         3 4 5 6 7];

We can extract column 1 from matrix M with the command

    x = M(:, 1)

which returns

    x =
            1
            2
            3.

We read this syntax as "all the rows in column 1." We can extract any of the columns in a similar manner. For instance,

```
y = M(:, 4)
```

returns

```
y =
      4
      5
      6
```

and can be interpreted as "all the rows in column 4." Similarly, to extract a row,

```
z = M(1,:)
```

returns

```
z =
      1   2   3   4   5
```

and is read as "row 1, all the columns."

We don't have to extract an entire row or an entire column. The colon operator can also be used to mean "from row to row" or "from column to column." To extract the two bottom rows of the matrix M, type

```
w = M(2:3,:)
```

which returns

```
w =
      2   3   4   5   6
      3   4   5   6   7
```

and reads "rows 2 to 3, all the columns." Similarly, to extract just the four numbers in the lower right-hand corner of matrix M,

```
w = M(2:3, 4:5)
```

returns

```
w =
      5   6
      6   7
```

and reads "rows 2 to 3 in columns 4 to 5."

In MATLAB®, it is valid to have a matrix that is empty. For example, each of the following statements will generate an empty matrix:

```
a = [ ];
b = 4:-1:5;
```

Finally, using the matrix name with a single colon, such as

```
M(:)
```

transforms the matrix into one long column.

KEY IDEA

You can identify an element using either a single number, or indices representing the row and column.

M =

1
2
3
2
3
4
3
4
5
4
5
6
5
6
7

This matrix was formed by first listing column 1, then adding column 2 onto the end, tacking on column 3, and so on. Actually, the computer does not store two-dimensional arrays in a two-dimensional pattern. Rather, it "thinks" of a matrix as one long list, just like the matrix **M** at the left. There are two ways you can extract a single value from an array: by using a single index number or by using the row, column notation. To find the value in row 2, column 3, use the following commands:

```
M
M =
        1   2   3   4   5
        2   3   4   5   6
        3   4   5   6   7
M(2, 3)
ans =
        4
```

Alternatively, you can use a single index number. The value in row 2, column 3 of matrix M is element number 8. (Count down column 1, then down column 2, and finally down column 3 to the correct element.) The associated MATLAB® command is

```
M(8)
ans = 4.
```

HINT

You can use the word "end" to identify the final row or column in a matrix, even if you don't know how big it is. For example,

```
    M(1,end)
```

returns

```
    ans =
            5
```

and

```
    M(end, end)
```

returns

```
    ans =
            7
```

as does

```
    M(end)
    ans =
            7.
```

PRACTICE EXERCISE 4.1

Create MATLAB® variables to represent the following matrices, and use them in the exercises that follow. The correct answers can be found on the Pearson website.

$$a = [12 \quad 17 \quad 3 \quad 6] \quad b = \begin{bmatrix} 5 & 8 & 3 \\ 1 & 2 & 3 \\ 2 & 4 & 6 \end{bmatrix} \quad c = \begin{bmatrix} 22 \\ 17 \\ 4 \end{bmatrix}$$

1. Assign to the variable x1 the value in the second column of matrix a. This is sometimes represented in mathematics textbooks as element $a_{1,2}$ and could be expressed as x1 = $a_{1,2}$.
2. Assign to the variable x2 the third column of matrix b.
3. Assign to the variable x3 the third row of matrix b.
4. Assign to the variable x4 the values in matrix b along the diagonal (i.e., elements $b_{1,1}$, $b_{2,2}$, and $b_{3,3}$).
5. Assign to the variable x5 the first three values in matrix a as the first row, and all the values in matrix b as the second through the fourth row.
6. Assign to the variable x6 the values in matrix c as the first column, the values in matrix b as columns 2, 3, and 4, and the values in matrix a as the last row.
7. Assign to the variable x7 the value of element 8 in matrix b, using the single-index-number identification scheme.
8. Convert matrix b to a column vector named x8.

EXAMPLE 4.1

USING TEMPERATURE DATA

The data collected by the National Weather Service are extensive but are not always organized in exactly the way we would like (see Figure 4.1). Take, for example, the

Figure 4.1
Temperature data collected from a weather satellite were used to create this composite false-color image. (NASA)

summary of the 1999 Asheville, North Carolina, Climatological Data. We'll use these data to practice manipulating matrices—both extracting elements and recombining elements to form new matrices.

The numeric information has been extracted from the table (Appendix D) and is in an Excel file called **Asheville_1999.xls.** Use MATLAB® to confirm that the reported values on the annual row are correct for the mean maximum temperature and the mean minimum temperature, as well as for the annual high temperature and the annual low temperature. Combine these four columns of data into a new matrix called **temp_data.**

1. State the problem
   Calculate the annual mean maximum temperature, the annual mean minimum temperature, the highest temperature reached during the year, and the lowest temperature reached during the year for 1999 in Asheville, North Carolina.
2. Describe the input and output
   Input   Import a matrix from the Excel file **Asheville_1999.xls.**
   Output Find the following four values: annual mean maximum temperature
                                              annual mean minimum temperature
                                              highest temperature
                                              lowest temperature
   Create a matrix composed of the mean maximum temperature values, the mean minimum temperature values, the highest monthly temperatures, and the lowest monthly temperatures. Do not include the annual data.
3. Develop a hand example
   Using a calculator, add the values in column 2 of the table and divide by 12.
4. Develop a MATLAB® solution
   First import the data from Excel, then save them in the current directory as **Asheville_1999.** Save the variable **Asheville_1999** as the file **Asheville_1999.mat.** This makes it available to be loaded into the workspace from our M-file program:

```
%% Example 4.1
%  In this example, we extract data from a large matrix and
%  use the data analysis functions to find the mean high
%  and mean low temperatures for the year and to find the
%  high temperature and the low temperature for the year
%
clear, clc
%  load the data matrix from a file
load asheville_1999
%  extract the mean high temperatures from the large matrix
mean_max = asheville_1999(1:12,2);
%  extract the mean low temperatures from the large matrix
mean_min = asheville_1999(1:12,3);
%  Calculate the annual means
annual_mean_max = mean(mean_max)
annual_mean_min = mean(mean_min)
%  extract the high and low temperatures from the large
%  matrix
high_temp = asheville_1999(1:12,8);
low_temp = asheville_1999(1:12,10);
%  Find the max and min temperature for the year
```

(continued)

```
max_high = max(high_temp)
min_low = min(low_temp)
%  Create a new matrix with just the temperature
%  information
new_table =[mean_max, mean_min, high_temp, low_temp]
```

The results are displayed in the command window:

```
annual_mean_max =
    68.0500
annual_mean_min =
    46.3250
max_high =
    96
min_low =
    9
new_table =
    51.4000     31.5000     78.0000     9.0000
    52.6000     32.1000     66.0000     16.0000
    52.7000     32.5000     76.0000     22.0000
    ...
    67.6000     45.5000     78.0000     28.0000
    62.2000     40.7000     76.0000     26.0000
    53.6000     30.5000     69.0000     15.0000
```

5. Test the solution

Compare the results against the bottom line of the table from the Asheville, North Carolina, Climatological Survey. It is important to confirm that the results are accurate before you start to use any computer program to process data.

4.2 PROBLEMS WITH TWO VARIABLES—USING MESHGRID

All of the calculations we have done thus far have used only one variable. Of course, most physical phenomena can vary with many different factors. In this section, we consider how to perform the same calculations when the variables are represented by vectors.

Consider the following MATLAB® statements:

```
x = 3;
y = 5;
A = x * y
```

Since **x** and **y** are scalars, it's an easy calculation: **x*y** = 15, or

```
A =
        15.
```

Now, let's see what happens if **x** is a matrix and **y** is still a scalar:

```
x = 1:5;
```

returns five values of **x**. Because **y** is still a scalar with only one value (5),

```
A = x * y
```

returns

```
A =
         5   10   15   20   25.
```

This is still a review. But what happens if **y** is now a vector? Then,

```
y = 1:3;
A = x * y
```

returns an error statement:

```
??? Error using = => *
Inner matrix dimensions must agree.
```

KEY IDEA

When formulating
problems with two
variables, the matrix
dimensions must agree.

This error statement reminds us that the asterisk is the operator for matrix multiplication, which is not what we want. We want the dot-asterisk operator (. *), which will perform an element-by-element multiplication. However, the two vectors, **x** and **y**, will need to be the same length for this to work. Thus,

```
y = linspace(1,3,5)
```

creates a new vector **y** with five evenly spaced elements:

```
y =
      1.0000    1.5000    2.0000    2.5000    3.0000
A = x .* y
A =
      1    3    6    10    15
```

However, although this solution works, the result is probably not what you really want. You can think of the results as the diagonal on a matrix (see Table 4.1).

What if we want to know the result for element 3 of vector **x** and element 5 of vector **y**? This approach obviously doesn't give us all the possible answers. We want a two-dimensional matrix of answers that corresponds to all the combinations of **x** and **y**. In order for the answer **A**, to be a two-dimensional matrix, the input vectors must be two-dimensional matrices. MATLAB® has a built-in function called meshgrid that will help us accomplish this—and **x** and **y** don't even have to be the same size.

First, let's change **y** back to a three-element vector:

```
y = 1:3;
```

Table 4.1 Results of an Element-by-Element Calculation

		x				
		1	2	3	4	5
	1.0	1				
	1.5		3			
y	2.0			6		
	2.5				10	
	3.0			?		15

Then, we'll use `meshgrid` to create a new two-dimensional version of both **x** and **y** that we'll call new_x and new_y:

```
[new_x, new_y] = meshgrid(x,y)
```

The `meshgrid` command takes the two input vectors and creates two two-dimensional matrices. Each of the resulting matrices has the same number of rows and columns. The number of columns is determined by the number of elements in the first input vector (**x**), and the number of rows is determined by the number of elements in the second input vector (**y**). This operation is called *mapping the vectors into a two-dimensional array*:

KEY IDEA

Use the meshgrid function to map two one-dimensional variables into two-dimensional variables of equal size.

```
new_x =
        1   2   3   4   5
        1   2   3   4   5
        1   2   3   4   5
new_y =
        1   1   1   1   1
        2   2   2   2   2
        3   3   3   3   3
```

Notice that all the rows in new_x are the same, and all the columns in new_y are the same. Now, it's possible to multiply new_x by new_y and get the two-dimensional grid of results we really want:

```
A = new_x.*new_y
A =
        1   2   3    4    5
        2   4   6    8   10
        3   6   9   12   15
```

PRACTICE EXERCISE 4.2

USING MESHGRID

The correct answers can be found on the Pearson website.

1. The area of a rectangle (see Figure 4.2) is length times width (area = length × width). Find the areas of rectangles with lengths of 1, 3, and 5 cm, and with widths of 2, 4, 6, and 8 cm. (You should have 12 answers.)
2. The volume of a circular cylinder is, volume = $\pi r^2 h$. Find the volume of cylindrical containers with radii from 0 to 12 m, and heights from 10 to 20 m. Increment the radius dimension by 3 m and the height by 2 m as you span the two ranges.

Figure 4.2
Dimensions of a rectangle and a circular cylinder.

EXAMPLE 4.2

DISTANCE TO THE HORIZON

You've probably experienced standing on the top of a hill or a mountain and feeling like you can see forever. How far can you really see? It depends on the height of the mountain and the radius of the earth, as shown in Figure 4.3. The distance to the horizon is quite different on the moon than on the earth, because the radius is different for each. Using the Pythagorean theorem, we see that

$$R^2 + d^2 = (R + h)^2$$

and solving for d yields $d = \sqrt{h^2 + 2Rh}$.

From this last expression, find the distance to the horizon on the earth and on the moon, for mountains from 0 to 8000 m. (Mount Everest is 8850 m tall.) The radius of the earth is 6378 km, and the radius of the moon is 1737 km.

1. **State the problem**
   Find the distance to the horizon from the top of a mountain on the moon and on the earth.

2. **Describe the input and output**

   Input

Radius of the moon	1737 km
Radius of the earth	6378 km
Height of the mountains	0 to 8000 m

   Output

   Distance to the horizon, in kilometers.

3. **Develop a hand example**

$$d = \sqrt{h^2 + 2Rh}$$

   Using the radius of the earth and an 8000-m mountain yields

$$d = \sqrt{(8\ \text{km})^2 + 2 \times 6378\ \text{km} \times 8\ \text{km}} = 319\ \text{km}$$

4. **Develop a MATLAB® solution**

```
%% Example 4.2
%Find the distance to the horizon
%Define the height of the mountains
%in meters
clear, clc
format bank
%Define the height vector
height=0:1000:8000;
%Convert meters to km
height=height/1000;
%Define the radii of the moon and earth
radius = [1737 6378];
%Map the radii and heights onto a 2D grid
  [Radius,Height] = meshgrid(radius,height);
%Calculate the distance to the horizon
distance = sqrt(Height.^2 + 2*Height.*Radius)
```

Figure 4.3
Distance to the horizon.

(continued)

Executing the preceding script returns an array of the distances to the horizon on both the moon and the earth:

```
Distance =
         0        0
     58.95    112.95
     83.38    159.74
    102.13    195.65
    117.95    225.92
    131.89    252.60
    144.50    276.72
    156.10    298.90
    166.90    319.55
```

5. Test the solution
Compare the MATLAB® solution with the hand solution. The distance to the horizon from near the top of Mount Everest (8000 m) is over 300 km and matches the value calculated in MATLAB®.

EXAMPLE 4.3

FREE FALL

The general equation for the distance that a freely falling body has traveled (neglecting air friction) is

$$d = \frac{1}{2}gt^2$$

where

d = distance,

g = acceleration due to gravity, and

t = time.

When a satellite orbits a planet, it is in free fall. Many people believe that when the spacecraft enters orbit, it leaves gravity behind; gravity, though, is what keeps the spacecraft in orbit. The spacecraft (or any satellite) is actually falling toward the earth (see Figure 4.4). If it is going fast enough horizontally, it stays in orbit; if it's going too slowly, it hits the ground.

The value of the constant g, the acceleration due to gravity, depends on the mass of the planet. On different planets, g has different values (see Table 4.2).

Find how far an object would fall at times from 0 to 100 seconds on each planet in our solar system, and on our moon.

Figure 4.4
The spacecraft is constantly falling toward the earth. (NASA Headquarters)

1. State the problem
Find the distance traveled by a freely falling object on planets with different gravities.

2. Describe the input and output
Input Value of g, the acceleration due to gravity, on each of the planets and the moon.

Time = 0 to 100 s

Output   Distances calculated for each planet and the moon.

3. Develop a hand example

$$d = 1/2 \, gt^2, \text{ so on Mercury at 100 seconds:}$$
$$d = 1/2 \times 3.7 \text{ m/s}^2 \times 100^2 \text{s}^2$$
$$d = 18,500 \text{ m}$$

Table 4.2 Acceleration Due to Gravity in Our Solar System

Mercury	$g = 3.7$ m/s^2
Venus	$g = 8.87$ m/s^2
Earth	$g = 9.8$ m/s^2
Moon	$g = 1.6$ m/s^2
Mars	$g = 3.7$ m/s^2
Jupiter	$g = 23.12$ m/s^2
Saturn	$g = 8.96$ m/s^2
Uranus	$g = 8.69$ m/s^2
Neptune	$g = 11.0$ m/s^2
Pluto	$g = 0.58$ m/s^2

4. Develop a MATLAB® solution

```
%%    Example 4.3
%Free fall
clear, clc
%Try the problem first with only two planets, and a coarse
% grid
format shortg
%Define constants for acceleration due to gravity on
%Mercury and Venus
acceleration_due_to_gravity = [3.7, 8.87];
time=0:10:100; %Define time vector
%Map acceleration_due_to_gravity and time into 2D matrices
  [g,t] = meshgrid(acceleration_due_to_gravity, time);
%Calculate the distances
distance=1/2*g.*t.^2
```

Executing the preceding script returns the following values of distance traveled on Mercury and on Venus.

```
distance =
              0            0
            185        443.5
            740         1774
           1665       3991.5
           2960         7096
```

(continued)

4625	11087
6660	15966
9065	21731
11840	28384
14985	35923
18500	44350

5. Test the solution

Compare the MATLAB® solution with the hand solution. We can see that the distance traveled on Mercury at 100 seconds is 18,500 m, which corresponds to the hand calculation.

The program included the calculations for just the first two planets and was performed first to work out any programming difficulties. Once we've confirmed that the program works, it is easy to redo with the data for all the planets:

```
%Redo the problem with all the data
clear, clc
format shortg
%Define constants
acceleration_due_to_gravity = [3.7, 8.87, 9.8, 1.6, 3.7,
23.12 8.96, 8.69, 11.0, 0.58];
time=0:10:100;
%Map acceleration_due_to_gravity and time into 2D matrices
 [g,t] = meshgrid(acceleration_due_to_gravity,time);
%Calculate the distances
d=1/2*g.*t.^2
```

Figure 4.5
Results of the distance calculations for an object falling on each of the planets.

There are several important things to notice about the results shown in Figure 4.5. First, look at the workspace window—acceleration_due_to_gravity is a 1×10 matrix (one value for each of the planets and the moon), and time is a 1×11 matrix (11 values of time). However, both g and t are 11×10 matrices—the result of the meshgrid operation. The results shown in the command window were formatted with the format shortg command to make the output easier to read; otherwise there would have been a common scale factor.

HINT

As you create a MATLAB® program in the editing window, you may want to comment out sections of the code which you know work, then uncomment them later. Although you can do this by adding one % at a time to each line, it's easier to highlight the code you'd like to comment out, then select "Comment" on the editing toolstrip. You can also access this menu by right-clicking in the edit window.

4.3 SPECIAL MATRICES

MATLAB® contains a group of functions that generate special matrices; we present some of these functions in Table 4.3.

4.3.1 Matrix of Zeros

It is sometimes useful to create a matrix of all zeros. When the zeros function is used with a single scalar input argument, n, a square $n \times n$ matrix is generated:

```
A = zeros(3)
A =
        0    0    0
        0    0    0
        0    0    0
```

If we use two scalar arguments, the first value specifies the number of rows and the second the number of columns:

```
B = zeros(3,2)
B =
        0    0
        0    0
        0    0
```

4.3.2 Matrix of Ones

KEY IDEA

Use a matrix of zeros or ones as placeholders for future calculations.

The ones function is similar to the zeros function, but creates a matrix of ones:

```
A = ones(3)
A =
        1    1    1
        1    1    1
        1    1    1
```

Table 4.3 Functions to Create and Manipulate Matrices

`zeros(m)`	Creates an $m \times m$ matrix of zeros.	`zeros(3)`
		`ans =`
		`    0    0    0`
		`    0    0    0`
		`    0    0    0`

`zeros(m,n)`	Creates an $m \times n$ matrix of zeros.	`zeros(2,3)`
		`ans =`
		`    0    0    0`
		`    0    0    0`

`ones(m)`	Creates an $m \times m$ matrix of ones.	`ones(3)`
		`ans =`
		`    1    1    1`
		`    1    1    1`
		`    1    1    1`

`ones(m,n)`	Creates an $m \times n$ matrix of ones.	`ones(2,3)`
		`ans =`
		`    1    1    1`
		`    1    1    1`

`diag(A)`	Extracts the diagonal of a two-dimensional matrix **A**.	`A = [123;345;123];`
		`diag(A)`
		`ans =`
		`    1`
		`    4`
		`    3`

	For any vector **A**, creates a square matrix with **A** as the diagonal. Check the `help` function for other ways the `diag` function can be used.	`A = [123];`
		`diag(A)`
		`ans =`
		`    1    0    0`
		`    0    2    0`
		`    0    0    3`

`fliplr`	Flips a matrix into its mirror image, from right to left.	`A = [100;020;003];`
		`fliplr(A)`
		`ans =`
		`    0    0    1`
		`    0    2    0`
		`    3    0    0`

`flipud`	Flips a matrix vertically.	`flipud(A)`
		`ans =`
		`    0    0    3`
		`    0    2    0`
		`    1    0    0`

`magic(m)`	Creates an $m \times n$ "magic" matrix.	`magic(3)`
		`ans =`
		`    8    1    6`
		`    3    5    7`
		`    4    9    2`

As with the `zeros` function, if we use two inputs, we can control the number of rows and columns:

```
B = ones(3,2)
B =
       1   1
       1   1
       1   1
```

The `zeros` and `ones` functions are useful for creating matrices with "placeholder" values that will be filled in later. For example, if you wanted a vector of five numbers, all of which were equal to π, you might first create a vector of ones:

```
a = ones(1,5)
```

This gives

```
a =
       1   1   1   1   1.
```

Then, multiply by π.

```
b = a*pi
```

The result is

```
b =
       3.1416   3.1416   3.1416   3.1416   3.1416.
```

The same result could be obtained by adding π to a matrix of zeros. For example,

```
a = zeros(1,5);
b = a+pi
```

gives

```
b =
       3.1416   3.1416   3.1416   3.1416   3.1416.
```

A placeholder matrix is especially useful in MATLAB® programs with a loop structure, because it can reduce the time required to execute the loop.

4.3.3 Diagonal Matrices

We can use the `diag` function to extract the diagonal from a matrix. For example, if we define a square matrix

```
A = [1 2 3; 3 4 5; 1 2 3];
```

then using the function

```
diag(A)
```

extracts the main diagonal and gives the following results:

```
ans =
       1.00
       4.00
       3.00
```

Figure 4.6
Each diagonal in a matrix can be described by means of the parameter **k**.

Other diagonals can be extracted by defining a second input, k, to diag. Positive values of k specify diagonals in the upper right-hand corner of the matrix, and negative values specify diagonals in the lower left-hand corner (see Figure 4.6).

Thus, the command

```
diag(A,1)
```

returns

```
ans =
    2
    5.
```

If, instead of using a two-dimensional matrix as input to the diag function, we use a vector such as

```
B = [1 2 3];
```

then, MATLAB® uses the vector for the values along the diagonal of a new matrix and fills in the remaining elements with zeros:

```
diag(B)
ans =
    1   0   0
    0   2   0
    0   0   3
```

By specifying a second parameter, we can move the diagonal to any place in the matrix:

```
diag(B,1)
ans =
    0   1   0   0
    0   0   2   0
    0   0   0   3
    0   0   0   0
```

4.3.4 Magic Matrices

MATLAB® includes a matrix function called magic that generates a matrix with unusual properties. At the present time, there does not seem to be any practical use for magic matrices—except that they are interesting. In a magic matrix, the sums of the columns are the same, as are the sums of the rows. An example is

```
A = magic(4)
A =
    16    2    3   13
     5   11   10    8
     9    7    6   12
     4   14   15    1
sum(A)
ans =
    34   34   34   34.
```

To find the sums of the rows, we can either transpose the matrix:

```
sum(A')
ans =
   34   34   34   34
```

or request that the function operate on rows by specifying the dimension in the second field

```
sum(A,2).
```

Not only are the sums of all the columns and rows the same, but the sums of the diagonals are also the same. The diagonal from left to right is

```
diag(A)
ans =
   16
   11
    6
    1.
```

The sum of the diagonal is the same number as the sums of the rows and columns:

```
sum(diag(A))
ans =
   34
```

Finally, to find the diagonal from lower left to upper right, we first have to "flip" the matrix, then find the sum of the diagonal:

```
fliplr(A)
ans =
   13    3    2   16
    8   10   11    5
   12    6    7    9
    1   15   14    4
diag(ans)
ans =
   13
   10
    7
    4
sum(ans)
ans =
   34
```

Figure 4.7 shows one of the earliest documented examples of a magic square— Albrecht Dürer's woodcut "Melancholia," created in 1514. Scholars believe the square was a reference to alchemical concepts popular at the time. The date 1514 is included in the two middle squares of the bottom row (see Figure 4.8).

Magic squares have fascinated both professional and amateur mathematicians for centuries. For example, Benjamin Franklin experimented with magic squares. You can create magic squares of any size greater than 2×2 in MATLAB®. MATLAB®'s solution is not the only one; other magic squares are possible.

Figure 4.7
"Melancholia" by Albrecht
Dürer, 1514. (INTERFOTO/
Alamy)

Figure 4.8
Albrecht Dürer included the
date of the woodcut (1514)
in the magic square.
(INTERFOTO/Alamy)

PRACTICE EXERCISE 4.3

The correct answers can be found on the Pearson website.

1. Create a 3×3 matrix of zeros.
2. Create a 3×4 matrix of zeros.
3. Create a 3×3 matrix of ones.
4. Create a 5×3 matrix of ones.
5. Create a 4×6 matrix in which all the elements have a value of pi.
6. Use the `diag` function to create a matrix whose diagonal has values of 1, 2, 3.
7. Create a 10×10 magic matrix.

   a. Extract the diagonal from this matrix.
   b. Extract the diagonal that runs from lower left to upper right from this matrix.
   c. Confirm that the sums of the rows, columns, and diagonals are all the same.

SUMMARY

This chapter concentrated on manipulating matrices, a capability that allows the user to create complicated matrices by combining smaller ones. It also lets you extract portions of an existing matrix. The colon operator is especially useful for these operations. The colon operator should be interpreted as "all of the rows" or "all of the columns" when used in place of a row or column designation. It should be interpreted as "from _ to _" when it is used between row or column numbers. For example,

```
A(:,2:3)
```

should be interpreted as "all the rows in matrix **A**, and all the columns from 2 to 3." When used alone as the sole index, as in **A(:)**, it creates a matrix that is a single column from a two-dimensional representation. The computer actually stores all array information as a list, making both single-index notation and row-column notation useful alternatives for specifying the location of a value in a matrix.

The meshgrid function is extremely useful, since it can be used to map vectors into two-dimensional matrices, making it possible to perform array calculations with vectors of unequal size.

MATLAB® contains a number of functions that make it easy to create special matrices:

- **zeros,** which is used to create a matrix composed entirely of zeros.
- **ones,** which is used to create a matrix composed entirely of ones.
- **diag,** which can be used to extract the diagonal from a matrix or, if the input is a vector, to create a square matrix.
- **magic,** which can be used to create a matrix with the unusual property that all the rows and columns add up to the same value, as do the diagonals.

In addition, a number of functions were included that allow the user to "flip" the matrix either from left to right, or from top to bottom.

MATLAB® SUMMARY

The following MATLAB® summary lists and briefly describes all of the special characters, commands, and functions that were defined in this chapter.

Special Characters	
:	colon operator
...	ellipsis, indicating continuation on the next line
[]	empty matrix

Commands and Functions	
meshgrid	maps vectors into a two-dimensional array
zeros	creates a matrix of zeros
ones	creates a matrix of ones
diag	extracts the diagonal from a matrix
fliplr	flips a matrix into its mirror image, from left to right
flipud	flips a matrix vertically
magic	creates a "magic" matrix

KEY TERMS

elements   magic matrices   subscripts
index numbers   mapping

PROBLEMS

Manipulating Matrices

4.1 Create the following matrices, and use them in the exercises that follow:

$$a = \begin{bmatrix} 15 & 3 & 22 \\ 3 & 8 & 5 \\ 14 & 3 & 82 \end{bmatrix} \quad b = \begin{bmatrix} 1 \\ 5 \\ 6 \end{bmatrix} \quad c = \begin{bmatrix} 12 & 18 & 5 & 2 \end{bmatrix}$$

(a) Create a matrix called **d** from the third column of matrix **a**.

(b) Combine matrix **b** and matrix **d** to create matrix **e**, a two-dimensional matrix with three rows and two columns.

(c) Combine matrix **b** and matrix **d** to create matrix **f**, a one-dimensional matrix with six rows and one column.

(d) Create a matrix **g** from matrix **a** and the first three elements of matrix **c**, with four rows and three columns.

(e) Create a matrix **h** with the first element equal to $a_{1,3}$, the second element equal to $c_{1,2}$, and the third element equal to $b_{2,1}$.

4.2 Load the file **thermo_scores.dat** provided by your instructor, or enter the matrix shown in Table P4.2 and name it *thermo_scores*. (Enter only the numbers.)

Table P4.2 Thermodynamics Test Scores

Student No.	Test 1	Test 2	Test 3
1	68	45	92
2	83	54	93
3	61	67	91
4	70	66	92
5	75	68	96
6	82	67	90
7	57	65	89
8	5	69	89
9	76	62	97
10	85	52	94
11	62	34	87
12	71	45	85
13	96	56	45
14	78	65	87
15	76	43	97
16	68	76	95
17	72	65	89
18	75	67	88
19	83	68	91
20	93	90	92

(a) Extract the scores and student number for student 5 into a row vector named **student_5**.
(b) Extract the scores for Test 1 into a column vector named **test_1**.
(c) Find the standard deviation and variance for each test.
(d) Assuming that each test was worth 100 points, find each student's final total score and final percentage. (Be careful not to add in the student number.)
(e) Create a table that includes the final percentages and the scores from the original table.
(f) Sort the matrix on the basis of the final percentage, from high to low (in descending order), keeping the data in each row together. (You may need to consult the help function to determine the proper syntax.)

4.3 Consider the the thermocouple data in Table P4.3:

Table P4.3 Thermocouple Data

Time (hr)	Thermocouple 1 °F	Thermocouple 2 °F	Thermocouple 3 °F
0	84.3	90.0	86.7
2	86.4	89.5	87.6
4	85.2	88.6	88.3
6	87.1	88.9	85.3
8	83.5	88.9	80.3
10	84.8	90.4	82.4
12	85.0	89.3	83.4
14	85.3	89.5	85.4
16	85.3	88.9	86.3
18	85.2	89.1	85.3
20	82.3	89.5	89.0
22	84.7	89.4	87.3
24	83.6	89.8	87.2

(a) Create a column vector named **times** going from 0 to 24 in 2-hour increments.
(b) Your instructor may provide you with the thermocouple temperatures in a file called **thermocouple.dat**, or you may need to create a matrix named **thermocouple** yourself by typing in the data.
(c) Combine the **times** vector you created in part (a) with the data from **thermocouple** to create a matrix corresponding to the table in this problem.
(d) Recall that both the **max** and **min** functions can return not only the maximum values in a column, but also the element number where those values occur. Use this capability to determine the values of **times** at which the maxima and minima occur in each column.

4.4 Suppose that a file named **sensor.dat** contains information collected from a set of sensors. Your instructor may provide you with this file, or you may need to enter it by hand from the data in table P4.4.
Each row contains a set of sensor readings, with the first row containing values collected at 0 seconds, the second row containing values collected at 0.5 seconds, and so on.

(a) Read the data file and print the number of sensors and the number of seconds of data contained in the file. (**Hint:** Use the **size** function—don't just count the two numbers.)

Table P4.4 Sensor Data

Time (s)	Sensor 1	Sensor 2	Sensor 3	Sensor 4	Sensor 5
0.0000	70.6432	68.3470	72.3469	67.6751	73.1764
0.5000	73.2823	65.7819	65.4822	71.8548	66.9929
1.0000	64.1609	72.4888	70.1794	73.6414	72.7559
1.5000	67.6970	77.4425	66.8623	80.5608	64.5008
2.0000	68.6878	67.2676	72.6770	63.2135	70.4300
2.5000	63.9342	65.7662	2.7644	64.8869	59.9772
3.0000	63.4028	68.7683	68.9815	75.1892	67.5346
3.5000	74.6561	73.3151	59.7284	68.0510	72.3102
4.0000	70.0562	65.7290	70.6628	63.0937	68.3950
4.5000	66.7743	63.9934	77.9647	71.5777	76.1828
5.0000	74.0286	69.4007	75.0921	77.7662	66.8436
5.5000	71.1581	69.6735	62.0980	73.5395	58.3739
6.0000	65.0512	72.4265	69.6067	79.7869	63.8418
6.5000	76.6979	67.0225	66.5917	72.5227	75.2782
7.0000	71.4475	69.2517	64.8772	79.3226	69.4339
7.5000	77.3946	67.8262	63.8282	68.3009	71.8961
8.0000	75.6901	69.6033	71.4440	64.3011	74.7210
8.5000	66.5793	77.6758	67.8535	68.9444	59.3979
9.0000	63.5403	66.9676	70.2790	75.9512	66.7766
9.5000	69.6354	63.2632	68.1606	64.4190	66.4785

(b) Find both the maximum value and the minimum value recorded on each sensor. Use MATLAB® to determine at what times they occurred.

(c) Find the mean and standard deviation for each sensor and for all the data values collected. Remember, column 1 does not contain sensor data; it contains time data.

4.5 The American National Oceanic and Atmospheric Administration (NOAA) measures the intensity of a hurricane season with the accumulated cyclone energy (ACE) index. The ACE for a season is the sum of the ACE for each tropical storm with winds exceeding 35 knots (65 km/h). The maximum sustained winds (measured in knots) in the storm are measured or approximated every six hours. The values are squared and summed over the duration of the storm. The total is divided by 10,000, to make the parameter easier to use.

$$ACE = \frac{\Sigma v_{max}^2}{10^4}$$

This parameter is related to the energy of the storm, since kinetic energy is proportional to velocity squared. However, it does not take into account the size of the storm, which would be necessary for a true total energy estimate. Reliable storm data have been collected in the Atlantic Ocean since 1950 and are shown in table P4.5. These data may also be available to you from your instructor as an EXCEL worksheet, **ace.xlsx**, and was extracted from the *Accumulated Cyclone Energy* article in Wikipedia. (http://en.wikipedia.org/wiki/Accumulated_cyclone_energy). It was collected by the National Oceanic and Atmospheric Administration (http://www.aoml.noaa.gov/hrd/tcfaq/E11.html).

Table P4.5 Atlantic Basin Hurricane Seasons, 1950–2016

Year	ACE Index	# Tropical Storms	# Hurricanes Cat. 1–5	# Major Hurricanes Cat. 3–5
1950	243	13	11	8
1951	137	10	8	5
1952	87	7	6	3
1953	104	14	6	4
1954	113	11	8	2
1955	199	12	9	6
1956	54	8	4	2
1957	84	8	3	2
1958	121	10	7	5
1959	77	11	7	2
1960	88	7	4	2
1961	205	11	8	7
1962	36	5	3	1
1963	118	9	7	2
1964	170	12	6	6
1965	84	6	4	1
1966	145	11	7	3
1967	122	8	6	1
1968	35	7	4	0
1969	158	17	12	5
1970	34	10	5	2
1971	97	13	6	1
1972	28	4	3	0
1973	43	7	4	1
1974	61	7	4	2
1975	73	8	6	3
1976	81	8	6	2
1977	25	6	5	1
1978	62	11	5	2
1979	91	8	5	2
1980	147	11	9	2
1981	93	11	7	3
1982	29	5	2	1
1983	17	4	3	1
1984	71	12	5	1
1985	88	11	7	3
1986	36	6	4	0
1987	34	7	3	1
1988	103	12	5	3
1989	135	11	7	2
1990	91	14	8	1
1991	34	8	4	2
1992	75	6	4	1
1993	39	8	4	1
1994	32	7	3	0
1995	228	19	11	5
1996	166	13	9	6
1997	40	7	3	1
1998	182	14	10	3
1999	177	12	8	5
2000	116	14	8	3

(continued)

Table P4.5 (continued)

Year	ACE Index	# Tropical Storms	# Hurricanes Cat. 1–5	# Major Hurricanes Cat. 3–5
2001	106	15	9	4
2002	65	12	4	2
2003	175	16	7	3
2004	225	14	9	6
2005	248	28	15	7
2006	79	10	5	2
2007	72	15	6	2
2008	145	16	8	5
2009	51	9	3	2
2010	165	19	12	5
2011	126	19	7	4
2012	133	19	10	2
2013	36	14	2	0
2014	67	8	6	2
2015	63	11	4	2
2016*	112	14	6	2

*As of October 12, 2016

(a) Import the data into MATLAB®, and name the array **ace_data**.

(b) Extract the data from each column, into individual arrays. You should have arrays named
- **years**
- **ace**
- **tropical_storms**
- **hurricanes**
- **major_hurricanes**

(c) Use the `max` function to determine which year had the highest
- ACE value
- Number of tropical storms
- Number of hurricanes
- Number of major hurricanes

(d) Determine the **mean** and the **median** values for each column in the array, except for the year.

(e) Use the `sortrows` function to rearrange the **ace_data** array based on the ACE value, sorted from high to low.

The data presented in this problem are updated regularly.

4.6 ACE data similar to those presented in 4.5 are collected by NOAA for the eastern and central Pacific oceans, and can be found online from a number of sources including Wikipedia. Repeat 4.5 using the Pacific data.

Problems with Two Variables

4.7 The area of a triangle is, area = ¹/₂ base × height (see Figure P4.7). Find the area of a group of triangles whose base varies from 0 to 10 m, and whose height varies from 2 to 6 m. Choose an appropriate spacing for your calculational variables. Your answer should be a two-dimensional matrix.

4.8 A barometer (see Figure P4.8) is used to measure atmospheric pressure and is filled with a high-density fluid. In the past, mercury was used, but because of its toxic properties it has been replaced with a variety of other fluids. The pressure P measured by a barometer is the height of the fluid column, h, times the density of the liquid, ρ, times the acceleration due to gravity, g, or

Figure P4.7
The area of a triangle.

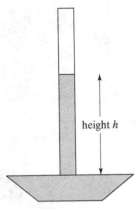

Figure P4.8

Barometer.

$$P = h\rho g.$$

This equation could be solved for the height:

$$h = \frac{P}{\rho g}$$

Find the height to which the liquid column will rise for pressures from 0 to 100 kPa for two different barometers. Assume that the first uses mercury, with a density of 13.56 g/cm³ (13,560 kg/m³) and the second uses water, with a density of 1.0 g/cm³ (1000 kg/m³). The acceleration due to gravity is 9.81 m/s². Before you start calculating, be sure to check the units in this calculation. The metric measurement of pressure is a pascal (Pa), equal to 1 kg/ms². A kPa is 1000 times as big as a Pa. Your answer should be a two-dimensional matrix.

4.9 The ideal gas law, $Pv = RT$, describes the behavior of many gases. When solved for v (the specific volume, m³/kg), the equation can be written

$$v = \frac{RT}{P}.$$

Find the specific volume for air, for temperatures from 100 to 1000 K and for pressures from 100 kPa to 1000 kPa. The value of R for air is 0.2870 kJ/(kg K). In this formulation of the ideal gas law, R is different for every gas. There are other formulations in which R is a constant, and the molecular weight of the gas must be included in the calculation. You'll learn more about this equation in chemistry classes and thermodynamics classes. Your answer should be a two-dimensional matrix.

Special Matrices

4.10 Create a matrix of zeros the same size as each of the matrices **a, b,** and **c** from 4.1. (Use the `size` function to help you accomplish this task.)

4.11 Create a 6 × 6 magic matrix.

(a) What is the sum of each of the rows?
(b) What is the sum of each of the columns?
(c) What is the sum of each of the diagonals?

4.12 Extract a 3 × 3 matrix from the upper left-hand corner of the magic matrix you created in 4.11. Is this also a magic matrix?

4.13 Create a 5 × 5 magic matrix named **a.**

(a) Is **a** times a constant such as 2 also a magic matrix?
(b) If you square each element of **a**, is the new matrix a magic matrix?
(c) If you add a constant to each element, is the new matrix a magic matrix?
(d) Create a 10 × 10 matrix out of the following components (see Figure P4.13):
  • The matrix **a**
  • 2 times the matrix **a**
  • A matrix formed by squaring each element of **a**
  • 2 plus the matrix **a**
Is your result a magic matrix? Does the order in which you arrange the components affect your answer?

4.14 Albrecht Dürer's magic square (see Figure 4.8) is not exactly the same as the 4 × 4 magic square created with the command

```
magic(4)
```

(a) Recreate Durer's magic square in MATLAB® by rearranging the columns.
(b) Prove that the sum of all the rows, columns, and diagonals is the same.

Figure P4.13

Create a matrix out of other matrices.

5

Plotting

Objectives

After reading this chapter, you should be able to:

- Create and label two-dimensional plots.
- Adjust the appearance of your plots.

- Divide the plotting window into subplots.
- Create three-dimensional plots.
- Use the interactive MATLAB® plotting tools.

INTRODUCTION

Large tables of data are difficult to interpret. Engineers use graphing techniques to make the information easier to understand. With a graph, it is easy to identify trends, pick out highs and lows, and isolate data points that may be measurement or calculation errors. Graphs can also be used as a quick check to determine whether a computer solution is yielding expected results.

5.1 TWO-DIMENSIONAL PLOTS

The most useful plot for engineers is the *x–y* plot. A set of ordered pairs is used to identify points on a two-dimensional graph; the points are then connected by straight lines. The values of *x* and *y* may be measured or calculated. Generally, the independent variable is given the name *x* and is plotted on the *x*-axis, and the dependent variable is given the name *y* and is plotted on the *y*-axis.

HINT

Major changes to MATLAB's graphing capabilities were introduced with version 2014a. If you are using earlier versions of the software, you may see differences in the output.

5.1.1 Basic Plotting

Simple x–y Plots

Once vectors of *x*-values and *y*-values have been defined, MATLAB® makes it easy to create plots. Suppose a set of time versus distance data were obtained through measurement.

We can store the time values in a vector called *x* (the user can define any convenient name) and the distance values in a vector called *y*:

```
x = [0:2:18];
y = [0 0.33 4.13 6.29 6.85 11.19 13.19 13.96 16.33 18.17];
```

To plot these points, use the `plot` command, with *x* and *y* as arguments:

```
plot(x, y)
```

Time, s	Distance, ft
0	0
2	0.33
4	4.13
6	6.29
8	6.85
10	11.19
12	13.19
14	13.96
16	16.33
18	18.17

A graphics window automatically opens, which MATLAB® names Figure 1. The resulting plot is shown in Figure 5.1(a). (Slight variations in scaling of the plot may

Figure 5.1
Simple plot of time versus distance created in MATLAB®. (a) The data are represented as an x–y plot. (b) The data are represented as an area plot.

(a)

(b)
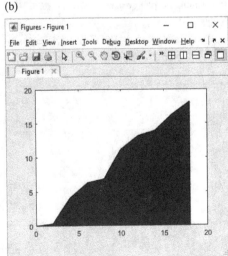

occur, depending on the size of the graphics window.) The area plot is quite similar, the only exception being that the area under the curve is filled in. The code

```
area(x,y)
```

results in the plot shown in Figure 5.1(b).

Titles, Labels, and Grids

KEY IDEA

Always include units on axis labels.

Good engineering practice requires that we include axis labels and a title in our plot. The following commands add a title, *x*- and *y*-axis labels, and a background grid:

```
plot(x,y)
title('Laboratory Experiment 1')
xlabel('Time, sec')
ylabel('Distance, ft')
grid on
```

These commands generate the plot in Figure 5.2. As with any MATLAB® commands, they could also be combined onto one or two lines to save space.

```
plot(x,y), title('Laboratory Experiment 1')
xlabel('Time, sec'), ylabel('Distance, ft'), grid
```

STRING

A list of characters enclosed by single quotes

As you type the preceding commands into MATLAB®, notice that the text color changes to red when you enter a single quote ('). This alerts you that you are starting a string. The color changes to purple when you type the final single quote ('), indicating that you have completed the string. Paying attention to these visual aids will help you avoid coding mistakes.

If you are working in the command window, the graphics window will open on the top of the other windows (see Figure 5.3). To continue working, either click in the command window, or minimize the graphics window. You can also resize the graphics window to whatever size is convenient for you, or add it to the MATLAB® desktop by selecting the docking arrow underneath the exit icon in the upper right-hand corner of the figure window.

Figure 5.2
Adding a grid, a title, and labels makes a plot easier to interpret.

Figure 5.3
The graphics window opens on the top of the command window. You can resize it to a convenient shape or dock it with the MATLAB® desktop.

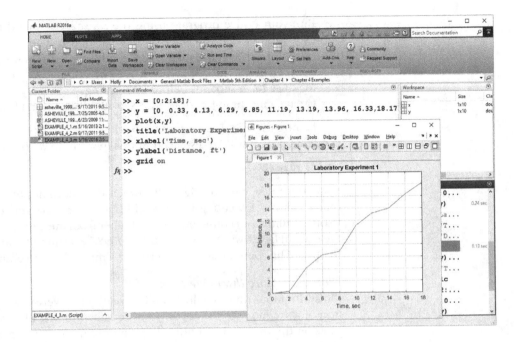

HINT

Once you click in the command window, the figure window is hidden behind the current window. To see the changes to your figure, you will need to select the figure from the Windows task bar at the bottom of the screen.

HINT

You must create a graph *before* you add the title and labels. If you specify the title and labels first, they are erased when the plot command executes.

HINT

Because a single quote is used to end the string used in `xlabel`, `ylabel`, and `title` commands, MATLAB® interprets an apostrophe (as in the word *it's*) as the end of the string. Entering the single quote twice, as in `xlabel('Holly"s Data')`, will allow you to use apostrophes in your text. (Don't use a double quote, which is a different character.)

Creating Multiple Plots

If you are working in a script when you request a plot, and then continue with more computations, MATLAB® will generate and display the graphics window and then return immediately to execute the rest of the commands in the program. If you request a second plot, the graph you created will be overwritten. There are three possible solutions to this problem:

- Use sections to execute your program interactively, one section at a-time—making sure that each section generates no more than one figure.

- Run your entire program using the `pause` command to temporarily halt the execution so that you can examine the figure. The `pause` command stops the program execution until any key is pressed. If you want to pause for a specified number of seconds, use the `pause(n)` command, which will cause execution to pause for n seconds before continuing.
- Create a multiple figure windows, using the `figure` function.

Issuing the `figure` command opens a new figure window. The next time you request a plot, it will be displayed in this new window. For example,

```
figure(2)
```

opens a window named "Figure 2," which then becomes the window used for subsequent plotting. Executing `figure` without an input parameter causes a new window to open, numbered consecutively one higher from the current window. For example, if the current figure window is named "Figure 2," executing `figure` will cause "Figure 3" to open. The commands used to create a simple plot are summarized in Table 5.1.

Plots with More than One Line

Plots with more than one line can be created in several ways. By default, the execution of a second `plot` statement will replace the first plot. However, you can layer plots on the top of one another by using the `hold on` command. Execute the following statements to create a plot with both functions plotted on the same graph, as shown in Figure 5.4:

```
x = 0:pi/100:2*pi;
y1 = cos(x*4);
plot(x,y1)
y2 = sin(x);
hold on;
plot(x, y2)
```

Semicolons are optional on both the `plot` statement and the `hold on` statement. MATLAB® will continue to layer the plots until the `hold off` command is executed:

```
hold off
```

Table 5.1 Basic Plotting Functions

`plot`	Creates an x–y plot	`plot(x,y)`
`title`	Adds a title to a plot	`title('My Graph')`
`xlabel`	Adds a label to the x-axis	`xlabel('Independent Variable')`
`ylabel`	Adds a label to the y-axis	`ylabel('Dependent Variable')`
`grid`	Adds a grid to the graph	`grid`
		`grid on`
		`grid off`
`pause`	Pauses the execution of the program, allowing the user to view the graph	`pause`
`figure`	Determines which figure will be used for the current plot	`figure`
		`figure(2)`
`hold`	Freezes the current plot, so that an additional plot can be overlaid	`hold on`
		`hold off`

Figure 5.4
The `hold on` command can be used to layer plots onto the same figure.

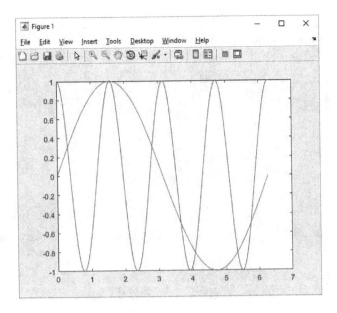

KEY IDEA
The most common plot used in engineering is the *x–y* scatter plot.

Another way to create a graph with multiple lines is to request both lines in a single `plot` command. MATLAB® interprets the input to `plot` as alternating **x** and **y** vectors, as in

```
plot(X1, Y1, X2, Y2)
```

where the variables `X1`, `Y1` form an ordered set of values to be plotted, and `X2`, `Y2` form a second ordered set of values. Using the data from the previous example,

```
plot(x, y1, x, y2)
```

produces the same graph as Figure 5.4.

If the `plot` function is called with a single matrix argument, MATLAB® draws a separate line for each column of the matrix. The *x*-axis is labeled with the row index vector, 1:*k*, where *k* is the number of rows in the matrix. This produces an evenly spaced plot, sometimes called a line plot. If `plot` is called with two arguments, one a vector and the other a matrix, MATLAB® successively plots a line for each row in the matrix. For example, we can combine `y1` and `y2` into a single matrix and plot against `x`:

```
Y = [y1; y2];
plot(x,Y)
```

This creates the same plot as Figure 5.4.

Here's another more complicated example:

```
X = 0:pi/100:2*pi;
Y1 = cos(X)*2;
Y2 = cos(X)*3;
Y3 = cos(X)*4;
Y4 = cos(X)*5;
Z = [Y1; Y2; Y3; Y4];
plot(X, Y1, X, Y2, X, Y3, X, Y4)
```

This code produces the same result (see Figure 5.5) as

```
plot(X, Z)
```

Figure 5.5
Multiple plots on the same graph.

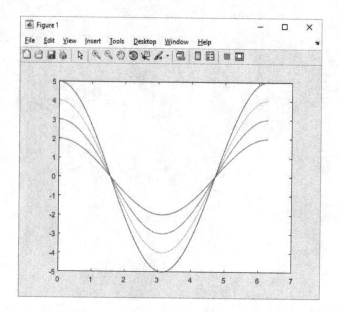

A function of two variables, the peaks function produces sample data that are useful for demonstrating certain graphing functions. (The data are created by scaling and translating Gaussian distributions.) Calling peaks with a single argument n will create an $n \times n$ matrix. We can use peaks to demonstrate the power of using a matrix argument in the plot function. The command

```
plot(peaks(100))
```

results in the impressive looking graph in Figure 5.6. The input to the plot function created by peaks is a 100×100 matrix. Notice that the x-axis goes from 1 to 100, the index numbers of the data. You undoubtedly can't tell, but there are 100 lines drawn to create this graph—one for each column.

Figure 5.6
The peaks function, plotted with a single argument in the plot command.

Plots of Complex Arrays

If the input to the `plot` command is a single array of complex numbers, MATLAB® plots the real component on the *x*-axis and the imaginary component on the *y*-axis. For example, if

```
A = [0+0i, 1+2i, 2+5i, 3+4i]
```

then

```
plot(A)
title('Plot of a Single Complex Array')
xlabel('Real Component')
ylabel('Imaginary Component')
```

returns the graph shown in Figure 5.7(a).

If we attempt to use two arrays of complex numbers in the `plot` function, the imaginary components are ignored. The real portion of the first array is used for the *x*-values, and the real portion of the second array is used for the *y*-values. To illustrate, first create another array called B by taking the sine of the complex array A:

```
B = sin(A)
```

returns

```
B = 0 3.1658 + 1.9596i 67.4789 - 30.8794i 3.8537 - 27.0168i
```

and

```
plot(A,B)
title('Plot of Two Complex Arrays')
xlabel('Real Component of the X array')
ylabel('Real Component of the Y array')
```

(a)   (b)

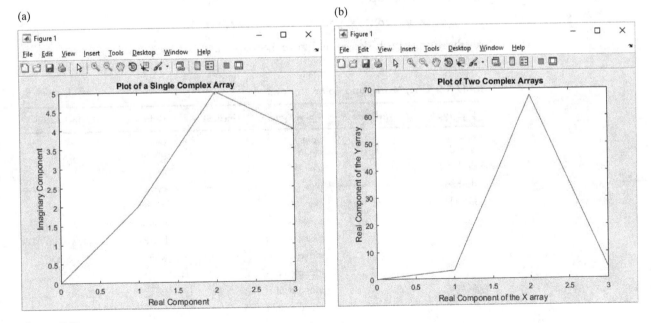

Figure 5.7

(a) Complex numbers are plotted with the real component on the *x*-axis and the imaginary component on the *y*-axis when a single array is used as input. (b) When two complex arrays are used in the `plot` function, the imaginary components are ignored.

gives us an error statement.

```
Warning: Imaginary parts of complex X and/or Y arguments
ignored.
```

The data are still plotted, as shown in Figure 5.7(b).

5.1.2 Line, Color, and Mark Style

You can change the appearance of your plots by selecting user-defined line styles and line colors, and by choosing to show the data points on the graph with user-specified mark styles. The command

```
help plot
```

returns a list of the available options. You can select solid (the default), dashed, dotted, and dash-dot line styles, and you can choose to show the points. The choices among marks include plus signs, stars, circles, and x-marks, among others. There are eight different color choices. (See Table 5.2 for a complete list.)

The following commands illustrate the use of line, color, and mark styles:

```
x = [1:10];
y = [58.5 63.8 64.2 67.3 71.5 88.3 90.1 90.6 89.5 90.4];
plot(x,y,':ok')
```

The resulting plot (see Figure 5.8(a)) consists of a dashed line, together with data points marked with circles. The line, the points, and the circles are drawn in black. The indicators were listed inside a string, denoted with single quotes. The order in which they are entered is arbitrary and does not affect the output.

To specify line, mark, and color styles for multiple lines, add a string containing the choices after each pair of data arrays. If the string is not included, the defaults are used. For example,

```
plot(x,y,':ok',x,y*2,'--xr',x,y/2,'-b')
```

results in the graph shown in Figure 5.8(b).

Table 5.2 Line, Mark, and Color Options

Line Type	Indicator	Point Type	Indicator	Color	Indicator
solid	-	point	.	blue	b
dotted	:	circle	o	green	g
dash-dot	-.	x-mark	x	red	r
dashed	--	plus	+	cyan	c
(none)	no line	star	*	magenta	m
		square	s	yellow	y
		diamond	d	black	k
		triangle down	v	white	w
		triangle up	^		
		triangle left	<		
		triangle right	>		
		pentagram	p		
		hexagram	h		

(a)   (b)

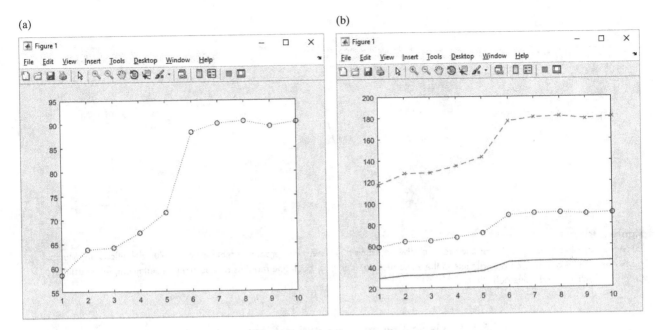

Figure 5.8
(a) Adjusting the line, mark, and color style. (b) Multiple plots with varying line styles and point styles.

The `plot` command offers additional options to control the way the plot appears. To control these properties you need to specify the property name and value. For example, plots intended for overhead presentations may look better with thicker lines. First, you'll need to define the data to be plotted, then add the two additional fields. In the first, specify the property as a string and in the second, specify the property value.

```
plot(x,y,'LineWidth',2)
```

creates a plot of a single line with a width of 2 (0.5 is the default) as shown in Figure 5.9(a), and

```
plot(x,y,'LineWidth',2,'Marker','o','MarkerSize',10)
```

creates a plot (see Figure 5.9(b)) with a line width of 2, circles for the markers, and a marker that is larger than the default (10 vs the default of 6). You can add as many property pairs as needed. Explore the possible combinations by searching the help documentation:

```
doc Chart Line Properties
```

Unfortunately, if you want to fine tune line properties using this technique, you'll have to define each line in a separate plot statement. To create a graph with multiple lines, use the `hold on` command, then a new `plot` statement for each line. Thus, to add more lines to the graph shown in Figure 5.9(b),

```
hold on
plot(x,y*2,'LineWidth',1,'Marker','h','MarkerSize',12)
plot(x,y/2,'LineWidth',3,'Marker','d','MarkerSize',8)
```

which results in the graph shown in Figure 5.9(c). Don't forget to issue the `hold off` command when you are done.

```
hold off
```

(a)

(b)

(c)

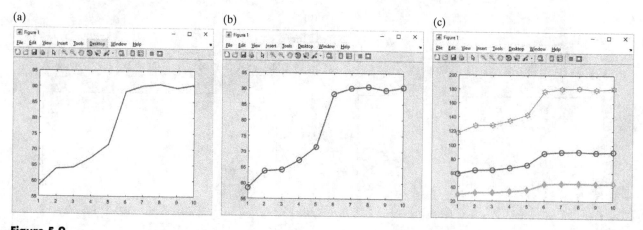

Figure 5.9

(a) More control can be exerted over line properties by adjusting them using line property identifiers and value definitions. (b) Multiple properties can be adjusted on a single line in the same plot statement. (c) Each line requires a separate plot statement, when using property identifiers and value definitions.

5.1.3 Axis Scaling and Annotating Plots

MATLAB® automatically selects appropriate x-axis and y-axis scaling, but sometimes, it is useful for the user to be able to control the scaling. Control is accomplished with the axis function, shown in Table 5.3. Executing the axis function without any input

axis

freezes the scaling of the plot. If you use the **hold on** command to add a second line to your graph, the scaling cannot change. To return control of the scaling to MATLAB®, simply re-execute the axis function.

The axis function also accepts input defining the x-axis and y-axis scaling. The argument is a single matrix, with four values representing:

- The minimum x value shown on the x-axis.
- The maximum x value shown on the x-axis.
- The minimum y value shown on the y-axis.
- The maximum y value shown on the y-axis.

Table 5.3 Axis Scaling and Annotating Plots

axis	When the **axis** function is used without inputs, it freezes the axis at the current configuration. Executing the function a second time returns axis control to MATLAB®.
axis(v)	The input to the **axis** command must be a four-element vector that specifies the minimum and maximum values for both the x- and y-axes—for example, [**xmin, xmax, ymin, ymax**].
axis equal	Forces the scaling on the x- and y-axis to be the same.
legend('string1', 'string 2', etc)	Allows you to add a legend to your graph. The legend shows a sample of the line and lists the string you have specified.
text(x_coordinate,y_coordinate, 'string')	Allows you to add a text box to the graph. The box is placed at the specified x- and y-coordinates and contains the string value specified.
gtext('string')	Similar to text. The box is placed at a location determined interactively by the user by clicking in the figure window.

Thus, the command

```
axis([-2, 3, 0, 10])
```

fixes the plot axes to x from -2 to $+3$ and y from 0 to 10.

It is often useful to create plots where the scaling is the same on the x- and y-axis. This is accomplished with the command

```
axis equal.
```

MATLAB® offers several additional functions, also listed in Table 5.3, that allow you to annotate your plots. The `legend` function requires the user to specify a legend in the form of a string for each line plotted, and defaults to a display in the upper right-hand corner of the plot. (Consult the help feature to figure out how to move the legend box to different locations.) The `text` function allows you to add a text box to your plot, which is useful for describing features on the graph. It requires the user to specify the location of the lower left-hand corner of the box in the plot window as the first two input fields, with a string specifying the contents of the text box in the third input field. The use of both `legend` and `text` is demonstrated in the following code, which modifies the graph from Figure 5.8(b). Additionally, the clear figure command, `clf`, was used to make sure a 'fresh' figure window was used.

```
clf
plot(x,y,':ok',x,y*2,'--xr',x,y/2,'-b')
legend('line 1', 'line 2', 'line3')
text(1,100,'Label plots with the text command')
```

We added a title, x and y labels, and adjusted the axis with the following commands:

```
xlabel('My x label'), ylabel('My y label')
title('Example graph for  Chapter 5')
axis([0,11,0,200])
```

The results are shown in Figure 5.10.

Figure 5.10
Final version of the sample graph, annotated with a legend, a text box, a title, x and y labels, and a modified axis.

HINT

You can use Greek letters in your titles and labels by putting a backslash (\\) before the name of the letter. For example,

```
title('\alpha \beta \gamma')
```

creates the plot title

$$\alpha \beta \gamma$$

To create a superscript, use a caret. Thus,

```
title('x^2')
```

gives

$$x^2$$

To create a subscript, use an underscore:

```
title('x_5')
```

gives

$$x_5$$

If your expression requires a group of characters as either a subscript or a superscript, enclose them in curly braces. For example,

```
title('k^{-1}')
```

returns

$$k^{-1}$$

Finally, to create a title with more than one line of text, you'll need to use a cell array. You can learn more about cell arrays in a later chapter, but the syntax is:

```
title({'First line of text'; 'Second line of text'})
```

MATLAB® has the ability to create other more complicated mathematical expressions for use as titles, axis labels, and other text strings, using the TeX markup language. To learn more, consult the help feature. (Search on "text properties.")

```
doc text properties
```

PRACTICE EXERCISE 5.1

The correct answers can be found on the Pearson website.

1. Plot x versus y for $y = \sin(x)$. Let x vary from 0 to 2π in increments of 0.1π.
2. Add a title and labels to your plot.
3. Plot x versus y_1 and y_2 for $y_1 = \sin(x)$ and $y_2 = \cos(x)$. Let x vary from 0 to 2π in increments of 0.1π. Add a title and labels to your plot.

4. Re-create the plot from Exercise 3, but make the $\sin(x)$ line dashed and red. Make the $\cos(x)$ line green and dotted.
5. Add a legend to the graph in Exercise 4.
6. Adjust the axes so that the x-axis goes from -1 to $2\pi + 1$, and the y-axis from -1.5 to $+1.5$.
7. Plot x versus y for $y = \sin(2*x)$, with a line weight of 3, a line color of green and with markers as triangles with a weight of 10.
8. Create a new vector, a = cos(x). Let **x** vary from 0 to 2π in increments of 0.1π. Plot just a without specifying the **x** values (plot(a)) and observe the result. Compare this result with the graph produced by plotting **x** versus a.

EXAMPLE 5.1

USING THE CLAUSIUS–CLAPEYRON EQUATION

The Clausius–Clapeyron equation can be used to find the saturation vapor pressure of water in the atmosphere, for different temperatures. The saturation water vapor pressure is useful to meteorologists because it can be used to calculate relative humidity, an important component of weather prediction, when the actual partial pressure of water in the air is known.

The Clausius–Clapeyron equation is

$$\ln (P^0/6.11) = \left(\frac{\Delta H_v}{R_{air}}\right) * \left(\frac{1}{273} - \frac{1}{T}\right)$$

where

P^0 = saturation vapor pressure for water, in mbar, at temperature T,
ΔH_v = latent heat of vaporization for water, 2.453×10^6 J/kg,
R_{air} = gas constant for moist air, 461 J/kg, and
T = temperature in kelvins.

1. State the problem
Find the saturation vapor pressure at temperatures from $-60°F$ to $120°F$, using the Clausius–Clapeyron equation, and present the results graphically.
2. Describe the input and output

Input

$$\Delta H_v = 2.453 \times 10^6 \text{ J/kg}$$
$$R_{air} = 461 \text{ J/kg}$$
$$T = -60°F \text{ to } 120°F$$

Since the number of temperature values was not specified, we'll choose to recalculate every 10°F.

Output

Table of temperature versus saturation vapor pressures
Graph of temperature versus saturation vapor pressures

(*continued*)

3. **Develop a hand example**

Change the temperatures from degrees Fahrenheit to kelvins:

$$T_k = \frac{(T_f + 459.6)}{1.8}$$

Solve the Clausius–Clapeyron equation for the saturation vapor pressure (P^0):

$$\ln\left(\frac{P^0}{6.11}\right) = \left(\frac{\Delta H_v}{R_{air}}\right) \times \left(\frac{1}{273} - \frac{1}{T}\right)$$

$$P^0 = 6.11*\exp\left(\left(\frac{\Delta H_v}{R_{air}}\right) \times \frac{1}{273} - \frac{1}{T}\right)$$

Notice that the expression for the saturation vapor pressure, P^0, is an exponential equation. We would thus expect the graph to have the shape shown in Figure 5.11.

4. **Develop a MATLAB® solution**

Figure 5.11
A sketch of the predicted equation behavior.

```
%%Example 5.1
%Using the Clausius-Clapeyron equation, find the
%saturation vapor pressure for water at different temperatures
%
  TF = [-60:10:120];        %Define temp matrix in F
  TK = (TF + 459.6)/1.8;    %Convert temp to K
  Delta_H=2.45e6;           %Define latent heat of
  R_air = 461;              %vaporization
                            %Define ideal gas constant
                            %for air
%
%Calculate the vapor pressures
  Vapor_Pressure=6.11*exp((Delta_H/R_air)*(1/273 - 1./TK));
  %Display the results in a table
  my_results=[TF',Vapor_Pressure']
%
%Create an x-y plot
  plot(TF,Vapor_Pressure)
  title('Clausius-Clapeyron Behavior')
  xlabel('Temperature, F')
  ylabel('Saturation Vapor Pressure, mbar')
```

The resulting table is

```
my_results =
         -60.0000        0.0698
         -50.0000        0.1252
         -40.0000        0.2184
         -30.0000        0.3714
         -20.0000        0.6163
         -10.0000        1.0000
                0        1.5888
          10.0000        2.4749
          20.0000        3.7847
```

30.0000	5.6880
40.0000	8.4102
50.0000	12.2458
60.0000	17.5747
70.0000	24.8807
80.0000	34.7729
90.0000	48.0098
100.0000	65.5257
110.0000	88.4608
120.0000	118.1931

A figure window opens to display the graphical results, shown in Figure 5.12.

5. Test the solution

The plot follows the expected trend. It is almost always easier to determine whether computational results make sense if a graph is produced. Tabular data are extremely difficult to interpret.

Figure 5.12
A plot of the Clausius–Clapeyron equation.

EXAMPLE 5.2

BALLISTICS

The range of an object (see Figure 5.13) shot at an angle θ with respect to the x-axis and an initial velocity v_0 is given by:

$$R(\theta) = \frac{v^2}{g}\sin(2\theta) \quad \text{for } 0 \le \theta \le \frac{\pi}{2} \text{(neglecting air resistance)}$$

Use $g = 9.9 \text{ m/s}^2$ and an initial velocity of 100 m/s. Show that the maximum range is obtained at $\theta = \pi/4$ by computing and plotting the range for values of θ from

(*continued*)

$$0 \le \theta \le \frac{\pi}{2}$$

Figure 5.13
The range is zero, if the cannon is perfectly vertical or perfectly horizontal.

in increments of 0.05.

Repeat your calculations with an initial velocity of 50 m/s, and plot both sets of results on a single graph.

1. State the problem
   Calculate the range as a function of the launch angle.
2. Describe the input and output

   Input

   $g = 9.9$ m/s^2

   $\theta = 0$ to $\pi/2$, incremented by 0.05

   $v_0 = 50$ m/s and 100 m/s

   Output

   Range R
   Present the results as a plot

3. Develop a hand example
   If the cannon is pointed straight up, we know that the range is zero, and if the cannon is horizontal, the range is also zero (see Figure 5.12).

   This means that the range must increase with the cannon angle up to some maximum, and then decrease. A sample calculation at 45 degrees ($\pi/4$ radians) shows that

   $$R(\theta) = \frac{v^2}{g}\sin(2\theta)$$

   $$R\left(\frac{\pi}{4}\right) = \frac{100^2}{9.9}\sin\left(\frac{2\pi}{4}\right) = 1010 \text{ m when the initial velocity is 100 m/s.}$$

4. Develop a MATLAB® solution

```
%%Example 5.2
%The program calculates the range of a ballistic projectile
%
%Define the constants
  g = 9.9;
  v1 = 50;
  v2 = 100;
%Define the angle vector
  angle = 0:0.05:pi/2;
%Calculate the range
  R1 = v1^2/g*sin(2*angle);
  R2 = v2^2/g*sin(2*angle);
%Plot the results
  plot(angle,R1,angle,R2,'--')
  title('Cannon Range')
```

```
xlabel('Cannon Angle')
ylabel('Range, meters')
legend('Initial Velocity=50 m/s','Initial Velocity=100 m/s')
```

Notice that in the `plot` command, we requested MATLAB® to print the second set of data as a dashed line. A title, labels, and a legend were also added. The results are shown in Figure 5.14.

5. Test the solution

Compare the MATLAB® results with those from the hand example. Both graphs start and end at zero. The maximum range for an initial velocity of 100 m/s is approximately 1000 m, which corresponds well to the calculated value of 1010 m. Notice that both solutions peak at the same angle, approximately 0.8 radian. The numerical value for $\pi/4$ is 0.785 radian, confirming the hypothesis presented in the problem statement that the maximum range is achieved by pointing the cannon at an angle of $\pi/4$ radians (45 degrees).

Figure 5.14
The predicted range of a projectile.

HINT

To clear a figure, use the `clf` command. To close the active figure window, use the `close` command, and to close all open figure windows use `close all`.

5.2 SUBPLOTS

The `subplot` command allows you to subdivide the graphing window into a grid of m rows and n columns. The function

```
subplot(m,n,p)
```

$p = 1$	$p = 2$
$p = 3$	$p = 4$

Figure 5.15
Subplots are used to subdivide the figure window into an $m \times n$ matrix.

splits the figure into an $m \times n$ matrix. The variable p identifies the portion of the window where the next plot will be drawn. For example, if the command

```
subplot(2,2,1)
```

is used, the window is divided into two rows and two columns, and the plot is drawn in the upper left-hand window (see Figure 5.15).

The windows are numbered from left to right, top to bottom. Similarly, the following commands split the graph window into a top plot and a bottom plot:

```
x = 0:pi/20:2*pi;
subplot(2,1,1)
plot(x,sin(x))
subplot(2,1,2)
plot(x,sin(2*x))
```

The first graph is drawn in the top window, since p = 1. Then the subplot command is used again to draw the next graph in the bottom window. Figure 5.16 shows both graphs.

Titles are added above each subwindow as the graphs are drawn, as are *x*- and *y*-axis labels and any annotation desired. The use of the subplot command is illustrated in several of the sections that follow.

Figure 5.16
The subplot command allows the user to create multiple graphs in the same figure window.

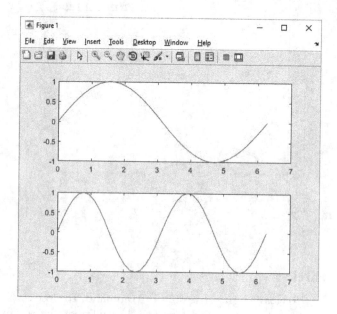

PRACTICE EXERCISE 5.2

The correct answers can be found on the Pearson website.

1. Subdivide a figure window into two rows and one column.
2. In the top window, plot $y = \tan(x)$ for $-1.5 \leq x \leq 1.5$. Use an increment of 0.1.

3. Add a title and axis labels to your graph.
4. In the bottom window, plot $y = \sinh(x)$ for the same range.
5. Add a title and labels to your graph.
6. Try the preceding exercises again, but divide the figure window vertically instead of horizontally.

5.3 OTHER TYPES OF TWO-DIMENSIONAL PLOTS

Although simple x–y plots are the most common type of engineering plot, there are many other ways to represent data. Depending on the situation, these techniques may be more appropriate than an x–y plot.

5.3.1 Polar Plots

MATLAB® provides plotting capability with polar coordinates.

```
polarplot(theta, r)
```

generates a polar plot of angle theta (in radians) and radial distance r. (Earlier versions of MATLAB® used `polar` instead of `polarplot`.)

For example, the code

```
x = 0:pi/100:pi;
y = sin(x);
polarplot(x,y)
```

generates the plot in Figure 5.17. A title was added in the usual way:

```
title('The sine function plotted in polar coordinates is a
circle.')
```

Figure 5.17
A polar plot of the sine function.

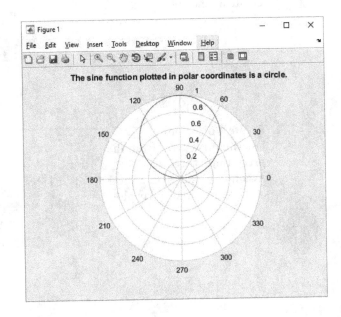

PRACTICE EXERCISE 5.3

The correct answers can be found on the Pearson website.
Use the `polarplot` function, not the older `polar` function.

1. Define an array called **theta**, from
   0 to 2π, in steps of 0.01π.
   Define an array of distances
   `r = 5*cos(4*theta)`.
   Make a polar plot of `theta` versus `r`.

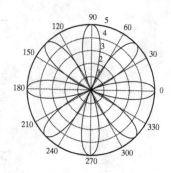

2. Use the `hold` on command to freeze
   the graph.
   Assign `r = 4*cos(6*theta)` and plot.
   Add a title.

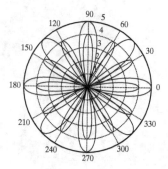

3. Create a new figure.
   Use the **theta** array from the
   preceding exercises.
   Assign `r = 5 - 5*sin(theta)` and
   create a new polar plot.

4. Create a new figure.
   Use the **theta** array from the
   preceding exercises.
   Assign `r = sqrt(5^2*cos(2*theta))`
   and create a new polar plot.

5. Create a new figure.
Define a theta array such that
`theta = pi/2:4/5*pi:4.8*pi`
Create a six-member array of
ones called `r`.
Create a new polar plot of
`theta` versus `r`.

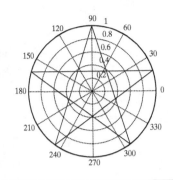

KEY IDEA

Logarithmic plots are
especially useful if the data
vary exponentially.

5.3.2 Logarithmic Plots

For most plots that we generate, the *x*- and *y*-axes are divided into equally spaced intervals; these plots are called *linear* or *rectangular* plots. Occasionally, however, we may want to use a logarithmic scale on one or both of the axes. A logarithmic scale (base 10) is convenient when a variable ranges over many orders of magnitude, because the wide range of values can be graphed without compressing the smaller values. Logarithmic plots are also useful for representing data that vary exponentially. Appendix B discusses in more detail when to use the various types of logarithmic scaling.

The MATLAB® commands for generating linear and logarithmic plots of the vectors x and y are listed in Table 5.4.

Remember that the logarithm of a negative number or of zero does not exist (although MATLAB® represents logs of negative numbers as complex values). If your data include these values, MATLAB® will issue a warning message and will not plot the points in question. However, it will generate a plot based on the remaining points.

Usually you will use logarithmic plots with two inputs, both the dependent and independent variables. However, each command for logarithmic plotting can be executed with a single argument, as we saw in `plot(y)` for a linear plot. In these cases, the plots are generated with the values of the indices of the vector *y* used as *x* values.

As an example, plots of $y = 5x^2$ were created using all four scaling approaches, as shown in Figure 5.18. The linear (rectangular) plot, semilog plot along the *x*-axis, semilog plot along the *y*-axis, and log–log plot are all shown on one figure, `plotted` with the `subplot` function in the following code:

```
x = 0:0.5:50;
y = 5*x.^2;
subplot(2,2,1)
plot(x,y)
```

Table 5.4 Rectangular and Logarithmic Plots

`plot(x,y)`	Generates a linear plot of the vectors x and y
`semilogx(x,y)`	Generates a plot of the values of x and y, using a logarithmic scale for x and a linear scale for y
`semilogy(x,y)`	Generates a plot of the values of x and y, using a linear scale for x and a logarithmic scale for y
`loglog(x,y)`	Generates a plot of the vectors x and y, using a logarithmic scale for both x and y

```
        title('Polynomial - linear/linear')
        ylabel('y'), grid
    subplot(2,2,2)
    semilogx(x,y)
        title('Polynomial - log/linear')
        ylabel('y'), grid
    subplot(2,2,3)
    semilogy(x,y)
        title('Polynomial - linear/log')
        xlabel('x'), ylabel('y'), grid
    subplot(2,2,4)
    loglog(x,y)
        title('Polynomial - log/log')
        xlabel('x'), ylabel('y'), grid
```

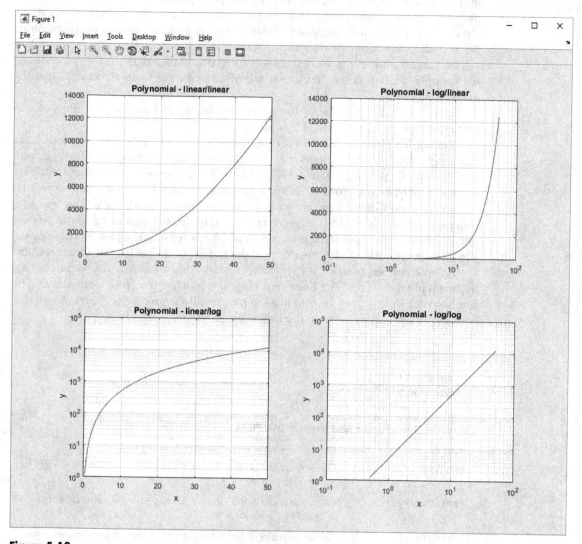

Figure 5.18
Linear and logarithmic plots, displayed using the subplot function.

KEY IDEA

Since MATLAB® ignores white space, use it to make your code more readable.

The indenting is intended to make the code easier to read—MATLAB® ignores white space. As a matter of style, notice that only the bottom two subplots have x-axis labels.

EXAMPLE 5.3

RATES OF DIFFUSION

Metals are often treated to make them stronger and therefore wear longer. One problem with making a strong piece of metal is that the metal becomes difficult to form it into a desired shape. A strategy that gets around this problem is to form a soft metal into the shape you desire, then harden the surface. This makes the metal wear well without making it brittle.

A common hardening process is called *carburizing*. The metal part is exposed to carbon, which diffuses into the part, making it harder. This is a very slow process if performed at low temperatures, but it can be accelerated by heating the part. The diffusivity is a measure of how fast diffusion occurs, and can be modeled as

$$D = D_0 \exp\left(\frac{-Q}{RT}\right)$$

where

D = diffusivity, cm^2/s,

D_0 = diffusion coefficient, cm^2/s,

Q = activation energy, J/mol, 8.314 J/mol K,

R = ideal gas constant, J/mol K, and

T = temperature, K.

As iron is heated, it changes structure and its diffusion characteristics change. The values of D_0 and Q are shown in the following table for carbon diffusing through each of iron's structures:

Type of Metal	D_0 (cm^2/s)	Q (J/mol K)
alpha Fe (BCC)	0.0062	80,000
gamma Fe (FCC)	0.23	148,000

Create a plot of diffusivity versus inverse temperature $(1/T)$, using the data provided. Try the rectangular, semilog, and log–log plots to see which you think might represent the results best. Let the temperature vary from room temperature (25°C) to 1200°C.

1. State the problem
   Calculate the diffusivity of carbon in iron.
2. Describe the input and output

   Input

   For C in alpha iron, $D_0 = 0.0062$ cm^2/s and $Q = 80,000$ J/mol K

   For C in gamma iron, $D_0 = 0.23$ cm^2/s and $Q = 148,000$ J/mol K

(continued)

$R = 8.314$ J/mol K

T varies from 25°C to 1200°C

Output

Calculate the diffusivity and plot it.

3. Develop a hand example

The diffusivity is given by

$$D = D_0 \exp\left(\frac{-Q}{RT}\right).$$

At room temperature, the diffusivity for carbon in alpha iron is

$$D = 0.0062 \exp\left(\frac{-80,000}{8.314 \times (25 + 273)}\right)$$

$$D = 5.9 \times 10^{-17}.$$

(Notice that the temperature had to be changed from Celsius to Kelvin.)

4. Develop a MATLAB® solution

```
%% Example 5.3
% Calculate the diffusivity of carbon in iron clear, clc
% Define the constants
  D0alpha = 0.0062;
  D0gamma = 0.23;
  Qalpha = 80000;
  Qgamma = 148000;
  R = 8.314;
  T = 25:5:1200;
% Change T from C to K
  T = T+273;
% Calculate the diffusivity
  Dalpha = D0alpha*exp(-Qalpha./(R*T));
  Dgamma = D0gamma*exp(-Qgamma./(R*T));
% Plot the results
  subplot(2,2,1)
  plot(1./T,Dalpha, 1./T,Dgamma)
  title('Diffusivity of C in Fe')
  xlabel('Inverse Temperature, K^{-1}'),
  ylabel('Diffusivity, cm^2/s')
  grid on

  subplot(2,2,2)
  semilogx(1./T,Dalpha, 1./T,Dgamma)
  title('Diffusivity of C in Fe')
  xlabel('Inverse Temperature, K^{-1}'),
  ylabel('Diffusivity, cm^2/s')
  grid on

  subplot(2,2,3)
  semilogy(1./T,Dalpha, 1./T,Dgamma)
```

```
title('Diffusivity of C in Fe')
xlabel('Inverse Temperature, K^{-1}'),
ylabel('Diffusivity, cm^2/s')
grid on

subplot(2,2,4)
loglog(1./T,Dalpha, 1./T,Dgamma)
title('Diffusivity of C in Fe')
xlabel('Inverse Temperature, K^{-1}'),
ylabel('Diffusivity, cm^2/s')
grid on
```

Subplots were used in Figure 5.19, so that all four variations of the plot are in the same figure. Notice that x-labels were added only to the bottom two graphs, to reduce clutter, and that a legend was added only to the first plot. The `semilogy` plot resulted in straight lines and allows a user to read values off the graph easily

Figure 5.19
Diffusivity data plotted on different scales. The data follows a straight line when the $\log_{10}$ of the diffusivity is plotted on the y-axis versus the inverse temperature on the x-axis.

(*continued*)

over a wide range of both temperatures and diffusivities. This is the plotting scheme usually used in textbooks and handbooks to present diffusivity values.

5. Test the solution

Compare the MATLAB® results with those from the hand example.

We calculated the diffusivity to be

$$5.9 \times 10^{-17} \text{ cm}^2/\text{s at } 25°C$$

for carbon in alpha iron. To check our answer, we'll need to change 25°C to kelvins and take the inverse:

$$\frac{1}{(25 + 273)} = 3.36 \times 10^{-3}$$

From the semilogy graph (lower left-hand corner), we can see that the diffusivity for alpha iron is approximately 10^{-17} cm²/s.

PRACTICE EXERCISE 5.4

The correct answers can be found on the Pearson website.

Create appropriate x and y arrays to use in plotting each of the expressions that follow. Use the `subplot` command to divide your figures into four sections, and create each of these four graphs for each expression:

- Rectangular
- Semilogx
- Semilogy
- Loglog

1. $y = 5x + 3$

2. $y = 3x^2$

3. $y = 12e^{(x+2)}$

4. $y = 1/x$

Physical data usually are plotted so that they fall on a straight line. Which of the preceding types of plot results in a straight line for each problem?

5.3.3 Bar Graphs and Pie Charts

Bar graphs, histograms, and pie charts are popular forms for reporting data. Some of the commonly used MATLAB® functions for creating bar graphs and pie charts are listed in Table 5.5.

Examples of some of these graphs generated by the following code are shown in Figure 5.20. The graphs make use of the `subplot` function to allow four plots in the same figure window:

```
clear, clc
x = [1,2,5,4,8];
y = [x;1:5];
subplot(2,2,1)
  bar(x),title('A bar graph of vector x')
subplot(2,2,2)
  bar(y),title('A bar graph of matrix y')
subplot(2,2,3)
  bar3(y),title('A three-dimensional bar graph')
subplot(2,2,4)
  pie(x),title('A pie chart of x')
```

Table 5.5 Bar Graphs and Pie Charts

`bar(x)`	When **x** is a vector, bar generates a vertical bar graph. When x is a two-dimensional matrix, bar groups the data by row.
`barh(x)`	When **x** is a vector, barh generates a horizontal bar graph. When **x** is a two-dimensional matrix, barh groups the data by row.
`bar3(x)`	Generates a three-dimensional bar chart.
`bar3h(x)`	Generates a three-dimensional horizontal bar chart.
`pie(x)`	Generates a pie chart. Each element in the matrix is represented as a slice of the pie.
`pie3(x)`	Generates a three-dimensional pie chart. Each element in the matrix is represented as a slice of the pie.
`histogram(x)`	Generates a histogram.

Figure 5.20
Sample bar graphs and pie charts. The subplot function was used to divide the window into quadrants.

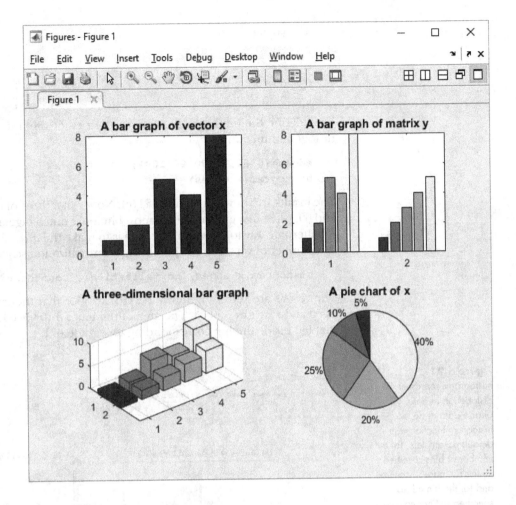

KEY IDEA
Histograms are useful in statistical analysis.

5.3.4 Histograms

A histogram is a plot showing the distribution of a set of values, especially useful in statistical analysis. In MATLAB®, the histogram computes the number of values falling into a number of bins (categories) that are equally spaced between the minimum and maximum values. For example, if we define a matrix **x** as the set of grades from the Introduction to Engineering final, the scores could be represented in a histogram, shown in Figure 5.21(a) and generated with the following code:

```
x = [100,95,74,87,22,78,34,82,93,88,86,69,55,72];
histogram(x)
```

The histogram function determines an appropriate number of bins automatically, but also allows for the user to specify the number of bins. For example, to create a histogram with 5 bins, the command would be

```
histogram(x, 5).
```

The results are shown in Figure 5.21(b).

Although it usually makes sense to space the bins equally between the minimum and maximum data value, sometimes it is more meaningful to define the bins based on some other criteria. For example, consider the grade data. It would be preferable to define each bin so that they correspond to specific grades as follows:

A   90–100
B   80–90
C   70–80
D   60–70
E   0–60

First, define the bin edges as an array, then enter them in the second field in the histogram function.

```
edges=[0,60,70,80,90,100];
histogram(x,edges)
```

The results are shown in Figure 5.21(c). Notice that three of the scores fell between 0 and 60, yet at first glance the left-most bin looks much bigger than the other results. An alternate way to represent the data is to make the *area* of the bin proportional to the number of values in the bin, using a normalization scheme.

```
histogram(x,edges,'normalization','countdensity')
```

The results are shown in Figure 5.21(d). Notice that the left-most bin has a width of 60 and a height of 0.05. The area of the bin is 3 (0.05*60), the number of scores that fell inside the bin corresponding to a grade of E.

Figure 5.21

Histograms represent the distribution of data. (a) Grade data using the histogram function with default parameters, (b) the number of bins specified, (c) the bin edges specified, and (d) the bin edges specified but normalized so that the area of each block corresponds to the number of items in each bin.

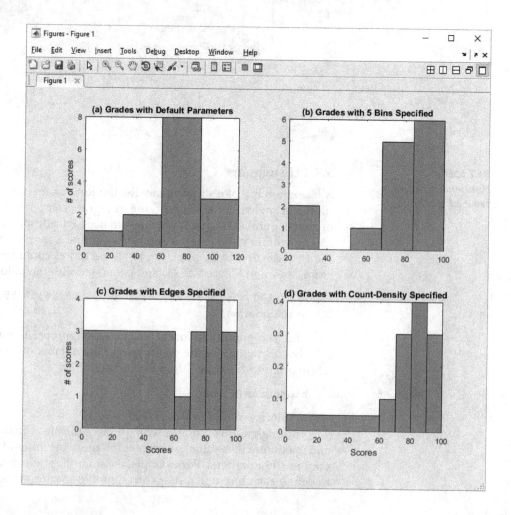

Setting the results of the histogram function equal to a variable creates a *handle* to the plot. You can think of a handle as a nickname. Handles are covered in more detail in a latter chapter. If you would like to save the plotting data, such as the number of values in each bin, use the `histcounts` function,

```
a = histcounts(x)
```

which creates an array representing the number of values used to create Figure 5.21(a).

```
a =
    1 2 8 3
```

The `histogram` and `histcounts` functions replace the earlier `hist` and `histc` functions used before version 2014a. Older code should be updated to the newer functions.

EXAMPLE 5.4

WEIGHT DISTRIBUTIONS

The average 18-year-old American male weighs 152 pounds. A group of 100 young men were weighed and the data stored in a file called **weight.dat**. Create a graph to represent the data.

1. State the problem
   Use the data file to create a line graph and a histogram. Which is a better representation of the data?
2. Describe the input and output

Input	**weight.dat**, an ASCII data file that contains weight data
Output	A line plot of the data A histogram of the data

3. Develop a hand example
   Since this is a sample of actual weights, we would expect the data to approximate a normal random distribution (a Gaussian distribution). The histogram should be bell-shaped.
4. Develop a MATLAB® solution
   The following code generates the plots shown in Figure 5.22:

```
%% Example 5.4
% Using Weight Data
%
load weight.dat
% Create the line plot of weight data
subplot(1,2,1)
plot(weight)
title('Weight of Freshman Class Men')
xlabel('Student Number')
ylabel('Weight, lb')
grid on
```

(continued)

Figure 5.22
Histograms and line plots are two different ways to visualize numeric information.

```
% Create the histogram of the data
subplot(1,2,2)
histogram(weight)
xlabel('Weight, lb')
ylabel('Number of students')
title('Weight of Freshman Class Men')
```

5. Test the solution

The graphs match our expectations. The weight appears to average about 150 lb and varies in what looks like a normal distribution. We can use MATLAB® to find the average and the standard deviation of the data, as well as the maximum and minimum weights in the data set. The MATLAB® code

```
average_weight = mean(weight)
standard_deviation = std(weight)
maximum_weight = max(weight)
minimum_weight = min(weight)
```

returns

```
average_weight = 151.1500
standard_deviation = 32.9411
maximum_weight = 228
minimum_weight = 74.
```

5.3.5 x–y Graphs with Two y-Axes

Sometimes, it is useful to overlay two x–y plots onto the same figure. However, if the orders of magnitude of the y-values are quite different, it may be difficult to see how the data behave. Consider, for example, a graph of $\sin(x)$ and e^x drawn on the same figure. The results, obtained with the following code, are shown in Figure 5.23(a):

```
x = 0:pi/20:2*pi;
y1 = sin(x);
y2 = exp(x);
subplot(1,2,1)
plot(x,y1,x,y2)
```

The plot of $\sin(x)$ looks like it runs straight along the line $x = 0$, because of the scale. The `yyaxis` function allows us to create a graph with two y-axes, one on the left and one on the right, by specifying which axis to use.

```
subplot(1,2,2)
yyaxis  left % default - this line of code is not necessary
plot(x,y1)
xlabel('x')
ylabel('sin function')
yyaxis  right
plot(x,y2)
ylabel('exponential function')
```

The `yyaxis` function replaces `plotyy`, which accomplished the same thing, but was more awkward to use. Although MATLAB still supports `plotyy` older code should be updated to use `yyaxis`.

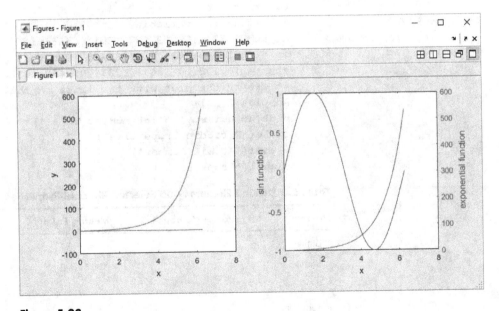

Figure 5.23
MATLAB® allows the y-axis to be scaled differently on the left-hand and right-hand sides of the figure. (a) Both lines were drawn using the same scaling. (b) The sine curve was drawn using the scaling on the left axis, while the exponential curve was drawn using the scaling on the right axis.

EXAMPLE 5.5

PERIODIC PROPERTIES OF THE ELEMENTS

The properties of elements in the same row or column in the periodic table usually display a recognizable trend as we move across a row or down a column. For example, the melting point usually goes down as we move down a column, because the atoms are farther apart and the bonds between the atoms are therefore weaker. Similarly, the radius of the atoms goes up as we move down a column, because there are more electrons in each atom and correspondingly bigger orbitals. It is instructive to plot these trends against atomic weight on the same graph.

1. **State the problem**
   Plot the melting point and the atomic radius of the Group I elements against the atomic weight, and comment on the trends you observe.
2. **Describe the input and output**

   Input   The atomic weights, melting points, and atomic radii of the Group I elements are listed in Table 5.6.

   Output   Plot with both melting point and atomic radius on the same graph.

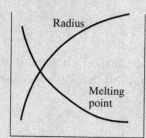

3. **Develop a hand example**
   We would expect the graph to look something like the sketch shown in Figure 5.24.
4. **Develop a MATLAB® solution**
   The following code produces the plot shown in Figure 5.25:

Figure 5.24
Sketch of the predicted data behavior.

```
%% Example 5.5
% Periodic Properties of the Elements
clear, clc,clf
%% Define the variables
at_num = [3, 11, 19, 37, 55];   %atomic number
mp = [181, 98, 63, 34, 28.4];   %melting point
at_r = [0.152, 0.186, 0.227, 0.2480, 0.2650];   %atomic radius
%% Create the plot with two lines on the same scale
subplot(1,2,1)
plot(at_num,mp,'-o',at_num,at_r,'-x')
title('Periodic Properties')
xlabel('Atomic Number')
ylabel('Properties')
```

Table 5.6 Group I Elements and Selected Physical Properties

Element	Atomic Number	Melting Point, °C	Atomic Radius, pm
Lithium	3	181	0.1520
Sodium	11	98	0.1860
Potassium	19	63	0.2270
Rubidium	37	34	0.2480
Cesium	55	28.4	0.2650

Figure 5.25
In the left-hand figure, the two sets of values were plotted using the same scale. Using two y-axes allows us to plot data with different units on the same graph, as shown in the right-hand figure.

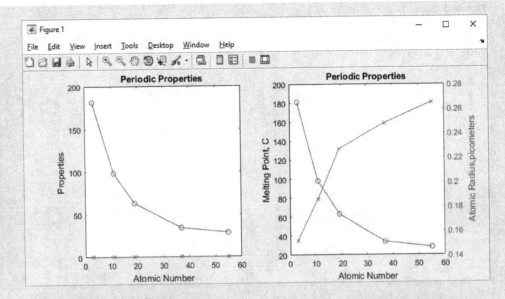

```
%% Create the second plot with two different y scales
subplot(1,2,2)
plot(at_num,mp,'-o')
title('Periodic Properties')
xlabel('Atomic Number')
ylabel('Melting Point, C')
yyaxis  right
plot(at_num,at_r,'-x')
ylabel('Atomic Radius,picometers')
```

On the second graph, which has two different y scales, we used yyaxis to define the right-hand axis. This forced the addition of a second scale, on the right-hand side of the plot. We needed it because atomic radius and melting point have different units, and the values for each have different magnitudes. Notice that in the first plot, it is almost impossible to see the atomic-radius line; it is on top of the x-axis because the numbers are so small.

5. Test the solution
   Compare the MATLAB® results with those from the hand example. The trend matches our prediction. Clearly, the graph with two y-axes is the superior representation, because we can see the property trends.

5.3.6 Function Plots

The fplot function allows you to plot a function without defining arrays of corresponding x- and y-values. For example,

```
fplot(@(x)sin(x),[-2*pi,2*pi])
```

creates a plot (see Figure 5.26) of x versus sin (x) for x-values from -2π to 2π. MATLAB® automatically calculates the spacing of x-values to create a smooth curve. The first argument in the fplot function starts with the @ symbol to specify the independent variable and continues with the function to be plotted. The second argument is

Figure 5.26
Function plots do not require the user to define arrays of ordered pairs.

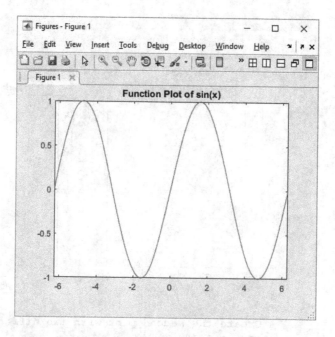

an array defining the plotting range. For more complicated functions that may be inconvenient to enter in this way, you may define an anonymous function and enter the function handle. Anonymous functions and function handles are described in a later chapter devoted to functions. The correct syntax for this case would be

```
f = @(x) sin(x)
fplot(f, [-2*pi,2*pi]).
```

PRACTICE EXERCISE 5.5

Create a plot of the functions that follow, using `fplot`. You'll need to select an appropriate range for each plot. Don't forget to title and label your graphs.

The correct answers can be found on the Pearson website.

1. $f(t) = 5t^2$
2. $f(t) = 5\sin^2(t) + t\cos^2(t)$
3. $f(t) = te^t$
4. $f(t) = \ln(t) + \sin(t)$

HINT

The correct MATLAB® syntax for the mathematical expression $\sin^2(t)$ is `sin(t).^2`.

5.4 THREE-DIMENSIONAL PLOTTING

MATLAB® offers a variety of three-dimensional plotting commands, several of which are listed in Table 5.7.

Table 5.7 Three-Dimensional Plots

`plot3(x,y,z)`	Creates a three-dimensional line plot
`comet3(x,y,z)`	Generates an animated version of `plot3`
`mesh(z) or mesh(x,y,z)`	Creates a meshed surface plot
`surf(z) or surf(x,y,z)`	Creates a surface plot; similar to the mesh function
`shading interp`	Interpolates between the colors used to illustrate surface plots
`shading flat`	Colors each grid section with a solid color
`colormap(map_name)`	Allows the user to select the color pattern used on surface plots
`contour(z) or` `contour(x,y,z)`	Generates a contour plot
`contourf(z) or` `contour(x,y,z)`	Generates a filled-contour plot
`surfc(z) or surfc(x,y,z)`	Creates a combined surface plot and contour plot
`pcolor(z) or` `pcolor(x,y,z)`	Creates a pseudo color plot

5.4.1 Three-Dimensional Line Plot

The `plot3` function is similar to the `plot` function, except that it accepts data in three dimensions. Instead of just providing x and y vectors, the user must also provide a z vector. These ordered triples are then plotted in three-space and connected with straight lines. For example,

```
clear, clc
x = linspace(0,10*pi,1000);
y = cos(x);
z = sin(x);
plot3(x,y,z)
grid
xlabel('angle'), ylabel('cos(x)'), zlabel('sin(x)'), title('A
Spring')
```

KEY IDEA
The axes used for three-dimensional plotting correspond to the right-hand rule.

The title, labels, and grid are added to the graph in Figure 5.27 in the usual way, with the addition of `zlabel` for the z-axis.

The coordinate system used with `plot3` is oriented using the right-handed coordinate system familiar to engineers.

HINT

Just for fun, recreate the plot shown in Figure 5.27, but this time with the `comet3` function:

```
comet3(x,y,z)
```

This plotting function "draws" the graph in an animation sequence. If your animation runs too quickly, add more data points. For two-dimensional line graphs, use the `comet` function.

5.4.2 Surface Plots

Surface plots allow us to represent data as a surface. We will be experimenting with two types of surface plots: mesh plots and surf plots.

Figure 5.27
A three-dimensional plot of a spring. MATLAB® uses a coordinate system consistent with the right-hand rule.

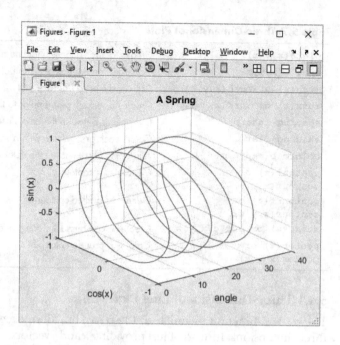

Mesh Plots

There are several ways to use mesh plots. They can be used to good effect with a single two-dimensional $m \times n$ matrix. In this application, the value in the matrix represents the z-value in the plot. The x- and y-values are based on the matrix dimensions. Take, for example, the following very simple matrix:

```
z = [1, 2, 3, 4, 5, 6, 7, 8, 9, 10;
     2, 4, 6, 8, 10, 12, 14, 16, 18, 20;
     3, 4, 5, 6, 7, 8, 9, 10, 11, 12];
```

The code

```
mesh(z)
xlabel('x-axis')
ylabel('y-axis')
zlabel('z-axis')
```

generates the graph in Figure 5.28.

The graph is a "mesh" created by connecting the points defined in z into a rectilinear grid. Notice that the x-axis goes from 0 to 10 and y goes from 1 to 3. The matrix index numbers were used for the axis values. For example, note that $z_{1,5}$—the value of z in row 1, column 5—is equal to 5. This element is circled in Figure 5.28.

The mesh function can also be used with three arguments: mesh(x,y,z). In this case, x is a list of x-coordinates, y is a list of y-coordinates, and z is a list of z-coordinates.

```
x = linspace(1,50,10)
y = linspace(500,1000,3)
z = [1, 2, 3, 4, 5, 6, 7, 8, 9, 10;
     2, 4, 6, 8, 10, 12, 14, 16, 18, 20;
     3, 4, 5, 6, 7, 8, 9, 10, 11, 12]
```

Figure 5.28

Simple mesh created with a single two-dimensional matrix.

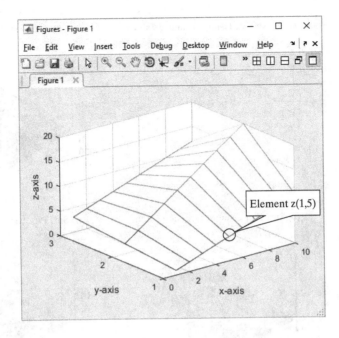

The *x* vector must have the same number of elements as the number of columns in the *z* vector and the *y* vector must have the same number of elements as the number of rows in the *z* vector. The command

```
mesh(x,y,z)
```

creates the plot in Figure 5.29(a). Notice that the *x*-axis varies from 0 to 50, with data plotted from 1 to 50. Compare this scaling with that in Figure 5.28, which used the **z** matrix index numbers for the *x* - and *y*-axes.

Surf Plots

Surf plots are similar to mesh plots, but `surf` creates a three-dimensional colored surface instead of a mesh. The colors vary with the value of **z**.

The `surf` command takes the same input as `mesh`: either a single input—for example, `surf(z)`, in which case it uses the row and column indices as *x* - and *y*-coordinates—or three matrices. Figure 5.29(b) was generated with the same commands as those used to generate Figure 5.29(a), except that `surf` replaced `mesh`.

The shading scheme for surface plots is controlled with the shading command. The default, shown in Figure 5.29(b), is "faceted." Interpolated shading can create interesting effects. The plot shown in Figure 5.29(c) was created by adding

```
shading interp
```

to the previous list of commands. Flat shading without the grid is generated when

```
shading flat
```

is used, as shown in Figure 5.29(d).

The color scheme used in surface plots can be controlled with the `colormap` function. For example,

```
colormap(gray)
```

KEY IDEA

The colormap function controls the colors used on surface plots.

Figure 5.29
Mesh and surf plots are
created with three input
arguments.

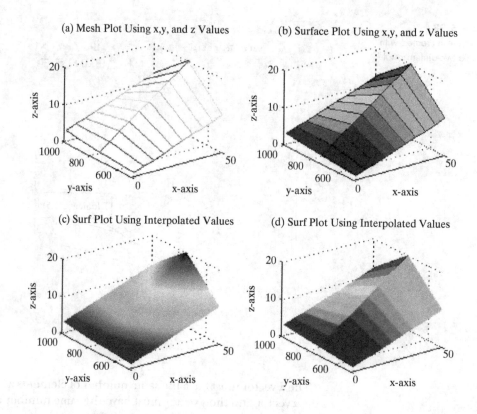

(a) Mesh Plot Using x,y, and z Values

(b) Surface Plot Using x,y, and z Values

(c) Surf Plot Using Interpolated Values

(d) Surf Plot Using Interpolated Values

forces a grayscale representation for surface plots. This may be appropriate if you'll be making black-and-white copies of your plots. Other available `colormaps` are

autumn	bone	hot
spring	colorcube	hsv
summer	cool	pink
winter	copper	prism
jet	flag	white
parula (default)	gray	lines

Use the `help` command to see a description of the various options:

```
help colormap
```

Another Example
A more complicated surface can be created by calculating the values of Z:

```
x = [-2:0.2:2];
y = [-2:0.2:2];
[X,Y] = meshgrid(x,y);
Z = X.*exp(-X. ^2 - Y. ^2);
```

In the preceding code, the `meshgrid` function is used to create the two-dimensional matrices X and Y from the one-dimensional vectors x and y. The values in Z are then calculated. The following code plots the calculated values:

```
subplot(2,2,1)
mesh(X,Y,Z)
```

Figure 5.30
Surface and contour plots are different ways of visualizing the same data.

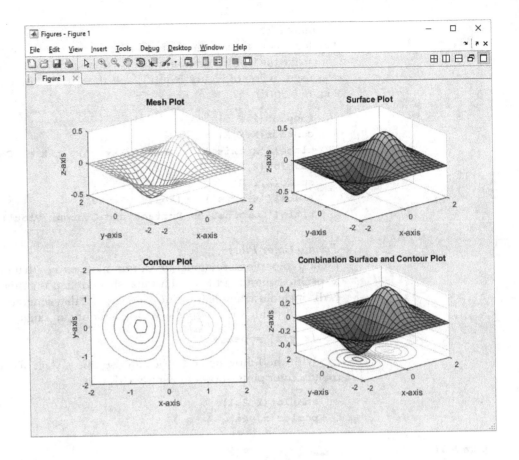

```
title('Mesh Plot'), xlabel('x-axis'), ylabel('y-axis'),
zlabel('z-axis')
subplot(2,2,2)
surf(X,Y,Z)
title('Surface Plot'), xlabel('x-axis'), ylabel('y-axis'),
zlabel('z-axis')
```

Either the *x*, *y* vectors or the *x*, *y* matrices can be used to define the *x*- and *y*-axes. Figure 5.30(a) is a mesh plot of the given function, and Figure 5.30(b) is a surf plot of the same function.

HINT

If a single vector is used in the meshgrid function, the program interprets it as

```
[X,Y] = meshgrid(x,x)
```

You could also use the vector definition as input to meshgrid:

```
[X,Y] = meshgrid(-2:0.2:2)
```

Both of these lines of code would produce the same result as the commands listed in the example.

Contour Plots

Contour plots are two-dimensional representations of three-dimensional surfaces, much like the familiar contour maps used by many hikers. The `contour` command was used to create Figure 5.30(c), and the `surfc` command was used to create Figure 5.30(d):

```
subplot(2,2,3)
contour(X,Y,Z)
xlabel('x-axis'), ylabel('y-axis'), title('Contour Plot')
subplot(2,2,4)
surfc(X,Y,Z)
xlabel('x-axis'), ylabel('y-axis')
title('Combination Surface and Contour Plot')
```

Pseudo Color Plots

Pseudo color plots are similar to contour plots, except that instead of lines outlining a specific contour, a two-dimensional shaded map is generated over a grid. MATLAB® includes a sample function called `peaks` that generates the **x**, **y**, and **z** matrices of an interesting surface that looks like a mountain range:

```
[x,y,z] = peaks;
```

With the following code, we can use this surface to demonstrate the use of pseudo color plots, shown in Figure 5.31:

```
subplot(2,2,1)
pcolor(x,y,z-
```

Figure 5.31

A variety of contour plots is available in MATLAB®.

The grid is deleted when interpolated shading is used:

```
subplot(2,2,2)
pcolor(x,y,z)
shading interp
```

You can add contours to the image by overlaying a contour plot:

```
subplot(2,2,3)
pcolor(x,y,z)
shading interp
hold on
contour(x,y,z,20,'k')
hold off
```

A similar result can be obtained by using the filled contour function:

```
contourf(x,y,z,20,'k')
```

The number 20 specifies that 20 contour lines are drawn, and the `'k'` indicates that the lines should be black. If we hadn't specified black lines, they would have been the same color as the pseudo color plot, and would have disappeared into the image. Finally, a simple contour plot was added to the figure for comparison:

```
subplot(2,2,4)
contour(x,y,z)
```

Additional options for using all the three-dimensional plotting functions are included in the help window. One particularly useful option is to add labels to the contour lines, which is accomplished using graphics object names, previously called handle graphics. The plot is given a name, (the handle) which is used as input to the `clabel` function.

```
h = contour(x,y,z); clabel(h)
```

5.5 EDITING PLOTS FROM THE MENU BAR

KEY IDEA

When you interactively edit a plot, your changes will be lost if you rerun the program.

In addition to controlling the way your plots look by using MATLAB® commands, you can edit a plot once you've created it. The plot in Figure 5.32 was created with the `sphere` command, which is one of several sample functions, like `peaks`, used to demonstrate plotting.

```
sphere
```

In the figure, the **Insert menu** has been selected. Notice that you can insert labels, titles, legends, text boxes, and so on, all by using this menu. The **Tools menu** allows you to change the way the plot looks, by zooming in or out, changing the aspect ratio, and so on. The figure toolbar, underneath the menu toolbar, offers icons that allow you to do the same thing.

The plot in Figure 5.32 doesn't really look like a sphere; it's also missing labels and a title, and the meaning of the colors may not be clear. We edited this plot by first adjusting the shape:

- Select **Edit** → **Axes Properties** from the menu toolbar.
- From the **Property Editor—Axes window**, select **More Properties** → **Data Aspect Ratio Mode.**
- Set the mode to manual (see Figure 5.33).

Figure 5.32
MATLAB® offers interactive tools, such as the insert tool, that allow the user to adjust the appearance of graphs.

Figure 5.33
MATLAB® allows you to edit plots by using commands from the toolbar.

Figure 5.34
Edited plot of a sphere.

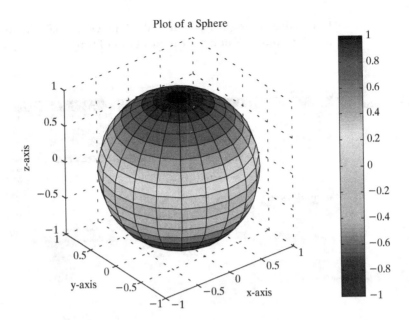

Similarly, labels, a title, and a color bar were added (see Figure 5.34) using the Property Editor. They could also have been added by using the **Insert menu** option on the menu bar. Editing your plot in this manner is more interactive and allows you to fine-tune the plot's appearance. The only problem with editing a figure interactively is that if you run your MATLAB® program again, you will lose all of your improvements.

HINT

You can force a plot to space the data equally on all the axes by using the `axis equal` command. This approach has the advantage that you can program **axis equal** into an M-file and retain your improvements.

5.6 CREATING PLOTS FROM THE WORKSPACE WINDOW

A great feature of MATLAB® 9 is its ability to create plots interactively using the variables in the workspace window. Select the variables you would like to plot, then select the **PLOTS** tab from the MATLAB® desktop (shown in Figure 5.35). MATLAB® will list the plotting options it "thinks" are reasonable for the data stored in your variable(s). Simply select the appropriate option, and your plot is created in the current figure window. If you don't like any of the suggested types of plot, choose the drop-down menu, and a new window will open with the complete list of available plotting options for you to choose from. This is especially useful, because it may suggest options that had not occurred to you. For example, Figure 5.35 shows a scatter plot of the x and y matrices highlighted in the figure. The matrices were created by loading the seamount data set, which is built into MATLAB®.

If you want to plot more than one variable, highlight the first, then hold down the *Ctrl* key and select the additional variables. To annotate your plots, use the interactive editing process described in Section 5.5. The interactive environment is a rich resource. You'll get the most out of it by exploring and experimenting.

Figure 5.35
Plotting from the workspace window, using the interactive plotting feature.

5.7 SAVING YOUR PLOTS

There are several ways to save plots created in MATLAB®:

- If you created the plot with programming code stored in a script, simply rerunning the code will recreate the figure.
- You can also save the figure from the file menu, using the **Save As ...** option. You'll be presented with several choices:

  1. You may save the figure as a **.fig** file, which is a MATLAB®-specific file format. To retrieve the figure, just double-click on the file in the current folder.
  2. You may save the figure in a number of different standard graphics formats, such as jpeg (**.jpg**) and enhanced metafile (**.emf**). These versions of the figure can be inserted into other documents, such as a Word document.
  3. You can select Edit from the menu bar, then select **copy figure**, and paste the figure into another document.
  4. You can use the file menu to create a script that will recreate the figure.

PRACTICE EXERCISE 5.6

Create a plot of $y = \cos(x)$. Practice saving the file and inserting it into a Word document. The correct answers can be found on the Pearson-website.

SUMMARY

The most commonly used graph in engineering is the $x-y$ plot. This two-dimensional plot can be used to graph data or to visualize mathematical functions. No matter what a graph represents, it should always include a title and x- and y-axis labels. Axis labels should be descriptive and should include units, such as ft/s or kJ/kg.

MATLAB® includes extensive options for controlling the appearance of your plots. The user can specify the color, line style, and marker style for each line on a graph. A grid can be added to the graph, and the axis range can be adjusted. Text boxes and a legend can be employed to describe the graph. The subplot function is used to divide the plot window into an $m \times n$ grid. Inside each of these subwindows, any of the MATLAB® plots can be created and modified.

In addition to $x-y$ plots, MATLAB® offers a variety of plotting options, including polar plots, pie charts, bar graphs, histograms, and $x-y$ graphs with two y-axes. The scaling on $x-y$ plots can be modified to produce logarithmic plots on either or both x- and y-axes. Engineers often use logarithmic scaling to represent data as a straight line.

The function `fplot` allows the user to plot a function without defining a vector of x- and y-values. MATLAB® automatically chooses the appropriate number of points and spacing to produce a smooth graph. Additional function-plotting capability is available in the symbolic toolbox.

The three-dimensional plotting options in MATLAB® include a line plot, a number of surface plots, and contour plots. Most of the options available in two-dimensional plotting also apply to these three-dimensional plots. The `meshgrid` function is especially useful in creating three-dimensional surface plots.

Interactive tools allow the user to modify existing plots. These tools are available from the figure menu bar. Plots can also be created with the interactive plotting option from the workspace window. The interactive environment is a rich resource. You'll get the most out of it by exploring and experimenting.

Figures created in MATLAB® can be saved in a variety of ways, either to be edited later or to be inserted into other documents. MATLAB® offers both proprietary file formats that minimize the storage space required to store figures and standard file formats suitable to import into other applications.

MATLAB® SUMMARY

The following MATLAB® summary lists all the special characters, commands, and functions that were defined in this chapter:

Special Characters					
Line Type	**Indicator**	**Point Type**	**Indicator**	**Color**	**Indicator**
solid	–	point	.	blue	b
dotted	:	circle	o	green	g
dash-dot	–.	x-mark	x	red	r
dashed	– –	plus	+	cyan	c
		star	*	magenta	m
		square	s	yellow	y
		diamond	d	black	k
		triangle down	v	white	w
		triangle up	∧		

(continued)

Special Characters	(continued)				
Line Type	**Indicator**	**Point Type**	**Indicator**	**Color**	**Indicator**
		triangle left	<		
		triangle right	>		
		pentagram	p		
		hexagram	h		

Commands and Functions

autumn	optional colormap used in surface plots
axis	freezes the current axis scaling for subsequent plots or specifies the axis dimensions
axis equal	forces the same scale spacing for each axis
bar	generates a bar graph
bar3	generates a three-dimensional bar graph
barh	generates a horizontal bar graph
bar3h	generates a horizontal three-dimensional bar graph
bone	optional colormap used in surface plots
clabel	add labels to a contour plot
clf	clear figure
close	close the current figure window
close all	close all open figure windows
colorcube	optional colormap used in surface plots
colormap	color scheme used in surface plots
comet	draws an x–y plot in a pseudo animation sequence
comet3	draws a three-dimensional line plot in a pseudo animation sequence
contour	generates a contour map of a three-dimensional surface
contourf	generates a filled contour map of a three-dimensional surface
cool	optional colormap used in surface plots
copper	optional colormap used in surface plots
figure	opens a new figure window
flag	optional colormap used in surface plots
fplot	creates an x–y plot based on a function
gtext	similar to text; the box is placed at a location determined interactively by the user by clicking in the figure window
grid	adds a grid to the current plot only
grid off	turns the grid off
grid on	adds a grid to the current and all subsequent graphs in the current figure
histogram	generates a histogram
histcounts	returns the number of data points in each bin
hold off	instructs MATLAB® **to** erase figure contents before adding new information
hold on	instructs MATLAB® **not to** erase figure contents before adding new information
hot	optional colormap used in surface plots
hsv	optional colormap used in surface plots
jet	default colormap used in surface plots
legend	adds a legend to a graph
linspace	creates a linearly spaced vector

Commands and Functions

`loglog`	generates an x–y plot with both axes scaled logarithmically
`mesh`	generates a mesh plot of a surface
`meshgrid`	places each of two vectors into separate two-dimensional matrices, the size of which is determined by the source vectors
`pause`	pauses the execution of a program until any key is hit
`pcolor`	creates a pseudo color plot similar to a contour map
`peaks`	creates a sample matrix used to demonstrate graphing functions
`pie`	generates a pie chart
`pie3`	generates a three-dimensional pie chart
`pink`	optional colormap used in surface plots
`plot`	creates an x–y plot
`plot3`	generates a three-dimensional line plot
`polarplot`	creates a polar plot
`prism`	optional colormap used in surface plots
`semilogx`	generates an x–y plot with the x-axis scaled logarithmically
`semilogy`	generates an x–y plot with the y-axis scaled logarithmically
`shading flat`	shades a surface plot with one color per grid section
`shading interp`	shades a surface plot by interpolation
`sphere`	sample function used to demonstrate graphing
`spring`	optional colormap used in surface plots
`subplot`	divides the graphics window into sections available for plotting
`summer`	optional colormap used in surface plots
`surf`	generates a surface plot
`surfc`	generates a combination surface and contour plot
`text`	adds a text box to a graph
`title`	adds a title to a plot
`white`	optional colormap used in surface plots
`winter`	optional colormap used in surface plots
`xlabel`	adds a label to the x-axis
`ylabel`	adds a label to the y-axis
`yyaxis`	specifies which y-axis to use
`zlabel`	adds a label to the z-axis

PROBLEMS

Two-Dimensional ($x - y$) Plots

5.1 Create plots of the following functions from $x = 0$ to 10.

(a) $y = e^x$

(b) $y = \sin(x)$

(c) $y = ax^2 + bx + c$, where $a = 5$, $b = 2$, and $c = 4$

(d) $y = \sqrt{x}$

Each of your plots should include a title, an x-axis label, a y-axis label, and a grid.

5.2 Plot the following set of data:

$$y = [12, 14, 12, 22, 8, 9]$$

Allow MATLAB® to use the matrix index number as the parameter for the x-axis.

5.3 Plot the following functions on the same graph for **x** values from $-\pi$ to π, selecting spacing to create a smooth plot:

$$y_1 = \sin(x)$$
$$y_2 = \sin(2x)$$
$$y_3 = \sin(3x)$$

(Hint: Recall that the appropriate MATLAB® syntax for $2x$ is **2* x**.)

5.4 Adjust the plot created in Problem 5.3 so that:
- Line 1 is red and dashed.
- Line 2 is blue and solid.
- Line 3 is green and dotted.
- Do not include markers on any of the graphs. In general, markers are included only on plots of measured data, not for calculated values.

5.5 Adjust the plot created in Problem 5.4 so that the x-axis goes from -6 to $+6$.
- Add a legend.
- Add a text box describing the plots.

x–y Plotting with Projectiles

Use the following information in Problems 5.6 through 5.10:
The distance a projectile travels when fired at an angle θ is a function of time, and can be divided into horizontal and vertical distances according to the formulas

$$\text{horizontal}(t) = tV_0 \cos(\theta)$$

and

$$\text{vertical}(t) = tV_0 \sin(\theta) - \tfrac{1}{2}gt^2$$

where

horizontal	=	distance traveled in the x direction,
vertical	=	distance traveled in the y direction,
V_0	=	initial velocity
g	=	acceleration due to gravity, 9.8 m/s^2, and
t	=	time, s.

5.6 Suppose the projectile just described is fired at an initial velocity of 100 m/s and a launch angle of $\pi/4(45°)$. Find the distance traveled both horizontally and vertically (in the x and y directions) for times from 0 to 20 s with a spacing of .01 s.

(a) Graph horizontal distance versus time.

(b) In a new figure window, plot vertical distance versus time (with time on the x-axis).

Don't forget a title and labels.

5.7 In a new figure window, plot horizontal distance on the x-axis and vertical distance on the y-axis.

5.8 Replot horizontal distance on the *x*-axis and vertical distance on the *y*-axis using the comet function. If the plot draws too quickly or too slowly on your computer, adjust the number of time values used in your calculations.

5.9 Calculate three new vectors for each of the vertical (v_1, v_2, v_3) and horizontal (h_1, h_2, h_3) distances traveled, assuming launch angles of $\pi/2$, $\pi/4$, and $\pi/6$.

- In a new figure window, graph horizontal distance on the *x*-axis and vertical distance on the *y*-axis, for all three cases. (You'll have three lines.)
- Make one line solid, one dashed, and one dotted. Add a legend to identify which line is which.

5.10 Recreate the plot from Problem 5.9. This time, create a matrix **theta** of the three angles, $\pi/2$, $\pi/4$, and $\pi/6$. Use the meshgrid function to create a mesh of **theta** and the time vector (**t**). Then use the two new meshed variables you create to recalculate vertical distance (v) and horizontal distance (h) traveled. Each of your results should be a 2001×3 matrix. Use the plot command to plot h on the *x*-axis and v on the *y*-axis.

5.11 A tensile testing machine such as the one shown in Figure P5.11(a) and (b) is used to determine the behavior of materials as they are deformed.

Figure P5.11
A tensile testing machine is used to measure stress and strain and to characterize the behavior of materials as they are deformed. (Courtesy of Instron)

(a)   (b)

Table P5.11 Tensile Testing Data

Load, lbf	Length, inches
0	2.0000
2000	2.0024
4000	2.0047
6000	2.0070
7500	2.0094
8000	2.0128
8500	2.0183
9000	2.0308
9500	2.0500
10000	2.075

In the typical test, a specimen is stretched at a steady rate. The force (load) required to deform the material is measured, as is the resulting deformation. An example set of data measured in one such test is shown in Table P5.11. These data can be used to calculate the applied stress and the resulting strain with the following equations.

$$\sigma = \frac{F}{A} \text{ and } \varepsilon = \frac{l - l_0}{l_0}$$

where

σ = stress in (Psi) $lb_f/in.^2$,
F = applied force in lb_f,
A = sample cross-sectional area in $in.^2$,
ε = strain in in./in.,
l = sample length, and
l_0 = original sample length.

(a) Use the provided data to calculate the stress and the corresponding strain for each data pair. The tested sample was a rod of diameter 0.505 in., so you'll need to find the cross-sectional area to use in your calculations.

(b) Create an x–y plot with strain on the x-axis and stress on the y-axis. Connect the data points with a solid black line, and use circles to mark each data point.

(c) Add a title and appropriate axis labels.

(d) The point where the graph changes from a straight line with a steep slope to a flattened curve is called the *yield stress* or *yield point*. This corresponds to a significant change in the material behavior. Before the yield point the material is elastic, returning to its original shape if the load is removed—much like a rubber band. Once the material has been deformed past the yield point, the change in shape becomes permanent and is called plastic deformation. Use a text box to mark the yield point on your graph.

5.12 In the previous chapter, the accumulated cyclone energy index (ACE) was introduced (see Problem 4.5). Use that data to solve the following problems. It may also be available to you as an EXCEL spreadsheet, named **ace_data.xlsx**.

(a) Create an x–y plot of the year (on the x-axis) versus the ACE index values (on the y-axis).

(b) Calculate the mean ACE value, and use it to draw the mean value on your graph. (*Hint:* You just need two points, one at the first year and one at the final year).

(c) Use the `filter` function to find a running weighted average of the ACE data, over a 10-year period, using the following syntax, assuming you have named the data extracted from the ACE column, `ace`.

```
running_avg_ace = filter(ones(1,10)/10,1,ace);
```

Create a plot of the year (on the x-axis) versus the ACE value and the weighted average on the y-axis. (You will have two lines.) From your graph, do you think hurricane intensity is increasing? You can find out more about the `filter` function by searching the `help` documentation.

Using Subplots

5.13 In Problem 5.1, you created four plots. Combine these into one figure with four subwindows, using the `subplot` function of MATLAB®.

5.14 In Problems 5.6, 5.7, and 5.9, you created a total of four plots. Combine these into one figure with four subwindows, using the `subplot` function of MATLAB®.

Polar Plots

5.15 Create a vector of angles from 0 to 2π. Use the `polarplot` plotting function to create graphs of the functions that follow. Remember, polar plots expect the angle and the radius as the two inputs to the `polarplot` function. Use the `subplot` function to put all four of your graphs in the same figure.

(a) $r = \sin^2(\theta) + \cos^2(\theta)$
(b) $r = \sin(\theta)$
(c) $r = e^{\theta/5}$
(d) $r = \sinh(\theta)$

5.16 In Practice Exercise 5.3, you created a number of interesting shapes in polar coordinates. Use those exercises as a help in creating the following figures:

(a) Create a "flower" with three petals.
(b) Overlay your figure with eight additional petals, half the size of the three original ones.
(c) Create a heart shape.
(d) Create a six-pointed star.
(e) Create a hexagon.

Logarithmic Plots

5.17 When interest is compounded continuously, the following equation represents the growth of your savings:

$$P = P_0 e^{rt}$$

In this equation,

P = current balance,
P_0 = initial balance,
r = growth constant, expressed as a decimal fraction, and
t = time invested.

Determine the amount in your account at the end of each year if you invest $1000 at 8% (0.08) for 30 years. (Make a table.)

Create a figure with four subplots. Plot time on the *x*-axis, and current balance P on the *y*-axis.

(a) In the first quadrant, plot t versus P in a rectangular coordinate system.
(b) In the second quadrant, plot t versus P, scaling the *x*-axis logarithmically.
(c) In the third quadrant, plot t versus P, scaling the *y*-axis logarithmically.
(d) In the fourth quadrant, plot t versus P, scaling both axes logarithmically.

Which of the four plotting techniques do you think displays the data best?

5.18 According to Moore's law (an observation made in 1965 by Gordon Moore, a co-founder of Intel Corporation), the number of transistors that would fit per square inch on a semiconductor integrated circuit doubles approximately every two years. Although Moore's law is often reported as predicting doubling every 18 months, this is incorrect. A colleague of Moore took into account the fact that transistor performance is also improving, and when combined with the increased number of transistors results in doubling of *performance* every 18 months. The year 2005 was the 40th-anniversary of the law. Over the last 40 years, Moore's projection has been consistently met. In 1965, the then state-of-the-art technology allowed for 30 transistors per square inch. Moore's law says that transistor density can be predicted by $d(t) = 30(2^{t/2})$, where t is measured in years.

(a) Letting $t = 0$ represent the year 1965 and $t = 46$ represent 2011, use this model to calculate the predicted number of transistors per square inch for the 46 years from 1965 to 2011. Let t increase in increments of 2 years. Display the results in a table with two columns—one for the year, and one for the number of transistors.

(b) Using the `subplot` feature, plot the data in a linear x–y plot, a semilog x plot, a semilog y plot, and a log–log plot. Be sure to title the plots and label the axes.

5.19 The total number of transistor count on integrated circuits produced over the last 45 years is shown in Table P5.19. Create a semilog plot (with the y-axis scaled logarithmically) of the actual data, using circles only to indicate

Table P5.19 Exponential Increase in Transistor Count on Integrated Circuits

Processor	Transistor Count	Date of Introduction	Manufacturer
Intel 4004	2300	1971	Intel
Intel 8008	2500	1972	Intel
Intel 8080	4500	1974	Intel
Intel 8088	29,000	1979	Intel
Intel 80286	134,000	1982	Intel
Intel 80386	275,000	1985	Intel
Intel 80486	1,200,000	1989	Intel
Pentium	3,100,000	1993	Intel
AMD K5	4,300,000	1996	AMD
Pentium II	7,500,000	1997	Intel
AMD K6	8,800,000	1997	AMD
Pentium III	9,500,000	1999	Intel
AMD K6-III	21,300,000	1999	AMD
AMD K7	22,000,000	1999	AMD
Pentium 4	42,000,000	2000	Intel
Barton	54,300,000	2003	AMD
AMD K8	105,900,000	2003	AMD
Itanium 2	220,000,000	2003	Intel
Itanium 2 with 9MB cache	592,000,000	2004	Intel
Cell	241,000,000	2006	Sony/IBM/Toshiba
Core 2 Duo	291,000,000	2006	Intel
Core 2 Quad	582,000,000	2006	Intel
G80	681,000,000	2006	NVIDIA
POWER6	789,000,000	2007	IBM

Processor	Transistor Count	Date of Introduction	Manufacturer
Dual-Core Itanium 2	1,700,000,000	2006	Intel
Quad-Core Itanium Tukwila (processor)[1]	2,000,000,000	2008	Intel
8-Core Xeon Nehalem-EX	2,300,000,000	2010	Intel
10-Core Xeon Westmere-EX	2,600,000,000	2011	Intel
61-Core Xeon Phi	5,000,000,000	2012	Intel
18-Core Xeon Haswell-E5	5,560,000,000	2014	Intel
IBM z13 Storage Controller	7,100,000,000	2015	IBM
22-core Xeon Broadwell-E5	7,200,000,000	2016	Intel
SPARC M7	10,000,000,000	2015	Oracle

the data points (no lines). Include a second line representing the predicted values using Moore's law, based on the 1971 count as the starting point. Add a legend to your plot.

5.20 Many physical phenomena can be described by the Arrhenius equation. For example, reaction-rate constants for chemical reactions are modeled as

$$k = k_0 e^{(-Q/RT)}$$

where

k_0 = constant with units that depend upon the reaction,
Q = activation energy, kJ/kmol,
R = ideal gas constant, kJ/kmol K, and
T = temperature in K.

For a certain chemical reaction, the values of the constants are

$$Q = 1000 \, \text{J/mol}$$
$$k_0 = 10 \, \text{s}^{-1}$$
$$R = 8.314 \, \text{J/mol K}$$

for T from 300 K to 1000 K. Find the values of k. Create the following two graphs of your data in a single figure window:

(a) Plot T on the x-axis and k on the y-axis.
(b) Plot your results as the $\log_{10}$ of k on the y-axis and $1/T$ on the x-axis.

Bar Graphs, Pie Charts, and Histograms

5.21 Use subplots to create the four plots in this problem. Let the vector

$$G = [68, 83, 61, 70, 75, 82, 57, 5, 76, 85, 62, 71, 96, 78, 76, 68, 72, 75, 83, 93]$$

represent the distribution of final grades in an engineering course.

(a) Use MATLAB® to sort the data, and create a bar graph of the scores.
(b) Create a histogram of the scores, using `histogram`.
(c) Assume the following grading scheme is used:

A > 90–100
B > 80–90
C > 70–80
D > 60–70
E > 0–60

Use the `histogram` function and an appropriate edges vector to create a histogram showing the grade distribution.

(d) Repeat part (c) but normalize the data using the countdensity option.

5.22 In the engineering class mentioned in Problem 5.21, there are

2 As
4 Bs
8 Cs
4 Ds
2 Es

(a) Use the `histcounts` function to create a vector called grades corresponding to this grade distribution, based on the grading scheme in Problem 5.21.

Create a pie chart of the grades vector. Add a legend listing the grade names (A, B, C, etc.).

(b) Use the `interactive` text option accessed from the figure window menu to add a text box to each slice of pie, with the grade shown in the text box. Save your modified graph as a **.fig** file.

(c) Create a three-dimensional pie chart of the same data, including a legend.

5.23 The National Oceanic and Atomospheric Administration (NOAA) provides climate information to the public through the National Centers for Environmental Information. You can probably find information there for your hometown or favorite vacation spot. (Perform an internet search to find the website.) Browse the available datasets and download one of the annual summaries that include monthly precipitation and temperature data. Your instructor may have the dataset for Orlando International Airport (MCO) available for you already from the Pearson website. Upload the data from the Excel spreadsheet, and create a histogram of the extreme maximum temperature data.

5.24 The inventory of a certain type of screw in a warehouse at the end of each month is listed in table P5.24:

Table P5.24 Screw Inventory

	2009	2010
January	2345	2343
February	4363	5766
March	3212	4534
April	4565	4719
May	8776	3422
June	7679	2200
July	6532	3454
August	2376	7865
September	2238	6543
October	4509	4508
November	5643	2312
December	1137	4566

Plot the data in a bar graph. Add an appropriate legend and title.

5.25 Use the `randn` function to create 1000 values in a normal (Gaussian) distribution of numbers with a mean of 70 and a standard deviation of 3.5. Create a histogram of the data set you calculated.

Graphs with Two y-Axes

5.26 In the introduction to Problems 5.6 through 5.10, we learned that the equations for the distance traveled by a projectile as a function of time are:

$$\text{horizontal}\,(t) = tV_0 \cos(\theta)$$
$$\text{vertical}\,(t) = tV_0 \sin(\theta) - \tfrac{1}{2}gt^2$$

For time from 0 to 20 s, plot both the horizontal distance versus time and the vertical distance versus time on the same graph, using separate y-axes for each line. Assume a launch angle of 45 degrees ($\pi/4$ radians) and an initial velocity of 100 m/s. Assume also that the acceleration due to gravity, g, is 9.8 m/s. Be sure to label both y-axes.

5.27 If the equation modeling the vertical distance traveled by a projectile as a function of time is

$$\text{vertical}\,(t) = tV_0 \sin(\theta) - 1/2\,gt^2$$

then, from calculus, the velocity in the vertical direction is

$$\text{velocity}\,(t) = V_0 \sin(\theta) - gt$$

Create a vector **t** from 0 to 20 s, and calculate both the vertical position and the velocity in the vertical direction, assuming a launch angle θ of $\pi/4$ radians and an initial velocity of 100 m/s. Plot both quantities on the same graph with separate y-axes. Be sure to label both y-axes.

   The velocity should be zero at the point where the projectile is the highest in the vertical direction. Does your graph support this prediction?

5.28 For many metals, deformation changes their physical properties. In a process called *cold work*, metal is intentionally deformed to make it stronger. The data in table P5.28 lists tabulate both the strength and ductility of a metal that has been cold worked to different degrees:

Table P5.28 Effect of Cold Work on a Hypothetical Metal

Percent Cold Work	Yield Strength, MPa	Ductility, %
10	275	43
15	310	30
20	340	23
25	360	17
30	375	12
40	390	7
50	400	4
60	407	3
68	410	2

Plot these data on a single x–y plot with two y-axes. Be sure to label both y-axes.

Three-Dimensional Line Plots

5.29 Create a vector x of values from 0 to 20π, with a spacing of $\pi/100$. Define vectors y and z as

$$y = x \sin(x)$$

and

$$z = x \cos(x)$$

(a) Create an x–y plot of **x** and **y**.
(b) Create a polar plot of **x** and **y**.
(c) Create a three-dimensional line plot of **x**, **y**, and **z**. Don't forget a title and labels.

5.30 Figure out how to adjust your input to `plot3` in Problem 5.29 so as to create a graph that looks like a tornado (see Figure P5.30). Use `comet3` instead of `plot3` to create the graph.

Three-Dimensional Surface and Contour Plots

5.31 Create x and y vectors from -5 to $+5$ with a spacing of 0.5. Use the `meshgrid` function to map x and y onto two new two-dimensional matrices called X and Y. Use your new matrices to calculate vector Z, with magnitude

$$Z = \sin(\sqrt{X^2 + Y^2})$$

(a) Use the `mesh` plotting function to create a three-dimensional plot of Z.
(b) Use the `surf` plotting function to create a three-dimensional plot of Z. Compare the results you obtain with a single input (Z) with those obtained with inputs for all three dimensions (X, Y, Z).
(c) Modify your surface plot with interpolated shading. Try using different `colormaps`.

Figure P5.30
Tornado plot.

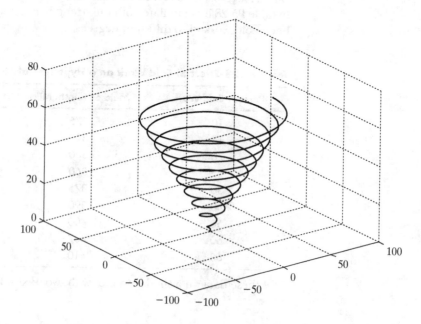

(d) Generate a contour plot of Z. Use handle graphics and the `clabel` function to label the contour lines.

(e) Generate a combination surface and contour plot of Z.

Challenge Problem

5.32 In Problem 5.31, you generated five different plots. Use subplots to plot the first four into a rectangular grid, much like we did in earlier problems. Consult the MATLAB® help feature to figure out how to add the fifth graph on top of the first four plots.

```
doc subplot
```

6 User-Defined Functions

Objectives

After reading this chapter, you should be able to:

- Create and use your own MATLAB® functions with both single and multiple inputs and outputs.
- Store and access your own functions in toolboxes.

- Create and use anonymous functions.
- Create and use function handles.
- Create and use sub-functions and nested subfunctions.

INTRODUCTION

The MATLAB® programming language is built around functions. A *function* is a piece of computer code that accepts an input argument from the user and provides output to the program. Functions allow us to program efficiently, enabling us to avoid rewriting the computer code for calculations that are performed frequently. For example, most computer programs contain a function that calculates the sine of a number. In MATLAB®, sin is the function name used to call up a series of commands that perform the necessary calculations. The user needs to provide an angle, and MATLAB® returns a result. It isn't necessary for the programmer to know how MATLAB® calculates the value of sin(x).

6.1 CREATING FUNCTION FILES

We have already explored many of MATLAB®'s built-in functions, but you may wish to define your own functions—those that are used commonly in your programming. User-defined functions are stored as M-files and can be accessed by MATLAB® if they are in the current folder.

6.1.1 Syntax

Both built-in MATLAB® functions and user-defined MATLAB® functions have the same structure. Each consists of a name, user-provided input, and calculated output. For example, the function

    cos(x)

- is named `cos`,
- takes the user input inside the parentheses (in this case, **x**), and
- calculates a result.

The user does not see the calculations performed, but just accepts the answer. User-defined functions work the same way. Imagine that you have created a function called `my_function`. Using

    my_function(x)

in a program or from the command window will return a result, as long as x is defined and the logic in the function definition works.

User-defined functions are created in M-files. Each must start with a function-definition line that contains the following:

- The word `function`
- A variable that defines the function output
- A function name
- A variable used for the input argument

KEY IDEA

Functions allow us to program more efficiently.

For example,

    function output = my_function(x)

is the first line of the user-defined function called `my_function`. It requires one input argument, which the program will call x, and will calculate one output argument, which the program will call `output`. The function name and the names of the input and output variables are arbitrary and are selected by the programmer. Here's an example of an appropriate first line for a function called `calculation`:

    function result = calculation(a)

In this case, the function name is `calculation`, the input argument will be called a in any calculations performed in the function program, and the output will be called `result`. Although any valid MATLAB® names can be used, it is good programming practice to use meaningful names for all variables, and for function names.

FUNCTION

A piece of computer code that accepts an input, performs a calculation, and provides an output

HINT

Students are often confused about the use of the word *input* as it refers to a function. We use it here to describe the input argument—the value that goes inside the parentheses when we call a function. In MATLAB®, input arguments are different from the input command, introduced in a later chapter.

Here's an example of a very simple MATLAB® function that calculates the value of a particular polynomial:

```
function output = poly(x)
%This function calculates the value of a third-order polynomial
output = 3*x.^3 + 5*x.^2 - 2*x +1;
```

The function name is `poly`, the input argument is x, and the output variable is named `output`.

Before this function can be used, it must be saved into the current folder. The file name *must be the same* as the function name in order for MATLAB® to find it. All of the MATLAB® naming conventions we learned for naming variables apply to naming user-defined functions. In particular,

KEY IDEA

Name functions using the standard MATLAB® naming conventions for variables.

- The function name must start with a letter.
- It can consist of letters, numbers, and the underscore.
- Reserved names cannot be used.
- Any length is allowed, although long names are not a good programming practice.

Once the function has been saved, it is available for use from the command window, from a script, or from another function. You cannot execute a function directly from the file itself. This makes sense, since the input parameters have not been defined until you call the function from the command window or a script. Consider the `poly` function just created. If, in the command window, we type

$$poly(4)$$

then MATLAB® responds with

```
ans =
      265.
```

If we set a equal to 4 and use a as the input argument, we get the same result:

```
a = 4;
poly(a)
ans =
      265
```

If we define a vector, we get a vector of answers. Thus,

```
y = 1:5;
poly(y)
```

gives

```
ans =
      7    41   121   265   491.
```

If, however, you try to execute the function by selecting the **Save-and-run** icon from the function menu bar, the following error message is displayed:

```
???Input argument "x" is undefined.
Error in ==> poly at 3
output = 3*x.^3 + 5*x.^2 - 2*x + 1;
```

The value of **x** must be passed to the function when it is used—either in the command window, or from within a script.

HINT

While you are creating a function, it may be useful to allow intermediate calculations to print to the command window. However, once you complete your "debugging," make sure that all your output is suppressed. If you don't, you'll see extraneous information in the command window.

PRACTICE EXERCISE 6.1

Create MATLAB® functions to evaluate the following mathematical functions (make sure you select meaningful function names) and test them. To test your functions, you'll need to call them from the command window, or use them in a script. Remember, each function requires its own file. The correct answers can be found on the Pearson website.

1. $y(x) = x^2$
2. $y(x) = e^{1/x}$
3. $y(x) = \sin(x^2)$

Create MATLAB® functions for the following unit conversions (you may need to consult a textbook or the Internet for the appropriate conversion factors). Be sure to test your functions, either from the command window, or by using them in a script.

1. Inches to feet
2. Calories to joules
3. Watts to BTU/hr
4. Meters to miles
5. Miles per hour (mph) to ft/s

EXAMPLE 6.1

CONVERTING BETWEEN DEGREES AND RADIANS

Engineers usually measure angles in degrees, yet most computer programs and many calculators require that the input to trigonometric functions be in radians. Write and test a function DR that changes degrees to radians, and another function RD that changes radians to degrees. Your functions should be able to accept both scalar and matrix input.

1. State the problem
   Create and test two functions, DR and RD, to change degrees to radians and radians to degrees respectively (see Figure 6.1).
2. Describe the input and output

Figure 6.1
Trigonometric functions require angles to be expressed in radians. Trigonometry is regularly used in engineering.

Input	A vector of degree values
	A vector of radian values
Output	A table converting degrees to radians
	A table converting radians to degrees

(*continued*)

3. Develop a hand example

$$\text{degrees} = \text{radians} \times 180/\pi$$
$$\text{radians} = \text{degrees} \times \pi/180$$

Degrees to Radians	
Degrees	**Radians**
0	0
30	$30(\pi/180) = \pi/6 = 0.524$
60	$601\,\pi/1802 = \pi/3 = 1.047$
90	$901\,\pi/1802 = \pi/2 = 1.571$

4. Develop a MATLAB® solution

```
%%Example 6.1
%
clear, clc
%Define a vector of degree values
degrees = 0:15:180;
% Call the DR function, and use it to find radians
radians = DR(degrees);
%Create a table to use in the output
degrees_radians = [degrees;radians]'
%Define a vector of radian values
radians = 0:pi/12:pi;
%Call the RD function, and use it to find degrees
degrees = RD(radians);
radians_degrees = [radians;degrees]'
```

The functions called by the program are

```
function output = DR(x)
%This function changes degrees to radians
output = x*pi/180;
```

and

```
function output = RD(x)
%This function changes radians to degrees
output = x*180/pi;
```

Remember that in order for the script to find the functions, they must be in the current folder and must be named **DR.m** and **RD.m**. The program generates the following results in the command window:

```
degrees_radians =
     0     0.000
    15     0.262
    30     0.524
    45     0.785
    60     1.047
    75     1.309
    90     1.571
```

```
            105    1.833
            120    2.094
            135    2.356
            150    2.618
            165    2.880
            180    3.142


radians_degrees =
            0.000       0.000
            0.262      15.000
            0.524      30.000
            0.785      45.000
            1.047      60.000
            1.309      75.000
            1.571      90.000
            1.833     105.000
            2.094     120.000
            2.356     135.000
            2.618     150.000
            2.880     165.000
            3.142     180.000
```

5. Test the solution
   Compare the MATLAB® solution with the hand solution. As the output is a
   table, it is easy to see that the conversions generated by MATLAB® correspond
   to those calculated by hand.

| EXAMPLE 6.2 |

ASTM GRAIN SIZE

You may not be used to thinking of metals as crystals, but they are. If you look at a
polished piece of metal under a microscope, the structure becomes clear, as seen in
Figure 6.2. As you can see, every crystal (called a grain in metallurgy) is a different
size and shape. The size of the grains affects the metal's strength; the finer the grains
are, the stronger will be the metal.

Because it is difficult to determine an "average" grain size, a standard technique
has been developed by ASTM (formerly known as the American Society for Testing
and Materials, but now known just by its initials). A sample of metal is examined
under a microscope at a magnification of 100, and the number of grains in 1 square
inch is counted. The parameters are related by

$$N = 2^{n-1}$$

where n is the ASTM grain size, and N is the number of grains per square inch at
100×. The equation can be solved for n to give

$$n = \frac{(\log(N) + \log(2))}{\log(2)}.$$

Figure 6.2
Microstructure of iron.
(Cultura Creative (RF)/
Alamy Stock Photo)

(*continued*)

This equation is not hard to use, but it's awkward. Instead, let's create a MATLAB® function called `grain_size`.

1. State the problem

   Create and test a function called `grain_size` to determine the ASTM grain size of a piece of metal.

2. Describe the input and output

   To test the function, we'll need to choose an arbitrary number of grains. For example:

   Input   16 grains per square inch at

   Output   ASTM grain size

3. Develop a hand example

$$n = \frac{(\log(N) + \log(2))}{\log(2)}$$

$$n = \frac{(\log(16) + \log(2))}{\log(2)} = 5$$

4. Develop a MATLAB® solution

   The function, created in a separate file, is

   ```
   function output = grain_size(N)
   %Calculates the ASTM grain size n
   output = (log10(N) + log10(2))./log10(2);
   ```

   which was saved as **grain_size.m** in the current folder. To use this function, we can call it from the command window:

   ```
   grain_size(16)
   ans =
         5
   ```

5. Test the solution

   The MATLAB® solution is the same as the hand solution. It might be interesting to see how the ASTM grain size varies with the number of grains per square inch. We could use the function with an array of values and plot the results in Figure 6.3.

   ```
   %%Example 6.2
   %ASTM Grain Size
   N = 1:100;
   n = grain_size(N);
   plot(N,n)
   title('ASTM Grain Size')
   xlabel('Number of grains per square inch at 100x')
   ylabel('ASTM Grain Size')
   grid
   ```

   As expected, the grain size increases as the number of grains per square inch increases.

Figure 6.3
A plot of a function's behavior is a good way to help determine whether you have programmed it correctly.

6.1.2 Comments

As with any computer program, you should comment your code liberally so that it is easy to follow. However, in a MATLAB® function, the comments on the line immediately following the very first line serve a special role. These lines are returned when the help function is queried from the command window. Consider, for example, the following function:

```
function results = f(x)
%This function converts seconds to minutes
results = x./60;
```

Querying the help function from the command window

```
help f
```

returns

```
This function converts seconds to minutes
```

6.1.3 Functions with Multiple Inputs and Outputs

Just as the predefined MATLAB® functions may require multiple inputs and may return multiple outputs, more complicated user-defined functions can be written. Recall, for example, the remainder function. This predefined function calculates the remainder in a division problem and requires the user to input the dividend and the divisor. For the problem $\frac{5}{3}$, the correct syntax is

KEY IDEA
Function comments are displayed when you use the help feature.

```
rem(5,3)
```

which gives

```
ans =
     2.
```

Similarly, a user-defined function could be written to multiply two vectors together:

```
function output = g(x,y)
% This function multiplies x and y together
% x and y must be the same size matrices
a = x .*y;
output = a;
```

When x and y are defined in the command window and the function g is called, a vector of output values is returned:

```
x = 1:5;
y = 5:9;
g(x,y)
ans =
      5    12    21    32    45
```

You can use the comment lines to let users know what kind of input is required and to describe the function. In this example, an intermediate calculation (**a**) was performed, but the only output from this function is the variable we've named output. This output can be a matrix containing a variety of numbers, but it's still only one variable.

You can also create functions that return more than one output variable. Many of the predefined MATLAB® functions return more than one result. For example, max returns both the maximum value in a matrix and the element number at which the maximum occurs. To achieve the same result in a user-defined function, make the output a matrix of answers instead of a single variable, as in

```
function [dist, vel, accel] = motion(t)
% This function calculates the distance, velocity, and
% acceleration of a particular car for a given value of t
% assuming all 3 parameters are initially 0.
accel = 0.5.*t;
vel = t.^2/4;
dist = t.^3/12;
```

Once saved as **motion.m** in the current folder, you can use the function to find values of distance, velocity, and acceleration at specified times:

```
[distance, velocity, acceleration] = motion(10)
distance =
      83.33
velocity =
      25
acceleration =
      5
```

If you call the `motion` function without specifying all three outputs, only the first output will be returned:

```
motion(10)
ans =
        500
```

Remember, all variables in MATLAB® are matrices, so it's important in the preceding example to use the .* operator, which specifies element-by-element multiplication. For example, using a vector of time values from 0 to 30 in the motion function

```
time = 0:10:30;
[distance, velocity, acceleration] = motion(time)
```

returns three vectors of answers:

```
distance =
     0   500   4000   13500
velocity =
     0   50   200   450
acceleration =
     0   5   10   15
```

It's easier to see the results if you group the vectors together, as in

```
results = [time',distance',velocity',acceleration']
```

which returns

```
results =
     0        0        0      0
    10      500       50      5
    20     4000      200     10
    30    13500      450     15
```

Because `time`, `distance`, `velocity`, and `acceleration` were row vectors, the transpose operator was used to convert them into columns.

PRACTICE EXERCISE 6.2

Assuming that the matrix dimensions agree, create and test MATLAB® functions to evaluate the following simple mathematical functions with multiple input vectors and a single output vector. The correct answers can be found on the Pearson website.

1. $z(x, y) = x + y$
2. $z(a, b, c) = ab^c$
3. $z(w, x, y) = we^{(x/y)}$
4. $z(p, t) = p/\sin(t)$

Assuming that the matrix dimensions agree, create and test MATLAB® functions to evaluate the following simple mathematical functions with a single input vector and multiple output vectors:

5. $f(x) = \cos(x)$
   $f(x) = \sin(x)$

6. $f(x) = 5x^2 + 2$
$f(x) = \sqrt{5x^2 + 2}$

7. $f(x) = \exp(x)$
$f(x) = \ln(x)$

Assuming that the matrix dimensions agree, create, and test MATLAB®
functions to evaluate the following simple mathematical functions with multiple input vectors and multiple output vectors:

8. $f(x, y) = x + y$
$f(x, y) = x - y$

9. $f(x, y) = ye^x$
$f(x, y) = xe^y$

EXAMPLE 6.3

HOW GRAIN SIZE AFFECTS METAL STRENGTH: A FUNCTION WITH THREE INPUTS

Metals composed of small crystals are stronger than metals composed of fewer large
crystals. The metal yield strength (the amount of stress at which the metal starts
to permanently deform) is related to the average grain diameter by the *Hall–Petch
equation*:

$$\sigma = \sigma_0 + Kd^{-1/2}$$

where the symbols σ_0 and K represent constants that are different for every metal.

Create a function called `HallPetch` that requires three inputs—σ_0, K, and
d—and calculates the value of yield strength. Call this function from a MATLAB®
program that supplies values of σ_0 and K, then plots the value of yield strength for
values of d from 0.1 to 10 mm.

1. **State the problem**
   Create a function called `HallPetch` that determines the yield strength of a
   piece of metal, using the Hall–Petch equation. Use the function to create a plot
   of yield strength versus grain diameter.

2. **Describe the input and output**
   Input $K = 9600$ psi $\sqrt{\text{min}}$
                            $\sigma = 1200$ psi
                            $d = 0.1$ to 10 mm
   Output   Plot of yield strength versus grain diameter

3. **Develop a hand example**

   The Hall–Petch equation is

   $$\sigma = \sigma_0 + Kd^{-1/2}.$$

   Substituting values of 12,000 psi and 9600 psi $\sqrt{\text{mm}}$ for σ_0 and K, respectively,
   then

   $$\sigma = 12{,}000 + 9600d^{-1/2}$$

For $d = 1$ mm,

$$\sigma = 12{,}000 + 9600 = 21{,}600$$

4. Develop a MATLAB® solution

The desired function, created in a separate file, is

```
function output = HallPetch(sigma0,k,d)
%Hall-Petch equation to determine the yield
%strength of metals
output = sigma0 + K*d.^(-0.5);
```

and was saved as **HallPetch.m** in the current folder.

```
%%Example 6.3
clear,clc
s0 = 12000; K = 9600 ;
%Define the values of grain diameter
diameter = 0.1:0.1:10;
yield = HallPetch(s0,K,d);
%Plot the results
figure(1)
plot(diameter,yield)
title('Yield strengths found with the Hall-Petch equation')
xlabel('diameter, mm')
ylabel('yield strength, psi')
```

The graph shown in Figure 6.4 was generated by the program.

5. Test the solution

We can use the graph to compare the results to the hand solution.

Figure 6.4
Yield strengths predicted with the Hall–Petch equation. Small grain diameters correspond to large values of the yield strength.

EXAMPLE 6.4

KINETIC ENERGY: A FUNCTION WITH TWO INPUTS

The kinetic energy of a moving object (see Figure 6.5) is

$$KE = 1/2\ mv^2.$$

Create and test a function called KE to find the kinetic energy of a moving car, if you know the mass m and the velocity v of the vehicle.

1. State the problem
   Create a function called KE to find the kinetic energy of a car.
2. Describe the input and output

   Input   Mass of the car, in kilograms
                 Velocity of the car, in m/s

   Output   Kinetic energy, in joules

3. Develop a hand example
   If the mass is 1000 kg, and the velocity is 25 m/s, then

   $$KE = {}^1\!/_2 \times 1000\ \text{kg} \times (25\ \text{m/s})^2 = 312{,}500\ \text{J} = 312.5\ \text{kJ}.$$

4. Develop a MATLAB® solution

   ```
   function output = ke(mass,velocity)
   output = 1/2*mass*velocity.^2;
   ```

5. Test the solution

   ```
   v = 25;
   m = 1000;
   ke(m,v)
   ans =
           312500
   ```

Figure 6.5
Race cars store a
significant amount of
kinetic energy. (Alex
Zanardi in Target/Ganassi
Car./Getty Images)

This result matches the hand example, confirming that the function works correctly and can now be used in a larger MATLAB® program.

6.1.4 Functions with No Input or No Output

Although most functions need at least one input and return at least one output value, in some situations no inputs or outputs are required. For example, consider this function, which draws a star in polar coordinates:

```
function [] = star( )
theta = pi/2:0.8*pi:4.8*pi;
r = ones(1,6);
polar(theta,r)
```

The square brackets on the first line indicate that the output of the function is an empty matrix (i.e., no value is returned). The empty parentheses tell us that no input is expected. If, from the command window, you type

```
star
```

then no values are returned, but a figure window opens showing a star drawn in polar coordinates (see Figure 6.6).

KEY IDEA
Not all functions require an input.

There are numerous built-in MATLAB® functions that do not require any input. For example,

```
A = clock
```

returns the current time:

```
A =
   1.0e+003 *
   Columns 1 through 4
     2.0050   0.0030   0.0200   0.0150
   Columns 5 through 6
     0.0250    0.0277
```

Also,

```
A = pi
```

returns the value of the mathematical constant π:

```
A =
     3.1416
```

HINT

You may ask yourself whether the `star` function is really an example of a function that does not return an output; after all, it does draw a star. But the output of a function is defined as a *value* that is returned when you call the function. If we ask MATLAB® to perform the calculation

```
A = star
```

an error statement is generated, because the `star` function does not return anything! Thus, there is nothing to set **A** equal to.

Figure 6.6
The user-defined function star requires no input and produces no output values, but it does draw a star in polar coordinates.

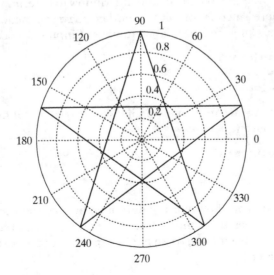

However, if we try to set the MATLAB® function tic equal to a variable name, an error statement is generated, because tic does not return an output value:

```
A = tic
???Error using ==> tic
Too many output arguments.
```

(The tic function starts a timer going for later use in the toc function.)

6.1.5 Determining the Number of Input and Output Arguments

There may be times when you want to know the number of input arguments or output values associated with a function. MATLAB® provides two built-in functions for this purpose.

KEY IDEA

Using the nargin or nargout functions is useful in programming functions with variable inputs and outputs.

The nargin function determines the number of input arguments in either a user-defined function or a built-in function. The name of the function may be specified as a string, as, for example, in

```
nargin('sin')
ans =
    1
```

or as a function handle. Function handles will be introduced later in this chapter. The remainder function, rem, requires two inputs; thus,

```
nargin('rem')
ans =
    2
```

When nargin is used inside a user-defined function, it determines how many input arguments were actually entered. This allows a function to have a variable number of inputs. Recall graphing functions such as surf. When surf has a single matrix input, a graph is created, using the matrix index numbers as the x- and y-coordinates. When there are three inputs, x, y, and z, the graph is based on the specified x- and y-values. The nargin function allows the programmer to determine how to create the plot, based on the number of inputs.

The surf function is an example of a function with a variable number of inputs. If we use nargin from the command window to determine the number of declared inputs, there isn't one correct answer. The nargin function returns a negative number to let us know that a variable number of inputs are possible:

```
nargin('surf')
ans =
    -1
```

The nargout function is similar to nargin, but it determines the number of outputs from a function:

```
nargout('sin')
ans =
    1
```

The number of outputs is determined by how many matrices are returned, not how many values are in the matrix. We know that size returns the number of rows and columns in a matrix, so we might expect nargout to return 2 when applied to size. However,

```
nargout('size')
ans =
     1
```

returns only one matrix, which has just two elements, as, in

```
x = 1:10;
size(x)
ans =
     1 10
```

An example of a function with multiple outputs is `max`:

```
nargout('max')
ans =
     2
```

When used inside a user-defined function, `nargout` determines how many outputs have been requested by the user. Consider this example, in which we have rewritten the function from Section 6.1.4 to create a star:

```
function A = star1( )
theta = pi/2:0.8*pi:4.8*pi;
r = ones(1,6);
polar(theta,r)
if nargout==1
    A = 'Twinkle twinkle little star';
end
```

If we use `nargout` from the command window, MATLAB® tells us that one output is specified.

```
nargout('star1')
ans =
     1
```

If we call the function simply as

```
star1
```

nothing is returned to the command window, although the plot is drawn. If we call the function by setting it equal to a variable, as in

```
x = star1
x =
Twinkle twinkle little star
```

a value for **x** is returned, based on the `if` statement embedded in the function, which used `nargout` to determine the number of output values.

If statements will be introduced in Chapter 8.

6.1.6 Local Variables

The variables used in function files are known as *local variables*. The only way a function can communicate with the workspace is through input arguments and the output it returns. Any variables defined within the function exist only for the function to use. For example, consider the g function previously described:

```
function output = g(x,y)
% This function multiplies x and y together
% x and y must be the same size matrices
```

```
a = x .*y;
output = a;
```

The variables a, x, y, and `output` are local variables. They can be used for additional calculations inside the g function, but they are not stored in the workspace. To confirm this, clear the workspace and the command window, then call the g function:

LOCAL VARIABLE
A variable that only has meaning inside a program or function

```
clear, clc
g(10,20)
```

The function returns

```
g(10,20)
ans =
    200.
```

Notice that the only variable stored in the workspace window is ans, which is characterized as follows:

Name	Value	Size	Bytes	Class
ans	200	1 × 1	8	double array

Just as calculations performed in the command window or from a script cannot access variables defined in functions, functions cannot access the variables defined in the workspace. This means that functions must be completely self-contained: The only way they can get information from your program is through the input arguments, and the only way they can deliver information is through the function output.

Consider a function written to find the distance an object falls due to gravity:

```
function result = distance(t)
%This function calculates the distance a falling object
%travels due to gravity
g = 9.8 %meters per second squared
result = 1/2*g*t.^2;
```

The value of g must be included *inside* the function. It doesn't matter whether g has or has not been used in the main program. How g is defined is hidden to the distance function, unless g is specified inside the function.

Of course, you could also pass the value of g to the function as an input argument:

```
function result = distance(g,t)
%This function calculates the distance a falling object
%travels due to gravity
result = 1/2*g*t.^2;
```

HINT

The same matrix names can be used in both a function and the program that references it. However, they do not *have* to be the same. Since variable names are local to either the function or the program that calls the function, the variables are completely separate. As a beginning programmer, you would be wise to use different variable names in your functions and your programs—just so you don't confuse *yourself*.

KEY IDEA

It is usually a bad idea to define global variables.

6.1.7 Global Variables

Unlike local variables, global variables are available to all parts of a computer program. In general, *it is a bad idea* to define global variables. However, MATLAB® protects users from unintentionally using a global variable by requiring that it be identified both in the command-window environment (or in a script) and in the function that will use it.

Consider the distance function once again:

GLOBAL VARIABLE

A variable that is available from multiple programs

```
function result = distance(t)
%This function calculates the distance a falling object
%travels due to gravity
global G
result = 1/2*G*t.^2;
```

The `global` command alerts the function to look in the workspace for the value of G. G must also have been defined in the command window (or script) as a global variable:

```
global G
G = 9.8;
```

This approach allows you to change the value of G without needing to redefine the distance function or providing the value of G as an input argument to the distance function.

HINT

As a matter of style, always make the names of global variables uppercase. MATLAB® doesn't care, but it is easier to identify global variables if you use a consistent naming convention.

HINT

It may seem like a good idea to use global variables because they can simplify your programs. However, consider this example of using global variables in your everyday life: It would be easier to order a book from an online bookseller if you had posted your credit card information on a site where any retailer could just look it up. Then the bookseller wouldn't have to ask you to type in the number. However, this might produce some unintended consequences (like other people using your credit card without your permission or knowledge!). When you create a global variable, it becomes available to other functions and can be changed by those functions, sometimes leading to unintended consequences.

6.1.8 Accessing Function Code

The functions provided with MATLAB® are of two types. One type is built in, and the code is not accessible for us to review. The other type consists of files, stored in toolboxes provided with the program. We can see these function files (or the function files written by users) with the `type` command. For example, the `sphere` function creates a three-dimensional representation of a sphere; thus,

```
type sphere
```

or

```
type('sphere')
```

returns the contents of the **sphere.m** file:

```
function [xx,yy,zz] = sphere(varargin)
%SPHERE Generate sphere.
%    [X,Y,Z] = SPHERE(N) generates three (N+1)-by-(N+1)
%    matrices so that SURF(X,Y,Z) produces a unit sphere.
%    [X,Y,Z] = SPHERE uses N = 20.
%    SPHERE(N) and just SPHERE graph the sphere as a SURFACE
%    and do not return anything.
%    SPHERE(AX, . . .) plots into AX instead of GCA.
%    See also ELLIPSOID, CYLINDER.
%    Clay M. Thompson 4-24-91, CBM 8-21-92.
%    Copyright 1984-2002 The MathWorks, Inc.
%    $Revision: 5.8.4.1 $ $Date: 2002/09/26 01:55:25 $
%    Parse possible Axes input
error(nargchk(0,2,nargin));
[cax,args,nargs] = axescheck(varargin{:});
n = 20;
if nargs > 0, n = args{1}; end
% -pi <= theta <= pi is a row vector.
% -pi/2 <= phi <= pi/2 is a column vector.
theta = (-n:2:n)/n*pi;
phi = (-n:2:n)'/n*pi/2;
cosphi = cos(phi); cosphi(1) = 0; cosphi(n+1) = 0;
sintheta = sin(theta); sintheta(1) = 0; sintheta(n+1) = 0;
x = cosphi*cos(theta);
y = cosphi*sintheta;
z = sin(phi)*ones(1,n+1);
if nargout == 0
    cax = newplot(cax);
    surf(x,y,z,'parent',cax)
else
    xx = x; yy = y; zz = z;
end
```

HINT

Notice that the `sphere` function uses `varargin` to indicate that it will accept a variable number of input arguments. The function also makes use of the `nargin` and `nargout` functions. Studying this function may give you ideas on how to program your own functions. Notice that the `sphere` function uses an if/else structure, which is introduced in a subsequent chapter of this text.

KEY IDEA
Group your functions
together into toolboxes.

6.2 CREATING YOUR OWN TOOLBOX OF FUNCTIONS

When you call a function in MATLAB®, the program first looks in the current folder to see if the function is defined. If it can't find the function listed there, it starts down a predefined search path, looking for a file with the function name. To view the path the program takes as it looks for files, select

Set Path

from the Home toolstrip or type

pathtool

in the command window (see Figure 6.7).

As you create more and more functions to use in your programming, you may wish to modify the path to look in a directory where you've stored your own personal tools. For example, suppose you have stored the degrees-to-radians and radians-to-degrees functions created in Example 6.1 in a directory called **My_functions**.

You can add this directory (folder) to the path by selecting **Add Folder** from the list of option buttons in the Set Path dialog window, as shown in Figure 6.7. You'll be prompted to either supply the folder location or browse to find it, as shown in Figure 6.8.

MATLAB® now first looks into the current folder for function definitions, then works down the modified search path, as shown in Figure 6.9.

Once you've added a folder to the path, the change applies only to the current MATLAB® session, unless you save your changes permanently. Clearly, you should never make permanent changes to a public computer. However, if someone else has made changes you wish to reverse, you can select the default button as shown in Figure 6.9 to return the search path to its original settings.

The path tool allows you to change the MATLAB® search path interactively; however, the addpath function allows you to insert the logic to add a search path to any MATLAB® program. Consult

Figure 6.7
The path tool allows
you to change where
MATLAB® looks for function
definitions.

Figure 6.8
The Browse for Folder window.

Figure 6.9
Modified MATLAB® search path.

```
help addpath or doc addpath
```

if you wish to modify the path in this way.

MATLAB® provides access to numerous toolboxes developed at The MathWorks or by the user community. For more information, see the developer's website, www.mathworks.com.

KEY IDEA

Anonymous functions may be included in MATLAB programs with other commands or may be defined from the command window.

6.3 ANONYMOUS FUNCTIONS AND FUNCTION HANDLES

Normally, if you go to the trouble of creating a function, you'll want to store it for use in other programming projects. However, MATLAB® includes a simpler kind of function, called an *anonymous function*. Anonymous functions are defined in the command window or in a script, and are available—much as are variable names—only until the workspace is cleared. To create an anonymous function, consider the following example:

```
ln = @(x)  log(x)
```

- The @ symbol alerts MATLAB® that ln is a function.
- Immediately following the @ symbol, the input to the function is listed in parentheses.
- Finally, the function is defined.

The function name appears in the variable window, listed as a function_handle:

Name	Value	Size	Bytes	Class
ln	@(x) log(x)	1 × 1	16	function_handle

HINT

Think of a function handle as a nickname for the function.

Anonymous functions can be used like any other function—for example,

```
ln(10)
ans =
        2.3026
```

Once the workspace is cleared, the anonymous function no longer exists. Anonymous functions can be saved as **.mat** files, just like any variable, and can be restored with the load command. For example, to save the anonymous function ln, type:

```
save my_ln_function ln
```

A file named **my_ln_function.mat** is created, which contains the anonymous ln function. Once the workspace is cleared, the ln function no longer exists, but it can be reloaded from the **.mat** file

```
load my_ln_function
```

It is possible to assign a function handle to any function. Earlier in this chapter, we created a function file called **distance.m**.

```
function result = distance(t)
result = 1/2*9.8*t.^2;
```

The command

```
distance_handle = @(t) distance(t)
```

assigns the handle **distance_handle** to the distance function.

Anonymous functions and the related function handles are useful in functions that require other functions as input (function functions). For example, earlier in this chapter we introduced the nargin function, which accepts either a function name represented as a string, or a function handle. If we define ln as an anonymous function

```
ln = @(x) log(x)
```

then we can use the function handle, `ln`, as input to `nargin`

```
nargin(ln)
ans =
    1
```

KEY IDEA

Function functions require
functions or function
handles as input.

6.4 FUNCTION FUNCTIONS

MATLAB®'s function functions have an odd, but descriptive name. They are functions that require other functions as input. One example of a MATLAB® built-in function function is the function plot, `fplot`. This function requires two inputs: a function or a function handle, and a range over which to plot. We can demonstrate the use of `fplot` with the function handle `ln`, defined as

```
ln = @(x) log(x)
```

The function handle can now be used as input to the `fplot` function:

```
fplot(ln,[0.1, 10])
```

A wide variety of MATLAB® functions accept function handles as input. For example, the `fzero` function finds the value of x where $f(x)$ is equal to 0. It accepts a function handle and a rough guess for x. From Figure 6.10, we see that the natural log has a zero between 0.5 and 1.5, so a rough guess for the zero point might be $x = 0.8$.

```
fzero(ln,0.8)
ans =
    1
```

We can check this result by substituting back into the ln function.

```
ln(ans)
ans =
    0
```

Figure 6.10
Function handles can be
used as input to a function
function, such as `fplot`.

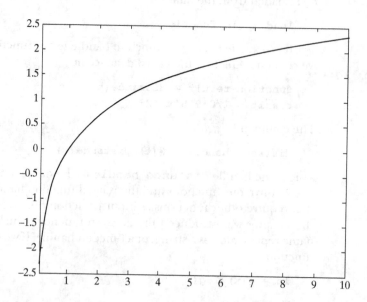

6.5 SUBFUNCTIONS

Subfunctions can be created by grouping functions together in a single file. There are two approaches: you can add subfunctions to a script (starting with R2016b), or you can use multiple subfunctions in a primary function. Subfunctions can be used to modularize your code and to make the primary code easier to read. They have the disadvantage that they are only available from the primary file, and cannot be used by other programs.

HINT

You should not attempt to create code using subfunctions until you have first mastered simple functions.

6.5.1 Using Subfunctions in Other Functions

Each MATLAB® function has *one* primary function. The name of the M-file must be the same as the *primary* function name. Thus, the primary function stored in the M-file **my_function.m** must be named `my_function`. Subfunctions are added after the primary function and can have any legitimate MATLAB® variable name. Figure 6.11 shows a very simple example of a function that both adds and subtracts two vectors. The primary function is named `subfunction_demo`. The file includes two subfunctions: `add` and `subtract`.

Notice in the editing window that the contents of each function are identified with a gray bracket. Each code section can be either collapsed or expanded, to make the contents easier to read, by clicking on the + or − sign included with the bracket. MATLAB® uses the term "folding" for this functionality.

Example 6.5 demonstrates the use of a more complicated example.

Figure 6.11
MATLAB® allows the user to create subfunctions within a function M-file. This file includes the primary function, `subfunction_demo`, and two subfunctions `add` and `subtract`.

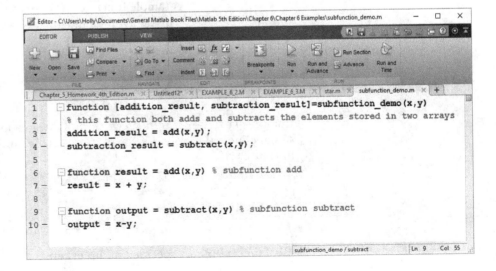

EXAMPLE 6.5

INTEGRATION: USING SUBFUNCTIONS

In a course in numerical methods, you will be introduced to multiple techniques to perform integrations, which can be thought of as finding the area under a curve. The simplest is the trapezoid rule, followed by Simpson's 13 technique and Simpson's 38 technique. A common strategy is to use each in the following conditions.

If only two values of the independent variable are specified, defining a single interval, use:	Trapezoid rule
If an odd number of points are defined, which results in an even number of segments, use:	Simpson's 13 technique
If 4 points are defined, which result in 3 segments, use:	Simpson's 38 technique
Otherwise use:	A combination of Simpson's 13 technique and Simpson's 38 techniques

Create a function that combines these techniques into a single function called `integrate` and test it on the polynomial

$$f(x) = 10 \sin(5x) + 5x^2$$

with the limits of integration equal to

$$0 \le x \le 2.$$

This is equivalent to finding the area under the curve as shown in Figure 6.12.

1. **State the problem**
   Create a function called `integrate` to find the area under a curve, using subfunctions.

2. **Describe the input and output**

Input	The logic for each of the subfunctions is provided
	A sample function, $f(x) = 0.5*x^3 - 3*x^2 + 5*x + 4$
Output	The value of the integral, for a variety of input parameters

3. **Develop a hand example**
   Choose a simpler function, for example the equation of a straight line such as

   $$f(x) = 5*x + 3$$

   from $x = 0$ to $x = 5$. It is then easy to find the area under the curve, which for a straight line is the average value of $f(x)$ times the difference in x values, as shown in Figure 6.13.

   $$area = \frac{(f(0) + f(5))}{2}*(5 - 0)$$

   $$area = \frac{(3 + 28)}{2}*5 = 77.5$$

All of the techniques specified in this example should give the same result.

Figure 6.12
The area under the
curve is equivalent
to the integral of a
function.

Figure 6.13
The area under a line is
equal to the average value
of *y* times the difference in
x values.

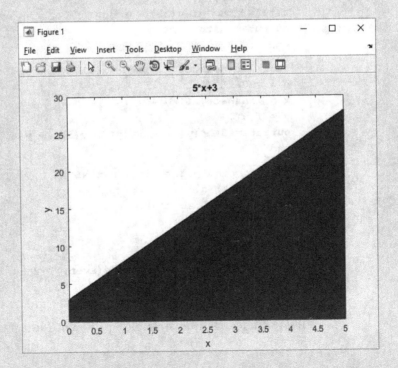

(*continued*)

4. Develop a MATLAB® solution

This solution uses if/else structures which will not be introduced until a later chapter. However, the structure of the function and subfunctions is the most important part of this example.

```matlab
function  I = integrate(f,xL,xU,n) %Primary function
% f is a function handle
% xL is the lower limit of integration
% xU is the upper limit of integration
% n is the number of segments to be used in the integration
% n+1 is the number of data points
remainder = rem(n,2);
if  n==1
    I = trapf(f,xL,xU,n);
elseif  remainder ==0
    I = simp13m(f,xL,xU,n);
elseif  n == 3
    I = simp38(f,xL,xU);
else h=(xU-xL)/n;
    xM=xU-h*3;
    s13 = simp13m(f,xL,xM,n-3);
    s38 = simp38(f,xM,xU);
    I = s13 + s38;
end
end

function  output = trapf(f,xL,xU,n) % The first subfunction
x=linspace(xL,xU,n+1);
y=f(x);
h = (xU-xL)/n;
total=2*sum(y)-y(1)-y(end);
output = h*total/2;
end

function  output = simp38(f,xL,xU) % The second subfunction
h = (xU-xL)/3;
x = linspace(xL,xU,4);
y = f(x);
output = 3*h*(y(1) + 3*(y(2)+y(3)) + y(4))/8;
end

function  output = simp13m(f,xL,xU,n) % The third subfunction
h = (xU-xL)/n;
x=linspace(xL,xU,n+1);
y = f(x);
even = 2:2:n+1;
odd = 3:2:n;
output = h*(y(1) + 4*(sum(y(even)))+2*sum(y(odd))+y(end))/3;
end
```

5. Test the solution

Test the function with the simple equation of a straight line for values of n from 1 to 5

```
f = @(x) 5*x + 3;
integrate(f,0,5,1)
integrate(f,0,5,2)
integrate(f,0,5,3)
integrate(f,0,5,4)
integrate(f,0,5,5)
```

As expected, every case returned the same value, 77.5. This result matches the hand example, suggesting that the function works correctly and can now be used with the more complicated function.

```
f = @(x) 10*sin(5*x)+ 5*x.^2
integrate(f,0,2,1)
ans =
      14.56
integrate(f,0,2,2)
ans =
      -1.2657
integrate(f,0,2,3)
ans =
      13.35
integrate(f,0,2,4)
ans =
      19.473
integrate(f,0,2,5)
ans =
      18.417
integrate(f,0,2,21)
ans =
      17.013
```

6.5.2 Subfunctions in MATLAB Programs

When could you use subfunctions effectively in a script? Imagine that your instructor has assigned three homework problems, each requiring you to create and test a function.

- **Problem 1** Create and test a function called `square` to square values of x. Assume x varies between -3 and $+3$.
- **Problem 2** Create and test a function called `cold_work` to find the percent cold work experienced by a metallic rod, as it is drawn into a wire. Cold work is described by the following equation

$$\% \text{ Cold Work} = \frac{r_i^2 - r_f^2}{r_i^2} \times 100$$

where r_i is the initial radius of the rod, and r_f is the final radius of the rod. To test your function, let $r_i = 0.5$ cm and let $r_f = 0.25$ cm.
- **Problem 3** Create and test a function called `potential_energy` to determine the potential energy change of a given mass. The change in potential energy is given by

$$\Delta \text{PE} = m \times g \times \Delta z.$$

Your function should have three inputs: m, g, and Δz. Use the following data to test your function:

$m = [1\ 2\ 3]$ kg (The array represents three different masses.)

$g = 9.8$ m/s^2

$\Delta z = 5$ m

To complete the assignment, you would need to create four files: one for each function, and one to call and test the functions. We can use subfunctions to reduce the number of files to one, as shown in Figure 6.14.

When the script executes, it calls the subfunctions, and the results are displayed in the command window, as follows:

```
Problem 1
The squares of the input values are listed below
     9    4    1    0    1    4    9
Problem 2
The percent cold work is
ans =
    0.7500
Problem 3
```

Figure 6.14
This M-file is an example of a script with sequential subfunctions. The subfunctions could also have been placed closer to the section of code where they were used.

```
1   function []= sample_homework()
2   %Example homework submission
3   % Problem 1
4   x = -3:3;
5   disp('Problem 1')
6   disp('The squares of the input values are listed below')
7   y=square(x);
8   disp(y)
9   % Problem 2
10  initial_radius = 0.5;
11  final_radius = 0.25;
12  disp('Problem 2')
13  disp('The percent cold work is')
14  cold_work(initial_radius, final_radius)
15  % Problem 3
16  m=[1,2,3];
17  g = 9.8;
18  delta_z = 5;
19  disp('Problem 3')
20  disp('The change in potential energy is ')
21  potential_energy(m,g,delta_z)
22  end
23  function result = square(x)
24      result = x.^2;
25  end
26  function result = cold_work(ri,rf)
27      result = (ri.^2 - rf.^2)/ri.^2;
28  end
29  function result = potential_energy(m,g,delta_z)
30      result = m.*g.*delta_z;
31  end
```

```
The change in potential energy is
ans =
     49 98 147
```

The primary downside to using subfunctions in script M-files is that you cannot execute the code successfully using sections that are executed one at a time. The only choice is to select the run button, and to run the entire file.

SUMMARY

MATLAB® contains a wide variety of built-in functions. However, you will often find it useful to create your own MATLAB® functions. The most common type of user-defined MATLAB® function is the stand-alone function file, which must start with a function-definition line that contains the following:

- the word `function`,
- a variable that defines the function output,
- a function name, and
- a variable used for the input argument.

For example,

```
function output = my_function(x)
```

The function name must also be the name of the M-file in which the function is stored. Function names follow the standard MATLAB® naming rules.

Like the built-in functions, user-defined functions can accept multiple inputs and can return multiple results.

Comments immediately following the function-definition line can be accessed from the command window with the `help` command.

Variables defined within a function are local to that function. They are not stored in the workspace and cannot be accessed from the command window. Global variables can be defined with the `global` command used in both the command window (or script file) and a MATLAB® function. Good programming style suggests that you define global variables with capital letters. In general, however, it is not wise to use global variables.

Groups of user-defined functions, called "toolboxes," may be stored in a common directory and accessed by modifying the MATLAB® search path. This is accomplished interactively with the path tool, either from the menu bar, as in

File → Set Path

or from the command line, with

```
pathtool
```

MATLAB® provides access to numerous toolboxes developed at The MathWorks or by the user community.

Another type of function is the anonymous function, which is defined in a MATLAB® session or in a script and exists only during that session. Anonymous functions are especially useful for very simple mathematical expressions, or as input to the more complicated function functions.

Multiple functions can be used either in a single script or in a single function, when they are listed as subfunctions. Subfunctions are only available to code inside the primary file, unlike stand alone function files, which are available to any code that can access the directory where they are stored.

MATLAB® SUMMARY

The following MATLAB® summary lists and briefly describes all of the special characters, commands, and functions that were defined in this chapter:

Special Characters	
@	identifies a function handle, such as that used with anonymous functions
%	comment

Commands and Functions	
addpath	adds a directory to the MATLAB® search path
fminbnd	a function function that accepts a function handle or function definition as input and finds the function minimum between two bounds
fplot	a function function that accepts a function handle or function definition as input and creates the corresponding plot between two bounds
fzero	a function function that accepts a function handle or function definition as input and finds the function zero point nearest a specified value
function	identifies an M-file as a function
global	defines a variable that can be used in multiple sections of code
meshgrid	maps two input vectors onto two two-dimensional matrices
nargin	determines the number of input arguments in a function
nargout	determines the number of output arguments from a function
pathtool	opens the interactive path tool
varargin	indicates that a variable number of arguments may be input to a function

KEY TERMS

anonymous	folding	in-line
argument	function	input argument
comments	function function	local variable
directory	function handle	M-file
file name	function name	nesting
folder	global variable	toolbox

PROBLEMS

Function Files

As you create functions in this section, be sure to comment them appropriately. Remember that, although many of these problems could be solved without a function, the objective of this chapter is to learn to write and use functions. Each of these functions (except for the anonymous functions) must be created in its own file, then called from the command window or a script.

6.1 As described in Example 6.2, metals are actually crystalline materials. Metal crystals are called grains. When the average grain size is small, the metal is strong; when it is large, the metal is weaker. Since every crystal in a particular sample of metal is a different size, it isn't obvious how we should describe the average crystal size. The American Society for Testing and Materials (ASTM) has developed the following correlation for standardizing grain-size measurements:

$$N = 2^{n-1}$$

The ASTM grain size (n) is determined by looking at a sample of a metal under a microscope at a magnification of 100× (100 power). The number of grains in a 1-square-inch area (actual dimensions of 0.01 in × 0.01 in) is estimated (N) and used in the preceding equation to find the ASTM grain size.

(a) Write a MATLAB® function called `num_grains` to find the number of grains in a 1-square-inch area (N) at 100× magnification when the ASTM grain size is known.

(b) Use your function to find the number of grains for ASTM grain sizes $n = 10$ to 100.

(c) Create a plot of your results.

6.2 Perhaps the most famous equation in physics is

$$E = mc^2$$

which relates energy E to mass m. The speed of light in a vacuum, c, is the property that links the two together. The speed of light in a vacuum is 2.9979×10^8 m/s.

(a) Create a function called `energy` to find the energy corresponding to a given mass in kilograms. Your result will be in joules, since $1 \text{ kg m}^2/\text{s}^2 = 1 \text{ J}$.

(b) Use your function to find the energy corresponding to masses from 1 kg to 10^6 kg. Use the `logspace` function (consult `help logspace`) to create an appropriate mass vector.

(c) Create a plot of your results. Try using different logarithmic plotting approaches (e.g., `semilogy`, `semilogx`, and `loglog`) to determine the best way to graph your results.

6.3 The future-value-of-money formula relates how much a current investment will be worth in the future, assuming a constant interest rate:

$$FV = PV \times (1 + I)^n$$

where

FV is the future value,

PV is the present value or investment,

I is the interest rate expressed as a fractional amount per compounding period—i.e., 5% is expressed as .05, and

N is the number of compounding periods.

(a) Create a MATLAB® function called `future_value` with three inputs: the investment (present value), the interest rate expressed as a fraction, and the number of compounding periods.

(b) Use your function to determine the value of a $1000 investment in 10 years, assuming the interest rate is 0.5% per month, and the interest is compounded monthly.

6.4 In freshman chemistry, the relationship between moles and mass is introduced:

$$n = \frac{m}{MW}$$

where

n = number of moles of a substance,
m = mass of the substance, and
MW = molecular weight (molar mass) of the substance.

(a) Create a function called `nmoles` that requires two vector inputs—the mass and molecular weight—and returns the corresponding number of moles. Because you are providing vector input, it will be necessary to use the `meshgrid` function in your calculations.

(b) Test your function for the compounds shown in Table P6.4, for masses from 1 to 10 g:

Table P6.4 Molar Mass of Model Compounds

Compound	Molecular Weight (Molar Mass)
Benzene	78.115 g/mol
Ethyl alcohol	46.07 g/mol
Refrigerant R134a	102.3 g/mol

Your result should be a 10 × 3 matrix.

6.5 By rearranging the preceding relationship between moles and mass, you can find the mass if you know the number of moles of a compound:

$$m = n \times MW$$

(a) Create a function called **mass.m** that requires two vector inputs—the number of moles and the molecular weight—and returns the corresponding mass. Because you are providing vector input, it will be necessary to use the `meshgrid` function in your calculations.

(b) Test your function with the compounds listed in the previous problem, for values of n from 1 to 10.

6.6 The distance to the horizon increases as you climb a mountain (or a hill). The expression

$$b = \sqrt{2rh + h^2}$$

where

d = distance to the horizon
r = radius of the earth
h = height of the hill

can be used to calculate that distance. The distance depends on how high the hill is, and on the radius of the earth (or another planetary body).

(a) Create a function called **distance.m** to find the distance to the horizon. Your function should accept two vector inputs—radius and height—and should return the distance to the horizon. Don't forget that you'll need to use `meshgrid` because your inputs are vectors.

(b) Create a MATLAB® program that uses your distance function to find the distance in miles to the horizon, both on the Earth and on Mars, for hills from 0 to 10,000 feet. Remember to use consistent units in your calculations. Note that

- Earth's diameter = 7926 miles
- Mars' diameter = 4217 miles

Report your results in a table. Each column should represent a different planet, and each row a different hill height.

6.7 A rocket is launched vertically. At time $t = 0$, the rocket's engine shuts down. At that time, the rocket has reached an altitude of 500 m and is rising at a velocity of 125 m/s. Gravity then takes over. The height of the rocket as a function of time is

$$h(t) = -\frac{9.8}{2}t^2 + 125t + 500 \text{ for } t > 0$$

(a) Create a function called `height` that accepts time as an input and returns the height of the rocket. Use your function in your solutions to parts b and c.

(b) Plot height vs. time for times from 0 to 30 seconds. Use an increment of 0.5 second in your time vector.

(c) Find the time when the rocket starts to fall back to the ground. (The `max` function will be helpful in this exercise.)

6.8 The distance a freely falling object travels is

$$x = \frac{1}{2}gt^2$$

where

$g =$ acceleration due to gravity, 9.8 m/s²,
$t =$ time in seconds, and
$x =$ distance traveled in meters.

If you have taken calculus, you know that we can find the velocity of the object by taking the derivative of the preceding equation. That is,

$$\frac{dx}{dt} = v = gt$$

We can find the acceleration by taking the derivative again:

$$\frac{dv}{dt} = a = g$$

(a) Create a function called `free_fall` with a single input vector t that returns values for distance x, velocity v, and acceleration g.

(b) Test your function with a time vector that ranges from 0 to 20 seconds.

6.9 Create a function called `polygon` that draws a polygon with any number of sides. Your function should require a single input: the number of sides desired. It should not return any value to the command window, but should draw the requested polygon in polar coordinates.

Creating Your Own Toolbox

6.10 This problem requires you to generate temperature-conversion tables. Use the following equations, which describe the relationships between temperatures in degrees Fahrenheit (T_F), degrees Celsius (T_C), kelvins (T_K), and degrees Rankine (T_R), respectively:

$$T_F = T_R - 459.67°R$$

$$T_F = \frac{9}{5}T_C + 32°F$$

$$T_R = \frac{9}{5}T_K$$

You will need to rearrange these expressions to solve some of the problems.

(a) Create a function called `F_to_K` that converts temperatures in Fahrenheit to Kelvin. Use your function to generate a conversion table for values from 0°F to 200°F.

(b) Create a function called `C_to_R` that converts temperatures in Celsius to Rankine. Use your function to generate a conversion table from 0°C to 100°C. Print 25 lines in the table. (Use the `linspace` function to create your input vector.)

(c) Create a function called `C_to_F` that converts temperatures in Celsius to Fahrenheit. Use your function to generate a conversion table from 0°C to 100°C. Choose an appropriate spacing.

(d) Group your functions into a folder (directory) called `my_temp_conversions`. Adjust the MATLAB® search path so that it finds your folder. (Don't save any changes on a public computer!)

Anonymous Functions and Function Handles

6.11 Barometers have been used for almost 400 years to measure pressure changes in the atmosphere. The first known barometer was invented by Evangelista Torricelli (1608–1647), a student of Galileo during his final years in Florence, Italy. The height of a liquid in a barometer is directly proportional to the atmospheric pressure, or

$$P = \rho g h$$

where P is the pressure, ρ is the density of the barometer fluid, and h is the height of the liquid column. For mercury barometers, the density of the fluid is 13,560 kg/m³. On the surface of the Earth, the acceleration due to gravity, g, is approximately 9.8 m/s². Thus, the only variable in the equation is the height of the fluid column, h, which should have the unit of meters.

(a) Create an anonymous function P that finds the pressure if the value of h is provided. The units of your answer will be

$$\frac{kg}{m^3}\frac{m}{s^2}m = \frac{kg}{ms^2}\frac{1}{} = Pa.$$

(b) Create another anonymous function to convert pressure in Pa (Pascals) to pressure in atmospheres (atm). Call the function `Pa_to_atm`. Note that

$$1 \text{ atm} = 101{,}325 \text{ Pa.}$$

(c) Use your anonymous functions to find the pressure for fluid heights from 0.5 m to 1.0 m of mercury.

(d) Save your anonymous functions as **.mat** files

6.12 The energy required to heat water at constant pressure is approximately equal to

$$E = mC_p \, \Delta T$$

where

  m = mass of the water, in grams,
  C_p = heat capacity of water, 1 cal/g K, and
  ΔT = change in temperature, K.

(a) Create an anonymous function called `heat` to find the energy required to heat 1 gram of water if the change in temperature is provided as the input.

(b) Your result will be in calories:

$$g \frac{\text{cal}}{\text{g K}} \frac{1}{} K = \text{cal}$$

Joules are the unit of energy used most often in engineering. Create another anonymous function `cal_to_J` to convert your answer from part (a) into joules. (There are 4.2 J/cal.)

(c) Save your anonymous functions as **.mat** files.

6.13. **(a)** Create an anonymous function called `my_function`, equal to

$$-x^2 - 5x - 3 + e^x.$$

(b) Use the `fplot` function to create a plot from $x = -5$ to $x = +5$. Recall that the `fplot` function can accept a function handle as input.

(c) Use the `fminbnd` function to find the minimum function value in this range. The `fminbnd` function is an example of a function function, since it requires a function or function handle as input. The syntax is

```
fminbnd(function_handle, xmin, xmax)
```

Three inputs are required: the function handle, the minimum value of x, and the maximum value of x. The function searches between the minimum value of x and the maximum value of x for the point where the function value is a minimum.

6.14 In Problem 6.7, you created an function called `height` to evaluate the height of a rocket as a function of time. The relationship between time, t, and height, $h(t)$, is:

$$h(t) = -\frac{9.8}{2}t^2 + 125t + 500 \text{ for } t > 0$$

(a) Create a function handle to the height function called height_handle.

(b) Use height_handle as input to the fplot function, and create a graph from 0 to 60 seconds.

(c) Use the fzero function to find the time when the rocket hits the ground (i.e., when the function value is zero). The fzero function is an example of a function function, since it requires a function or function handle as input. The syntax is

```
fzero(function_handle, x_guess)
```

The fzero function requires two inputs—a function handle, and your guess as to the time value where the function is close to zero. You can select a reasonable x_guess value by inspecting the graph created in part (b).

Subfunctions

6.15 In Problem 6.10, you were asked to create and use three different temperature-conversion functions, based on the following conversion equations:

$$T_F = T_R - 459.67°R$$

$$T_F = \frac{9}{5} T_C + 32°F$$

$$T_R = \frac{9}{5} T_K$$

Recreate Problem 6.10 using nested subfunctions. The primary function should be called temperature_conversions and should include the following subfunctions

```
F_to_K
C_to_R
C_to_F
```

Within the primary function, use the subfunctions to:

(a) Generate a conversion table for values from 0°F to 200°F. Include a column for temperature in Fahrenheit and Kelvin.

(b) Generate a conversion table from 0°C to 100°C. Print 25 lines in the table. (Use the linspace function to create your input vector.) Your table should include a column for temperature in Celsius and Rankine.

(c) Generate a conversion table from 0°C to 100°C. Choose an appropriate spacing. Include a column for temperature in Celsius and Fahrenheit.

Recall that you will need to call your primary function from the command window, or from a script.

7

User-Controlled Input and Output

Objectives

After reading this chapter, you should be able to:

- Prompt the user for input to a script.
- Create output with the `disp` function.
- Create tables using the `table` function.
- Create formatted output using `fprintf`.

- Create formatted output for use in other functions with the `sprintf` function.
- Use graphical techniques to provide program input.
- Use sections to modify and run MATLAB programs.

INTRODUCTION

So far, we have explored the use of MATLAB® in two modes: in the command window as a scratch pad, and in the editing window to write simple programs (scripts). The programmer has been the user. Now we move on to more complicated programs, written in scripts, where the programmer and the user may be different people. That will make it necessary to use input and output commands to communicate with the user, instead of rewriting the actual code to solve similar problems. MATLAB® offers built-in functions to allow a user to communicate with a program as it executes. The `input` command pauses the program and prompts the user for input; the `disp`, `table` and `fprintf` commands provide output to the command window.

7.1 USER-DEFINED INPUT

Although we have written MATLAB programs, we have assumed that the programmer (you) and the user are the same person. To run the program with different input values, we actually changed some of the code. We can create more general programs by allowing the user to input values of a matrix from the keyboard while the program is running, using the `input` function. The input function displays a text string in the command window, then waits for the user to provide the requested input. For example,

```
z = input('Enter a value')
```

displays

```
Enter a value
```

in the command window. If the user enters a value such as

```
5
```

the program assigns the value 5 to the variable z. If the `input` command does not end with a semicolon, the value entered is displayed on the screen:

```
z =
    5
```

The same approach can be used to enter a one- or two-dimensional matrix. The user must provide the appropriate brackets and delimiters (commas and semicolons). For example,

```
z = input('Enter values for z in brackets')
```

KEY IDEA
The `input` function can be used to communicate with the program user.

requests the user to input a matrix such as

```
[1, 2, 3; 4, 5, 6]
```

and responds with

```
z =
    1 2 3
    4 5 6.
```

This input value of z can then be used in subsequent calculations by the script.

Data entered with `input` does not need to be numeric information. Suppose we prompt the user with the command

```
x = input('Enter your name in single quotes')
```

and enter

```
'Holly'.
```

when prompted. Because we haven't used a semicolon at the end of the `input` command, MATLAB® will respond

```
x =
Holly.
```

Notice in the workspace window that **x** is listed as a 1×5 character array:

Name	Value	Size	Bytes	Class
x	'Holly'	1×5	6	char

If you are entering a string (in MATLAB®, strings are character arrays), you must enclose the characters in single quotes. However, an alternate form of the input command alerts the function to expect character input without the single quotes by specifying string input in the second field:

```
x = input('Enter your name', 's')
```

Now you need only enter the characters, such as

```
Ralph
```

and the program responds with

```
x =
   Ralph.
```

PRACTICE EXERCISES 7.1

The correct answers can be found on the Pearson website.

1. Calculate the area A of a triangle:

$$A = \frac{1}{2}\text{base} * \text{height}$$

   Prompt the user to enter the values for the base and for the height.
2. Find the volume V of a right circular cylinder:

$$V = \pi r^2 h$$

   Prompt the user to enter the values of r and h.
3. Create a vector from 0 to n, allowing the user to enter the value of n.
4. Create a vector that starts at a, ends at b, and has a spacing of c.
   Allow the user to input all of these parameters.

EXAMPLE 7.1

FREELY FALLING OBJECTS

Consider the behavior of a freely falling object under the influence of gravity (see Figure 7.1).

Figure 7.1
The Leaning Tower of Pisa. (QQ7/Fotolia)

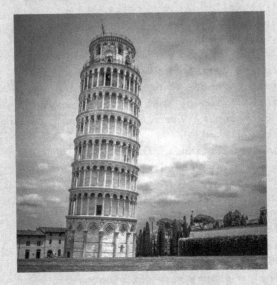

(continued)

The position of the object is described by

$$d = \frac{1}{2}gt^2$$

where

d = distance the object travels,

g = acceleration due to gravity, and

t = elapsed time.

We shall allow the user to specify the value of g—the acceleration due to gravity—and a vector of time values.

1. State the problem
   Find the distance traveled by a freely falling object and plot the results.
2. Describe the input and output

Input	Value of g, the acceleration due to gravity, provided by the user
	Time, provided by the user
Output	Plot of distance versus time

3. Develop a hand example

$$d = \frac{1}{2}gt^2, \text{ so, on the moon at 100 seconds}$$

$$d = \frac{1}{2} \times 1.6 \text{ m/s}^2 \times 100^2\text{s}^2$$

$$d = 8000 \text{ m}$$

4. Develop a MATLAB® solution

```
%%  Example 7.1
%Free fall
clear, clc
% Request input from the user
g = input('What is the value of acceleration due to
   gravity?')
start = input('What starting time would you like?')
finish = input('What ending time would you like?')
incr = input('What time increments would you like
   calculated?')
time = start:incr:finish;
%% Calculate the distance
distance = 1/2*g*time.^2;
%Plot the results
loglog(time,distance)
title('Distance Traveled in Free Fall')
xlabel('time, s'),ylabel('distance, m'),grid on
%Find the maximum distance traveled
final_distance = max(distance)
```

Figure 7.2
Distance traveled when the acceleration is 1.6 m/s². Notice that the figure is a loglog plot.

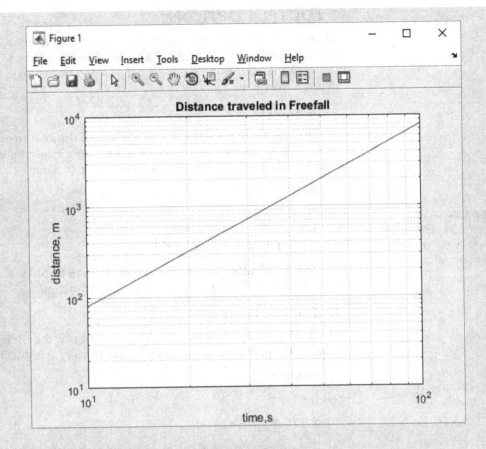

The interaction in the command window is:

```
What is the value of acceleration due to gravity? 1.6
g =
   1.6000
What starting time would you like? 0
start =
   0
What ending time would you like? 100
finish =
   100
What time increments would you like calculated? 10
incr =
   10
final_distance =
   8000
```

The results are plotted in Figure 7.2.

5. Test the solution
   Compare the MATLAB® solution with the hand solution. Since the user can control the input, we entered the data used in the hand solution. MATLAB® tells us that the final distance traveled is 8000 m, which, since we entered 100 seconds as the final time, corresponds to the distance traveled after 100 seconds.

7.2 OUTPUT OPTIONS

There are several ways to display the contents of a matrix. The simplest is to enter the name of the matrix, without a semicolon. The name will be repeated, and the values of the matrix will be displayed, starting on the next line. For example, first define a matrix **x**:

```
x = 1:5;
```

Because there is a semicolon at the end of the assignment statement, the values in **x** are not repeated in the command window. However, if you want to display **x** later in your program, simply type in the variable name

```
x
```

which returns

```
x =
    1   2   3   4   5
```

KEY IDEA
The disp function can display either character arrays or numeric arrays.

MATLAB® offers three other approaches to displaying results: the disp function, the table function, and the fprintf function.

7.2.1 Display Function

The display (disp) function can be used to display the contents of a matrix without printing the matrix name. It accepts a single array as input. Thus,

```
disp(x)
```

returns

```
1  2  3  4  5.
```

The display command can also be used to display a string (text enclosed in single quotation marks). For example,

```
disp('The values in the x matrix are:');
```

returns

```
The values in the x matrix are:.
```

When you enter a string as input into the disp function, you are really entering an array of character information. Try entering the following on the command line:

```
'The values in the x matrix are:'
```

MATLAB® responds

```
ans =
'The values in the x matrix are:'.
```

CHARACTER ARRAY
stores character information

The workspace window lists ans as a 1×32 character array.

Name	Size	Bytes	Class
ans	1×32	90	char array

Character arrays store character information in arrays similar to numeric arrays. Characters can be letters, numbers, punctuation, and even some nondisplayed characters. Each character, including spaces, is an element in the character array.

KEY IDEA

Characters can be letters, numbers, or symbols.

When we execute the two display functions

```
disp('The values in the x matrix are:')
disp(x)
```

MATLAB® responds

```
The values in the x matrix are:
1 2 3 4 5.
```

Notice that the two `disp` functions are displayed on separate lines. You can display all of the information on the same line by creating a combined matrix of your two outputs. However, the first output was a string, and the second was numeric information, and you can't normally combine data of different types into a single array. We can get around this problem by using the `num2str` (number to string) function, and then combining the two results into a single character array. The process is called *concatenation*. Thus,

```
disp(['The values in the x array are:' num2str(x)])
```

returns

```
The values in the x array are: 1 2 3 4 5.
```

The `num2str` function changes an array of numbers into an array of characters. In the preceding example, we used `num2str` to transform the **x** matrix to a character array, which was then combined with the first string (by means of square brackets, [ ]) to make a bigger character array. You can see the resulting matrix by typing

```
A = ['The values in the x array are: ' num2str(x)]
```

which returns

```
A =
    The values in the x array are: 1 2 3 4 5.
```

Checking in the workspace window, we see that **A** is a 1×45 matrix. The workspace window also tells us that the matrix contains character data instead of numeric information. This is evidenced both by the icon in front of **A** and in the class column.

Name	Size	Bytes	Class
A	1×45	90	char array

HINT

If you want to include an apostrophe in a string, you need to enter the apostrophe twice. If you don't do this, MATLAB® will interpret the apostrophe as terminating the string. An example of the use of two apostrophes is

```
disp('The moon''s gravity is 1/6th that of the earth')
```

You can use a combination of the `input` and `disp` functions to mimic a conversation. Try creating and running the following script:

```
disp('Hi There');
disp('I''m your MATLAB program');
```

```
name = input('Who are you?','s');
disp(['Hi',name]);
answer = input('Don"t you just love computers?','s');
disp([answer,'?']);
disp('Computers are very useful');
disp('You"ll use them a lot in college!!');
disp(Good luck with your studies')
pause(2);
disp('Goodbye')
```

This interaction made use of the `pause` function. If you execute `pause` without any input, the program waits until the user hits the Enter key. If a value is used as input to the `pause` function, the program waits for the specified number of seconds, then continues.

7.2.2 Formatted Output—The `fprintf` Function

The `fprintf` function (formatted print function) gives you even more control over the output than you have with the `disp` function. In addition to displaying both text and matrix values, you can specify the format to be used in displaying the values, and you can specify when to skip to a new line. If you are a C programmer, you will be familiar with the syntax of this function. With few exceptions, the MATLAB® `fprintf` function uses the same formatting specifications as the C `fprintf` function. This is hardly surprising, since MATLAB® was written in C. (It was originally written in Fortran and then later rewritten in C.)

The general form of the `fprintf` command contains two arguments, one a string, and the other a list of matrices:

```
fprintf(format-string, var,. . .)
```

Consider the following example:

```
cows = 5;
fprintf('There are %f cows in the pasture', cows)
```

The string, which is the first argument inside the `fprintf` function, contains a placeholder (%) where the value of the variable (in this case, `cows`) will be inserted. The placeholder also contains formatting information. In this example, the `%f` tells MATLAB® to display the value of `cows` in a default fixed-point format. The default format displays six places after the decimal point:

```
There are 5.000000 cows in the pasture
```

Besides defaulting to a fixed-point format, MATLAB® allows you to specify an exponential format, `%e`, or lets you allow MATLAB® to choose whichever is shorter, fixed point or exponential (`%g`). It also lets you display character information (`%c`) or a string of characters (`%s`). The decimal format (`%d`) is especially useful if the number you wish to display is an integer.

```
fprintf('There are %d cows in the pasture', cows)
There are 5 cows in the pasture
```

Table 7.1 illustrates the various formats supported by `fprintf`, and the related `sprintf` functions.

Additional type fields are described in the help feature.

Table 7.1 Type Field Format

Type Field	Result
%f	fixed-point notation
%e	exponential notation
%d	decimal notation—does not include trailing zeros if the value displayed is an integer. If the number includes a fractional component, it is displayed using exponential notation.
%g	whichever is shorter, %f or %e
%c	character information (displays one character at a time)
%s	string of characters (displays the entire string)

KEY IDEA

The fprintf function allows you to control how numbers are displayed.

MATLAB® does not automatically start a new line after an fprintf function is executed. If you tried out the preceding fprintf command example, you probably noticed that the command prompt is on the same line as the output:

```
There are 5.000000 cows in the pasture>>
```

If we execute another command, the results will appear on the same line instead of moving down. Thus, if we issue the new commands

```
cows = 6;
fprintf('There are %f cows in the pasture', cows);
```

from a script, MATLAB® continues the command window display on the same line:

```
There are 5.000000 cows in the pasture There are 6.000000 cows
in the pasture
```

KEY IDEA

The fprintf function allows you to display both character and numeric information with a single command.

To cause MATLAB® to start a new line, you'll need to use **\n,** called a linefeed, at the end of the string. For example, the code

```
cows = 5;
fprintf('There are %f cows in the pasture \n', cows)
cows = 6;
fprintf('There are %f cows in the pasture \n', cows)
```

returns the following output:

```
There are 5.000000 cows in the pasture
There are 6.000000 cows in the pasture
```

HINT

The backslash (\) and forward slash (/) are different characters. It's a common mistake to confuse them—and then the linefeed command doesn't work! Instead, the output to the command window will be

```
There are 5.000000 cows in the pasture /n
```

Other special format commands are listed in Table 7.2. The tab (**\t**) is especially useful for creating tables in which everything lines up neatly.

Table 7.2 Special Format Commands

Format Command	Resulting Action
\n	linefeed
\r	carriage return (similar to linefeed)
\t	tab
\b	backspace

You can further control how the variables are displayed using the optional width field and precision field with the format command. The width field controls the minimum total number of characters to be printed. It must be a positive decimal integer. The precision field is preceded by a period (.) and specifies the number of decimal places after the decimal point for exponential and fixed-point types. For example, %8.2f specifies that the minimum total width available to display your result is eight digits, two of which are after the decimal point. Thus, the code

```
voltage = 3.5;
fprintf('The voltage is %8.2f millivolts \n',voltage);
```

returns

The voltage is 3.50 millivolts.

Notice the empty space before the number 3.50. This occurs because we reserved six spaces (eight total, two after the decimal) for the portion of the number to the left of the decimal point.

Often when you use the fprintf function, your variable will be a matrix—for example,

```
x = 1:5;
```

MATLAB® will repeat the string in the fprintf command until it uses all the values in the matrix. Thus,

```
fprintf('%8.2f \n',x);
```

returns

```
    1.00
    2.00
    3.00
    4.00
    5.00.
```

If the variable is a two-dimensional matrix, MATLAB® uses the values one *column* at a time, going down the first column, then the second, and so on. Here's a more complicated example:

```
feet = 1:3;
inches = feet.*12;
```

Combine these two matrices:

```
conversions = [feet;inches]
```

MATLAB® then returns

```
conversions =
     1   2   3
    12  24  36.
```

The `conversions` array consists of two rows. The first row corresponds to feet, and the second row corresponds to inches. Now we can use the `fprintf` function to create output that is easier to interpret. For instance,

fprintf('%4.0f %7.2f \n',conversions)

sends the following to the command window:

```
1  12.00
2  24.00
3  36.00
```

Why don't the two outputs look the same? The `fprintf` statement we created uses two values at a time. It goes through the `conversions` array one *column* at a time to find the numbers it needs. Thus, the first two numbers used in the `fprintf` output are from the first column of the `conversions` array.

The `fprintf` function can accept a variable number of matrices after the string. It uses all of the values in each of these matrices, in order, before moving on to the next matrix. As an example, suppose we wanted to use the feet and inches matrices without combining them into a single matrix. Then we could type

fprintf('%4.0f %7.2f \n', feet, inches)
```
1      2.00
3     12.00
24    36.00.
```

The function works through the values of `feet` first, then uses the values in `inches`. It is unlikely that this is what you really want the function to do (in this example it wasn't), so the output values are almost always grouped into a single matrix to use in `fprintf`.

The `fprintf` command gives you considerably more control over the form of your output than MATLAB®'s simple format commands. It does, however, require some care and forethought to use.

In addition to creating formatted output for display in the command window, the `fprintf` function can be used to send formatted output to a file. First, you'll need to create and open an output file and assign it a file identifier (nickname). You do this with the `fopen` function

file_id = fopen('my_output_file.txt', 'wt');

The first field is the name of the file, and the second field makes it possible for us to write data to the file (hence the string `'wt'`). Once the file has been identified and opened for writing, we use the `fprintf` function, adding the file identifier as the first field in the function input.

fprintf(file_id, 'Some example output is %4.2f \n', pi*1000)

This form of the function sends the result of the formatted string

Some example output is 3141.59

to **my_output_file.txt.** To the command window, the function sends a count of the number of bytes transferred to the file.

```
ans =
  32
```

HINT

A common mistake new programmers make when using `fprintf` is to forget to include the field type identifier, such as `f`, in the placeholder sequence. The `fprintf` function won't work, but no error message is returned either.

HINT

If you want to include a percentage sign in an `fprintf` statement, you need to enter the % twice. If you don't, MATLAB® will interpret the % as a placeholder for data. For example,

```
fprintf('The interest rate is %5.2f %% \n', 5)
```

results in

```
The interest rate is 5.00 %.
```

EXAMPLE 7.2

FREE FALL: FORMATTED OUTPUT

Let's redo Example 7.1, but this time let's create a table of results instead of a plot, and let's use the `disp` and `fprintf` commands to control the appearance of the output.

1. **State the problem**
   Find the distance traveled by a freely falling object.
2. **Describe the input and output**

   Input   Value of g, the acceleration due to gravity, provided by the user
              Time t, provided by the user
   Output   Distances calculated for each planet and the moon

3. **Develop a hand example**

$$d = \frac{1}{2}gt^2, \text{ so on the moon at 100 seconds,}$$

$$d = \frac{1}{2} \times 1.6 \text{ m/s}^2 \times 100^2 \text{s}^2$$

$$d = 8000 \text{ m}$$

4. **Develop a MATLAB® solution**

```
%Example 7.2
%Free Fall
clear, clc
%Request input from the user
g = input('What is the value of acceleration due to
  gravity?')
start = input('What starting time would you like?')
```

```
finish = input('What ending time would you like?')
incr = input('What time increments would you like
 calculated?')
time = start:incr:finish;
%Calculate the distance
distance = 1/2*g*time.^2;
%Create a matrix of the output data
output = [time;distance];
%Send the output to the command window
fprintf('For an acceleration due to gravity of %5.1f seconds
\n the following data were calculated \n', g)
disp('Distance Traveled in Free Fall')
disp('time, s distance, m')
fprintf('%8.0f %10.2f\n',output)
```

This M-file produces the following interaction in the command window:

```
What is the value of acceleration due to gravity? 1.6
g =
   1.6000
What starting time would you like? 0
start =
   0
What ending time would you like? 100
finish =
   100
What time increments would you like calculated? 10
incr =
   10
For an acceleration due to gravity of 1.6 seconds the
following data were calculated
Distance Traveled in Free Fall
time, s distance, m
       0        0.00
      10       80.00
      20      320.00
      30      720.00
      40     1280.00
      50     2000.00
      60     2880.00
      70     3920.00
      80     5120.00
      90     6480.00
     100     8000.00
```

5. Test the solution

   Compare the MATLAB® solution with the hand solution. Since the output is a table, it is easy to see that the distance traveled at 100 seconds is 8000 m. Try using other data as input, and compare your results with the graph produced in Example 7.1.

PRACTICE EXERCISES 7.2

These exercises should be completed in a script. The correct answers can be found on the Pearson website.

1. Use the `disp` command to create a title for a table that converts inches to feet.
2. Use the `disp` command to create column headings for your table.
3. Create an `inches` vector from 0 to 120 with an increment of 10.
4. Calculate the corresponding values of `feet`.
5. Group the `inch` vector and the `feet` vector together into a `results` matrix.
6. Use the `fprintf` command to send your results to the command window.

KEY IDEA

The `sprintf` function is similar to `fprintf` and is useful for annotating plots.

7.2.3 Formatted Output—The `sprintf` Function

The `sprintf` function is similar to `fprintf`, but instead of just sending the result of the formatted string to the command window, `sprintf` assigns it a name and sends it to the command window.

```
a = sprintf('Some example output is %4.2f \n', pi*1000) =
a =
    Some example output is 3141.59
```

When would this be useful? In Example 7.3, the `sprintf` function is used to specify the contents of a text box, which is then used as an annotation on a graph.

EXAMPLE 7.3

PROJECTILE MOTION: ANNOTATING A GRAPH

Recall from earlier examples that the equation describing the range of a projectile fired from a cannon is

$$R(\theta) = \frac{v^2}{g} \sin(2\theta)$$

where

$R(\theta)$ is the range in meters,

v is the initial projectile velocity in m/s,

θ is the launch angle, and

g is the acceleration due to gravity, 9.9 m/s^2.

Plot the angle on the x-axis versus the range on the y-axis, and add a text box indicating the value of the maximum range.

1. State the problem
   Find and plot the distance traveled by projectile, as a function of launch angle. Annotate a plot, indicating the maximum range.

2. Describe the input and output

Input	Acceleration due to gravity, $g = 9.9$ m/s^2
	Launch angle
	Initial projectile velocity, 100 m/s
Output	An annotated graph indicating the maximum range.

3. Develop a hand example

We know from physics and from previous examples that the maximum range occurs at a launch angle of 45 degrees. Substituting into the provided equation,

$$R(45°) = \frac{100^2 \text{m}^2/\text{s}^2}{9.9 \text{ m/s}^2} \sin(2*45°)$$

Since the angle is specified in degrees, you must either set your calculator to accept degrees into the sine function, or else convert 45 degrees to the corresponding number of radians $(\pi/4)$. After you have done so, the result is

$$R(45°) = 1010 \text{ m}.$$

4. Develop a MATLAB® solution

```
%% Example 7.5
% Find the maximum projectile range for a given set of
  conditions
% Create an annotated graph of the results
% Define the input parameters
  g=9.9;    %Acceleration due to gravity
  velocity = 100; %Initial velocity, m/s^2
  theta = [0:5:90] %Launch angle in degrees
% Calculate the range
  range = velocity^2/g*sind(2*theta);
% Calculate the maximum range
  maximum = max(range);
% Create the input for the text box
  text_input=sprintf('The maximum range was %4.0f
  meters\n',maximum);
% Plot the results
  plot(theta,range)
  title('Range of a Projectile')
  xlabel('Angle, degrees'),
  ylabel('Range, meters')
  text(10,maximum,text_input)
```

There are several things to notice about this program. First, we took advantage of the sind function to calculate the value of sine, using degrees as input. Second, the location of the text box will always start on the graph at 10 degrees (measured on the *x*-axis), but the *y* location depends on the maximum range. This program produces the graph shown in Figure 7.3a.

5. Test the solution

Compare the MATLAB® solution with the hand solution. The text box used to annotate the graph lists the maximum range as 1010 m, the same value calculated by hand. We could also test the program with a different initial velocity, for example, 110 m/s. The result is shown in Figure 7.3.

(continued)

Figure 7.3
The contents of the text box change, depending on the input to the program, and are controlled by the `sprintf` function.

7.2.4 The `table` Function

Using `disp` and `fprintf` allows us to create tables of data in the command window, but there is no easy way to create output where the table columns are different data types, for example, characters and numbers. The `table` function actually uses a new data type called a *table* to accomplish this. We will focus on how to use the `table` function to display output.

Consider a calculation where we want to know how far an object will fall, both on the earth and the moon, after 100 seconds. The acceleration due to gravity in each location can be represented by a column vector, **g**:

$$\mathbf{g} = [9.8; 1.6]$$

The distance travelled is one half the acceleration due to gravity times the time squared, so

$$\mathbf{d} = 0.5*\mathbf{g}*100^2$$

which also returns a column vector.

We would like to have a table that lists the planet names in the first column, the value of **g** in the second column, and the distance travelled in the third. To do this, we need to define a column vector of planet names

```
p={'Earth';'Moon'}
```

The p variable created in this way is actually a data type we haven't used much called a cell array. Cell arrays are discussed in a later chapter. Once we've defined g, d and p they can be combined to create the table using the `table` function (all of the input vectors need to be columns.)

```
table(p,g,d)
```

which returns

```
ans =

        p        g        d
      _____   ___     _____

      'Earth'   9.8      49000
      'Moon'    1.6       8000
```

Notice that the column names default to the variable names. You can specify more meaningful column names by adding two additional fields

```
table(p,g,d,'VariableNames',{'Planet','g','Distance'})
ans =
```

Planet	g	Distance
'Earth'	9.8	49000
'Moon'	1.6	8000

Finally, the output table would be cleaner without the `ans = line`. To accomplish this, nest the code inside the `disp` function

```
disp(table(p,g,d,'VariableNames',{'Planet','g','Distance'}))
```

which gives

Planet	g	Distance
'Earth'	9.8	49000
'Moon'	1.6	8000

7.3 GRAPHICAL INPUT

MATLAB® offers a technique for entering ordered pairs of x- and y-values graphically. The `ginput` command allows the user to select points from a figure window and converts the points into the appropriate x- and y-coordinates. In the statement

```
[x,y] = ginput(n)
```

MATLAB® requests the user to select n points from the figure window. If the value of n is not included, as in

```
[x,y] = ginput
```

MATLAB® accepts points until the return key is entered
    This technique is useful for picking points off a graph. Consider the graph in Figure 7.4. The figure was created by defining x from 5 to 30 and calculating y:

```
x = 5:30;
y = x.^2 - 40.*x + 400;
plot(x, y)
axis([5,30, -50,250])
```

The axis values were defined so that the graph would be easier to trace.
    Once the `ginput` function has been executed, as in

```
[a,b] = ginput
```

MATLAB® adds a floating cross hair to the graph, as shown in Figure 7.4. After this cross hair is positioned to the user's satisfaction, right-clicking and selecting Return (Enter) sends the values of the x- and y-coordinates to the program:

```
a =
   24.4412
b =
   19.7368
```

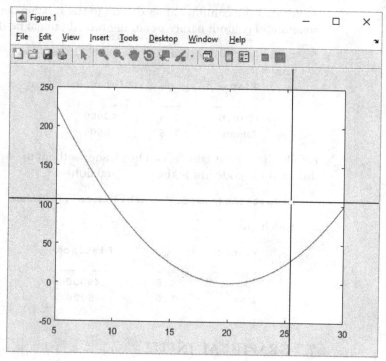

Figure 7.4
The `ginput` function allows the user to pick points off a graph.

KEY IDEA
Dividing your code into sections allows you to create reports in HTML, Word, and PowerPoint and pdf formats.

7.4 MORE FEATURES USING SECTION DIVIDERS

7.4.1 Publish

A useful feature to use in conjunction section dividers (%%) is Publish. It allows the user to publish a program and corresponding results to another file, for example, as HTML or a Word file. MATLAB® runs the program and creates a report showing the code in each section, as well as the calculational results that were sent to the command window. Any figures created are also included in the report. Figure 7.5 shows part of a script created to solve the homework problems from the chapter User-Defined Functions. It was created using sections, as can be seen from the section dividers. A portion of the report created using the Publish feature is shown in Figure 7.6. To access the Publish feature, select the Publish tab on the toolstrip, then select the **Publish** icon on the far right of the toolstrip.

HTML is the default format, but if you prefer a report in a different format, such as Word, PowerPoint or pdf, you can use the drop-down menu

Publish → **Edit Publishing Options** ...

to publish the results in your choice of several different formats. You'll need to select the "output file format" setting, and change it from HTML to your desired format, as shown in Figure 7.7. The Publish feature does not work well if you have programmed user interactions such as prompts for data input into the file. In this case, during the publishing process the script is executed, but no values are available for the user

Figure 7.5
This script, which was used to solve homework problems from the chapter User-Defined Functions, can be published using MATLAB®'s publish feature.

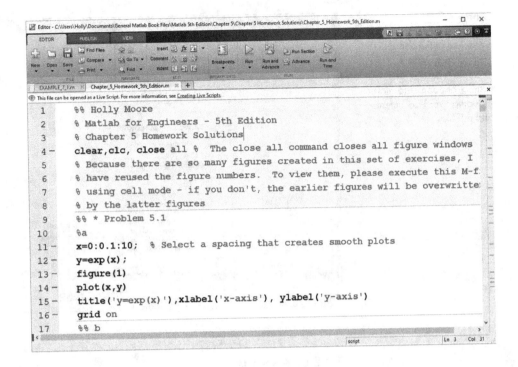

Figure 7.6
HTML report created from a MATLAB® script using the Publish feature.

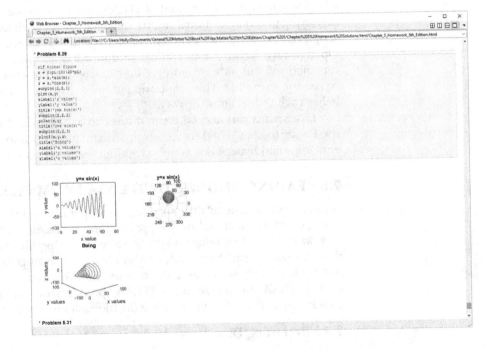

input. This results in an error message, which is included in the published version of the file. The Publish feature can be used to publish MATLAB programs that do not contain sections; however, the result is equivalent to a program that consists of only one section.

Figure 7.7
Change the output file format in the edit configuration window to create reports in a number of popular formats, including Word documents and pdf files.

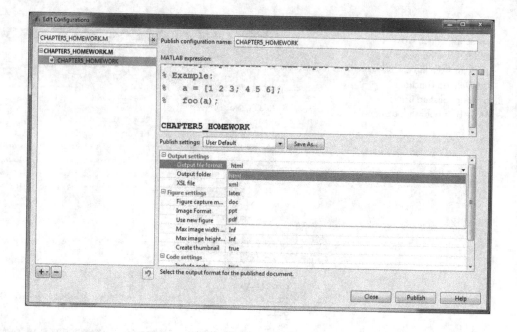

7.4.2 Live Scripts

New to MATLAB® 9 (first introduced in version 2016a) is Live Scripts. This format allows you to combine text and MATLAB® code in the same document, as well as displaying the computational results much like the Publish feature. From an existing script, right-click on the document tab in the editor as shown in Figure 7.8, and select Open as Live Script. A new editing window will open with a copy of your program, renamed with an **.mlx** extension. You can execute the code one section at a time, or run the entire file. The results will either be displayed to the right of the code, or below each cell. (Figure 7.9)

Live scripts can also be created directly by selecting **New → Live Script** from the Editor toolbar. The Live Editor opens and allows you to enter text, add images, equations and hyperlinks, as well as adding sections of MATLAB® code.

7.5 READING AND WRITING DATA FROM FILES

Data are stored in many different formats, depending on the devices and programs that created the data and on the application. For example, sound might be stored in **a .wav** file, and an image might be stored in a **.jpg** file. Many applications store data in Excel spreadsheets (**.xls** or **xlsx** files). The most generic of these files is the ASCII file, usually stored as a **.dat** or a **.txt** file. You may want to import these data into MATLAB® to analyze in a MATLAB® program, or you might want to save your data in one of these formats to make the file easier to export to another application.

7.5.1 Importing Data

Import Wizard

If you select a data file from the current folder and double-click on the file name, the Import Wizard launches. The Import Wizard determines what kind of data is in the file, and suggests ways to represent the data in MATLAB®. Table 7.3 is a list of some of the data types MATLAB® recognizes. Not every possible data format is

Figure 7.8
Convert an existing MATLAB program to a live script by right-clicking on the document tab or selecting **Save As → Live Script**.

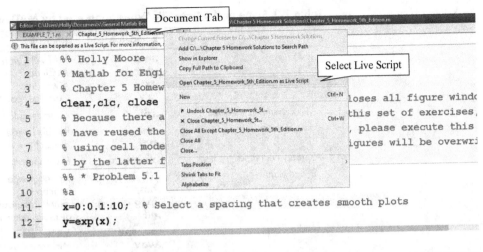

Figure 7.9
The Live Script editing window.

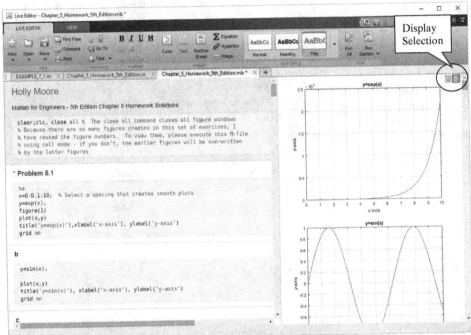

supported by MATLAB®. You can find a complete list by searching the help feature for supported file formats.

The Import Wizard can be used for simple ASCII files. Many of the other formats can also be imported with the Import Wizard, which can be launched from the command line, using the `uiimport` function:

```
uiimport(' filename.extension ')
```

For example, it is easy to record sound files using a variety of software tools, or to find existing files on the Internet. To import a sound file, such as one called **dave.wav**, type

```
uiimport('dave.wav ')
```

The Import Wizard then opens, as shown in Figure 7.10.

Table 7.3 Some of the Data File Types Supported by MATLAB®

File type	Extension	Remark
Text	.mat	MATLAB® workspace
	.dat	ASCII data
	.txt	ASCII data
	.csv	Comma-separated values
Other common scientific data formats	.cdf	common data format
	.fits	flexible image transport system data
	.hdf	hierarchical data format
Spreadsheet data	.xls, xlsx	Excel spreadsheet
Image data	.tiff	tagged image file format
	.bmp	bit map
	.jpeg or jpg	joint photographics expert group
	.gif	graphics interchange format
Audio data	.au, snd	audio
	.wav	Microsoft wave file
	.mp4	MPEG-4
Movie	.avi	audio/video interleaved file
	.mpg	motion picture experts group

Figure 7.10

The Import Wizard launches when the `uiimport` command is executed.

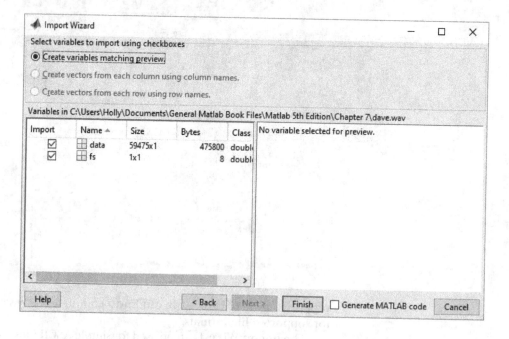

Either technique for launching the Import Wizard (double-clicking on the file name in the current folder window, or using the `uiimport` function in the command window) requires an interaction with the user (through the Wizard). If you want to load a data file from a MATLAB® program, you'll need a different approach.

Import Commands

You can bypass the Wizard interactions using one of the functions that are especially designed to read each of the supported file formats. For example, to read in **a .wav** file, use the `audioread` function:

```
[data,fs] = audioread('dave.wav')
```

Clearly, you need to understand what kind of data to expect, so that you can name the created variables appropriately. To use the files you have imported, you'll need to use a function appropriate to the data. In the case of **a .wav** file, the sound function is appropriate, so the code to play the **decision.wav** file is

```
sound(data,fs)
```

You should be aware that data storage formats are constantly changing, which can affect MATLAB®'s ability to interpret them. For example, some but not all **.wav** files use a data compression algorithm not supported by MATLAB®.

7.5.2 Exporting Data

The easiest way to find the appropriate function for writing a file is to use the help tutorial to find the correct function to read it, then to follow the links to the write function. For example, to read an Excel spreadsheet file (**.xls** or **.xlsx**), we'd use xlsread:

```
xlsread('filename.xlsx')
```

At the end of the tutorial page, we are referred to the correct function for writing an Excel file, namely,

```
xlswrite('filename.xlsx', M)
```

where M is the array you want to store in the Excel spreadsheet. An alternative approach to xlsread is to use the readtable function. This imports the data in the spreadsheet into a MATLAB table. The table data type is discussed in more detail in a later chapter.

7.6 DEBUGGING YOUR CODE

A software bug is a problem that exists in the code you have written. It can be a mistake that results in the code not working at all (a coding error), or it can be a logic error that results in a wrong answer. The term "bug" has its genesis in electronics, where actual insects sometimes caused equipment failure. Perhaps the most famous example is the moth (see Figure 7.11) found in the innards of one of the earliest computers, the Harvard Mark II Aiken Relay Calculator, in 1947.

MATLAB® includes a number of tools to help you debug your code, including the code analyzer (error bar) and more comprehensive tools that allow you to step through the code.

7.6.1 Code Analyzer

Whenever you use an M-file, notice that along the right-hand side of the figure window, a vertical bar appears that marks locations where there are actual errors or where MATLAB® has issued warnings. The portion of the code that concerns MATLAB® is highlighted. For example, in Figure 7.12 there are several places marked with a light orange highlight, which indicates a warning. If you run your cursor over the highlight (either in the code or along the bar), a message appears with a suggested fix for the problem. Not every warning corresponds to a real problem. For example, the warnings issued for the program in Figure 7.12 resulted from lines of code without semicolons at the end of the line. In this particular case, we wanted the code to report answers to the command window; in other cases you

Figure 7.11

The moth found trapped in a relay in Harvard's Mark II Aiken Relay Calculator. This is often erroneously reported to be the first use of the term "bug" as a synonym for a computer problem. This page from the computer log book is currently on exhibit in the Smithsonian Institute's National Museum of American History. (Image courtesy of the Naval Surface Warfare Center, Dalgren, VA, 1988.)

Figure 7.12

The code analyzer on the right-hand side of the screen identifies lines of code with potential errors. Locations in the code with potential errors are indicated with a light orange highlight.

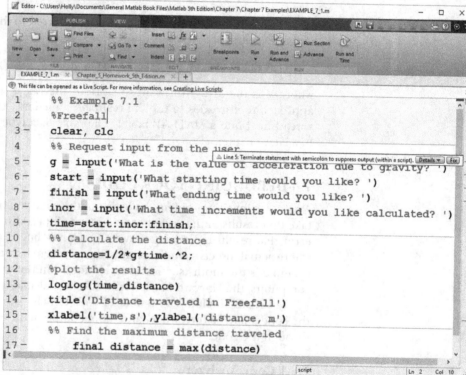

might want to suppress the output. You can edit which error messages are shown by selecting

   Preferences → Code Analyser

found on the Home tab.

If the errors shown on the code analyzer error bar are marked in red, they will cause the file to stop executing. In Figure 7.13, the code was adjusted to introduce such an error. On line 13, the right-hand parentheses are missing, as indicated by the error message. You can walk through the warnings and actual error messages by clicking on the square at the top of the error bar.

Figure 7.13
Script with an error on line 13.

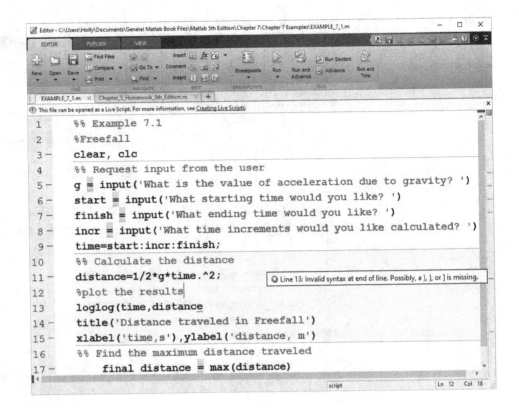

7.6.2 Debugging Toolbar

When trying to find logic errors in a piece of code, it is often useful to run sections of the program, then to stop, evaluate what has happened, and continue. Using sections is one way to accomplish this, but a more comprehensive approach is offered by the debugging toolbar. It allows you to set breakpoints (places in the code where the execution stops while you evaluate results) and to step through the code one line at a time. Breakpoints can't be enabled until all of the syntax errors have been resolved.

To set a breakpoint, click next to the line number on the left-hand side of the editing window, or select the **Set/Clear Breakpoint** icon on the toolbar. A red circle should appear, as shown in Figure 7.14. If the circle is gray, syntax errors still exist in the program, or you have not saved the most recent version of the code.

When you run the program, the debugging toolbar is activated, the execution will pause at the breakpoint, and the location will be marked with a green arrow (see Figure 7.15). To continue, select the continue icon from the breakpoint toolbar.

You can also choose to step through the code one line at a time, using the **Step** icon. If your code includes calls to user-defined functions, you can step into the function, then step through the function code one line at a time, using the **Step In** icon. To leave the user-defined function, select the **Step Out** icon. For example, Figure 7.16 shows a program that calls the user-defined function, RD. Both files are displayed in the editing window by selecting the VIEW tab, and choosing the left/right option. Notice that the line where we "stepped out" of the main program and into the function is marked with a white arrow.

Figure 7.14
MATLAB® includes code analysis tools that allow for easier debugging.

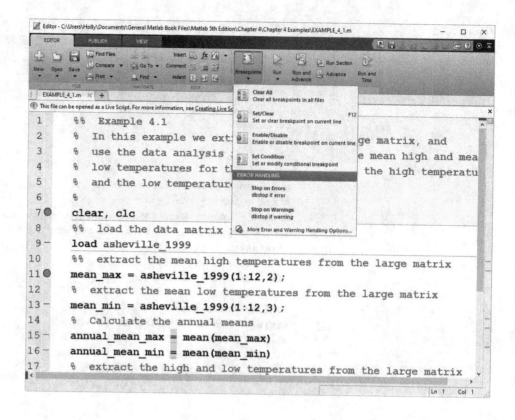

Figure 7.15
Breakpoints enable the user to move through the code in small pieces.

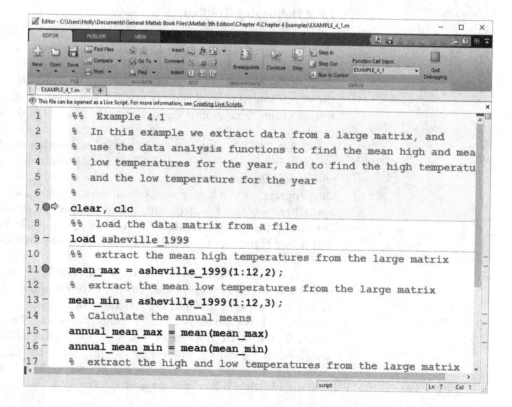

Figure 7.16
The step in option makes it possible to step through user-defined functions one line at a time, as they are called by the main program.

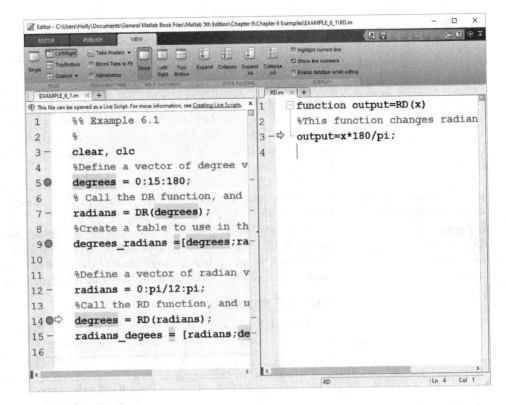

While you are executing the program using breakpoints to pause the code, the command window prompt is:

K>>

The prompt returns to the standard symbol

>>

when you have completed the process.

SUMMARY

MATLAB® provides functions that allow the user to interact with a program and allow the programmer to control the output to the command window.

The input function pauses the program and sends a prompt determined by the programmer to the command window. Once the user has entered a value or values and hits the return key, program execution continues.

The display (disp) function allows the programmer to display the contents of a string or a matrix in the command window. Although the disp function is adequate for many display tasks, the fprintf function gives the programmer considerably more control over the way results are displayed. The programmer can combine text and calculated results on the same line, and specify the number format used. The sprintf function behaves exactly the same way as the fprintf function. However, the result of sprintf is assigned a variable name and can be used with other functions that require strings as input. For example, the functions used to annotate graphs such as title, text, and xlabel all accept strings as input, and therefore will accept the result of the `sprintf` function as input. The `table` function creates tables that combine both text (strings) and numeric values.

For applications in which graphical input is required, the `ginput` command allows the user to provide input to a program by selecting points from a graphics window.

When sections are used with the `Publish` tool, a report is created containing both the code and results as well as any figures generated when the program executes. Results can be published in HTML or in a variety of common formats, such as Word or PowerPoint. Live Scripts are similar, but allow the user to execute one cell at a time, displaying the results either to the right of the code, or immediately below the cell.

MATLAB® includes functions that allow the user to import and export data in a number of popular file formats. A complete list of these formats is available in the help tutorial on the File Formats page.

The code analyzer error bar, located on the right-hand side of the editing window, identifies lines of code with potential errors. Warnings are indicated in orange, and errors that will cause the execution of the code to terminate are shown in red. More extensive debugging tools are available from the debugging toolbar.

KEY IDEA
MATLAB® includes debugging tools to help you find errors in your code.

KEY IDEA
MATLAB® can import data from files using a variety of formats.

MATLAB® SUMMARY

The following MATLAB® summary lists all the special characters, commands, and functions that were defined in this chapter:

Special Characters	
'	begins and ends a string
%	placeholder used in the `fprintf` command
%f	fixed-point, or decimal, notation
%d	signed integer notation
%e	exponential notation
%g	either fixed point or exponential notation
%s	string notation
%%	cell divider
\n	linefeed
\r	carriage return (similar to linefeed)
\t	tab
\b	backspace

Commands and Functions	
audioread	reads a variety of audio files
disp	displays a string or a matrix in the command window
fprintf	creates formatted output which can be sent to the command window or to a file
ginput	allows the user to pick values from a graph
input	allows the user to enter values
num2str	changes a number to a string
pause	pauses the program
sound	plays MATLAB® data through the speakers
sprintf	similar to `fprintf` creates formatted output which is assigned to a variable name and stored as a character array
table	creates a table containing multiple data types
uiimport	launches the Import Wizard
xlsimport	imports Excel data files
xlswrite	exports data as an Excel file

KEY TERMS

cell	formatted output	string
cell mode	precision field	width field
character array		

PROBLEMS

Input Function

7.1 Prompt the user to enter a value of x and then calculate the value of sin (x).

7.2 Prompt the user to enter a matrix, then use the `max` function to determine the largest value entered. Use the following matrix to test your program:

```
[1, 5, 3, 8, 9, 22]
```

7.3 The volume of a cone is

$$V = \frac{1}{3} \times \text{area of the base} \times \text{height}.$$

Prompt the user to enter the area of the base and the height of the cone (see Figure P7.3). Calculate the volume of the cone.

Figure P7.3
Volume of a cone.

Disp Function

7.4 One of the first computer programs many students write is called "Hello, World." The only thing the program does is print this message to the computer screen. Write a "Hello, World" program in an M-file, using the `disp` function.

7.5 Use two separate `input` statements to prompt a user to enter his or her first and last names. Use the `disp` function to display those names on one line. (You'll need to combine the names and some spaces into an array.)

7.6 Prompt the user to enter his or her age. Then use the `disp` function to report the age back to the command window. If, for example, the user enters 5 when prompted for her age, your display should read

```
Your age is 5
```

This output requires combining both character data (a string) and numeric data in the `disp` function—which can be accomplished using the `num2str` function.

7.7 Prompt the user to enter an array of numbers. Use the `length` function to determine how many values were entered, and use the `disp` function to report your results to the command window.

fprintf

7.8 Repeat Problem 7.7, and use `fprintf` to report your results.

7.9 Use `fprintf` to create the multiplication tables from 1 to 13 for the number 6. Your table should look like this:

$$1 \text{ times } 6 \text{ is } 6$$
$$2 \text{ times } 6 \text{ is } 12$$
$$3 \text{ times } 6 \text{ is } 18$$
$$\vdots$$

7.10 Before calculators were readily available (about 1974), students used tables to determine the values of mathematical functions like sine, cosine, and log. Create such a table for sine, using the following steps:
- Create a vector of angle values from 0 to 2π in increments of $\pi/10$.
- Calculate the sine of each of the angles, and group your results into an array that includes the angle and the sine.
- Use `disp` to create a title for the table, and a second `disp` command to create column headings.
- Use the `fprintf` function to display the numbers. Display only two values past the decimal point.

7.11 Very small dimensions—those on the atomic scale—are often measured in angstroms. An angstrom is represented by the symbol Å and corresponds to a length of 10^{-10} m. Create an inches-to-angstroms conversion table as follows for values of inches from 1 to 10:
- Use `disp` to create a title and column headings.
- Use `fprintf` to display the numerical information.
- Because the length represented in angstroms is so big, represent your result in scientific notation, showing two values after the decimal point. This corresponds to three significant figures (one before and two after the decimal point).

7.12 Use your favorite Internet search engine and browser to identify recent currency conversions for British pounds sterling, Japanese yen, and the European euro to US dollars. Use the conversion tables to create the following tables (use the `disp` and `fprintf` commands in your solution, which should include a title, column labels, and formatted output):

(a) Generate a table of conversions from yen to dollars. Start the yen column at 5 and increment by 5 yen. Print 25 lines in the table.

(b) Generate a table of conversions from the euros to dollars. Start the euro column at 1 euro and increment by 2 euros. Print 30 lines in the table.

(c) Generate a table with four columns. The first should contain dollars, the second the equivalent number of euros, the third the equivalent number of pounds, and the fourth the equivalent number of yen. Let the dollar column vary from 1 to 10.

`table`

7.13 Consider the patient data contained in table P7.13.

Table P7.13 Patient Data

Patient Last Name	Patient First Name	Age	Height (inches)	Weight (lb)
Smith	Fred	6	47	82
Jones	Kathy	22	66	140
Webb	Milton	92	62	110
Anderson	John	45	72	190

(a) Create a column vector of last names called last, using curly braces.
(b) Create a column vector of first names called first, using curly braces.
(c) Create column vectors for age, height and weight.
(d) Display the information using the `table` function.

Problems combining the `input`, `disp`, and `fprintf` and `table` functions

7.14 This problem requires you to generate temperature conversion tables. Use the following equations, which describe the relationships between temperatures in degrees Fahrenheit (T_F), degrees Celsius (T_C), kelvins (T_K), and degrees Rankine (T_R), respectively:

$$T_F = T_R - 459.67°R$$

$$T_F = \frac{9}{5} T_C + 32°F$$

$$T_R = \frac{9}{5} T_K$$

You will need to rearrange these expressions to solve some of the problems.

(a) Generate a table of conversions from Fahrenheit to Kelvin for values from $0°F$ to $200°F$. Allow the user to enter the increments in degrees F between lines. Use `disp` and `fprintf` to create a table with a title, column headings, and appropriate spacing.

(b) Generate a table of conversions from Celsius to Rankine. Allow the user to enter the starting temperature and the increment between lines. Print 25 lines in the table. Use `disp` and `fprintf` to create a table with a title, column headings, and appropriate spacing.

(c) Generate a table of conversions from Celsius to Fahrenheit. Allow the user to enter the starting temperature, the increment between lines, and the number of lines for the table. Use `disp` and `fprintf` to create a table with a title, column headings, and appropriate spacing.

7.15 Engineers use both English and SI (Système International d'Unités) units on a regular basis. Some fields use primarily one or the other, but many combine the two systems. For example, the rate of energy input to a steam power plant from burning fossil fuels is usually measured in Btu/hour. However, the electricity produced by the same plant is usually measured in joules/s (watts). Automobile engines, by contrast, are often rated in horsepower or in ft $lb_{f/s}$. Here are some conversion factors relating these different power measurements:

$$1 \text{ kW} = 3412.14 \text{ Btu/h} = 737.56 \text{ ft } lb_{f/s}$$

$$1 \text{ hp} = 550 \text{ ft } lb_{f/s} = 2544.5 \text{ Btu/h}$$

(a) Generate a table of conversions from kW to hp. The table should start at 0 kW and end at 15 kW. Use the `input` function to let the user define the increment between table entries. Use `disp` and `fprintf` to create a table with a title, column headings, and appropriate spacing.

(b) Repeat part a using the `table` function.

(c) Generate a table of conversions from ft $lb_{f/s}$ to Btu/h. The table should start at 0 ft $lb_{f/s}$ but let the user define the increment between table entries and the final table value. Use `disp` and `fprintf` to create a table with a title, column headings, and appropriate spacing.

(d) Repeat part (c) using the `table` function.

(e) Generate a table that includes conversions from kW to Btu/h, hp, and ft $lb_{f/s}$. Let the user define the initial value of kW, the final value of kW, and the number of entries in the table. Use `disp` and `fprintf` to create a table with a title, column headings, and appropriate spacing.

(f) Repeat part (d) using the `table` function.

ginput

7.16 At time $t = 0$, when a rocket's engine shuts down, the rocket has reached an altitude of 500 m and is rising at a velocity of 125 m/s. At this point, gravity takes over. The height of the rocket as a function of time is

$$h(t) = -\frac{9.8}{2}t^2 + 125t + 500 \text{ for } t > 0.$$

Plot the height of the rocket from 0 to 30 seconds, and
- Use the `ginput` function to estimate the maximum height the rocket reaches and the time when the rocket hits the ground.
- Use the `disp` command to report your results to the command window.

7.17 The `ginput` function is useful for picking distances off a graph. Demonstrate this feature by doing the following:
- Create a graph of a circle by defining an array of angles from 0 to 2π, with a spacing of $\pi/100$.
- Use the `ginput` function to pick two points on the circumference of the circle.
- Use `hold on` to keep the figure from refreshing, and plot a line between the two points you picked.
- Use the data from the points to calculate the length of the line between them. (*Hint*: Use the Pythagorean theorem in your calculation.)

7.18 In recent years, the price of gasoline has fluctuated dramatically. Automobile companies have responded with more fuel-efficient cars, in particular, hybrid models. But will you save money by purchasing a hybrid such as the Toyota Camry rather than a Camry with a standard engine? The hybrid vehicles are considerably more expensive, but get better gas mileage. Consider the vehicle prices and gas efficiencies shown in Table P7.18.

Table P7.18 A Comparison of Standard and Hybrid Vehicles

Year	Model	Base MSRP	Gas Efficiency, in-town/ highway (mpg)
2016	Toyota Camry	$23,070	25/35
2016	Toyota Camry Hybrid IE	$26,790	43/39 (hybrids may actually get better mileage in town than on the road)
2016	Toyota Highlander Limited	$40,915	20/25
2016	Toyota Highlander Limited Hybrid	$47,870	28/28
2016	Ford Fusion S	$22,120	23/34
2016	Ford Fusion S Hybrid	$25,185	43/41

One way to compare two vehicles is to find the "cost to own."

Cost to own = Purchase cost + Upkeep + Gasoline cost

Assume for this exercise that the upkeep costs are the same, so in our comparison we'll set them equal to zero.

(a) What do you think the cost of gasoline will be over the next several years? Prompt the user to enter an estimate of gasoline cost in dollars/gallon.
(b) Find the "cost to own" as a function of the number of miles driven for a pair of vehicles from the table, based on the fuel price estimate from

part (a). Plot your results on an *x–y* graph. The point where the two lines cross is the break-even point.

(c) Use the `ginput` function to pick the break-even point off the graph.

(d) Use `sprintf` to create a string identifying the break-even point, and use the result to create a text-box annotation on your graph. Position the text box using the `gtext` function.

Using Sections

7.19 Publish your program and results from Problem 7.17 to HTML, using the Publish to HTML feature. Unfortunately, because this chapter's assignment requires interaction with the user, the published results will include errors.

7.20 Save your homework assignment as a Live Script. Run the file, with the results displayed on the right-hand-side of the page. You will achieve a better looking and more functional result if you start each problem as a new section.

8 Logical Functions and Selection Structures

Objectives

After reading this chapter, you should be able to:

- Understand how MATLAB® interprets relational and logical operators.

- Use the `find` function.
- Understand the appropriate uses of the `if/else` family of commands.
- Understand the `switch/case` structure.

INTRODUCTION

One way to think of a computer program (not just MATLAB®) is to consider how the statements that compose it are organized. Usually, sections of computer code can be categorized as *sequences*, *selection structures*, and *repetition structures* (see Figure 8.1). So far, we have written code that contains sequences, but none of the other structures:

- A sequence is a list of commands that are executed one after another.
- A selection structure allows the programmer to execute one command (or set of commands) if some criterion is true and a second command (or set of commands) if the criterion is false. A selection statement provides the means of choosing between these paths, based on a *logical condition*. The conditions that are evaluated often contain both *relational* and *logical* operators or functions.
- A repetition structure, or loop, causes a group of statements to be executed multiple times. The number of times a loop is executed depends on either a counter or the evaluation of a logical condition.

Figure 8.1
Programming structures used in MATLAB®.

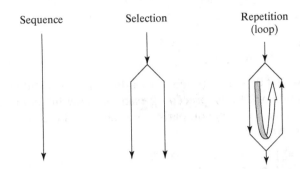

Sequence   Selection   Repetition
                                     (loop)

8.1 RELATIONAL AND LOGICAL OPERATORS

The selection and repetition structures used in MATLAB® depend on relational and logical operators. MATLAB® has six relational operators for comparing two matrices of equal size, as shown in Table 8.1.

Comparisons are either true or false, and most computer programs (including MATLAB®) use the number 1 for true and 0 for false. (MATLAB® actually takes any number that is not 0 to be true.) If we define two scalars

```
x = 5;
y = 1;
```

and use a relational operator such as <, the result of the comparison

```
x<y
```

is either true or false. In this case, **x** is not less than **y**, so MATLAB® responds

```
ans =
      0
```

indicating that the comparison is false. MATLAB® uses this answer in selection statements and in repetition structures to make decisions.

Of course, variables in MATLAB® usually represent entire matrices. If we redefine x and y, we can see how MATLAB® handles comparisons between matrices. For example,

```
x = 1:5;
y = x -4;
x<y
```

KEY IDEA

Relational operators compare values.

Table 8.1 Relational Operators

Relational Operator	Interpretation
<	less than
<=	less than or equal to
>	greater than
>=	greater than or equal to
==	equal to
~=	not equal to

returns

```
ans =
    0  0  0  0  0
```

MATLAB® compares corresponding elements and creates an answer matrix of zeros and ones. In the preceding example, **x** was greater than **y** for every comparison of elements, so every comparison was false, and the answer was a string of zeros. If, instead, we have

```
x = [ 1, 2, 3, 4, 5];
y = [-2, 0, 2, 4, 6];
x<y
```

then

```
ans =
    0  0  0  0  1
```

The results tell us that the comparison was false for the first four elements, but true for the last. For a comparison to be true for an entire matrix, it must be true for *every* element in the matrix. In other words, all the results must be ones.

HINT

One common source of confusion is the difference between the equals operator (==) and the assignment operator (=). The equals operator (==) compares two values and returns a result of true if they are the same and false if they are different. The assignment operator (=) assigns the value on the right-hand side of the expression to a memory location. For example, the statement

```
x = 5
```

assigns the value 5 to a memory location named x. Once we've made that assignment the comparison

```
x == 3
```

returns a value of 0, since the comparison is false

```
ans =
    0
```

KEY IDEA
Logical operators are used to combine comparison statements.

MATLAB® also allows us to combine comparisons with the logical operators *and*, *not*, and *or* (see Table 8.2).

Table 8.2 Logical Operators

Logical Operator	Interpretation
&	and
~	not
		or
xor	exclusive or
&&	short circuit and (used with scalars)
||	short circuit or (used with scalars)

The code

```
x = [ 1, 2, 3, 4, 5];
y = [-2, 0, 2, 4, 6];
z = [ 8, 8, 8, 8, 8];
z>x & z>y
```

returns

```
ans =
    1  1  1  1  1
```

because **z** is greater than both **x** and **y** for every element. The statement

```
x>y | x>z
```

is read as "**x** is greater than **y** or **x** is greater than **z**" and returns

```
ans =
  1  1  1  0  0
```

This means that the condition is true for the first three elements, and false for the last two.

MATLAB® supports the && (shortcut and) and || (shortcut or) operators; however, these operators apply only to scalar quantities. To save computational time, they evaluate only enough of the statement to determine whether it is true or false. For example, in the statement

```
5<3 && 10>2
```

the first comparison is false, so the result of the second comparison is irrelevant. Similarly, in the statement

```
12>3 || 2>5
```

the first comparison is true, making the second comparison irrelevant.

These relational and logical operators are used in both selection structures and loops to determine what commands should be executed.

8.2 FLOWCHARTS AND PSEUDOCODE

With the addition of selection and repetition structures to your group of programming tools, it becomes even more important to plan your program before you start coding. Two common approaches are to use flowcharts and pseudocode. A flowchart is a graphical approach to creating your coding plan. Pseudocode is a verbal description of your plan. You may want to use either or both for your programming projects.

For simple programs, pseudocode may be the best (or at least the simplest) planning approach:

KEY IDEA
Flowcharts and pseudocode are used to plan programming tasks.

- Outline a set of statements describing the steps you will take to solve a problem.
- Convert these steps into comments in a MATLAB program.
- Insert the appropriate MATLAB® code into the file between the comment lines.

Here's a really simple example: Suppose you've been asked to create a program to convert mph to ft/s. The output should be a table, complete with a title and column headings. Here's an outline of the steps you might follow:

- Define a vector of mph values.
- Convert mph to ft/s.

- Combine the mph and ft/s vectors into a matrix.
- Create a table title.
- Create column headings.
- Display the table.

Once you've identified the steps, put them into a MATLAB® M-file as comments:

```
%Define a vector of mph values
%Convert mph to ft/s
%Combine the mph and ft/s vectors into a matrix
%Create a table title
%Create column headings
%Display the table
```

Now you can insert the appropriate MATLAB® code into the script

```
%%Define a vector of mph values
  mph = 0:10:100;
%Convert mph to ft/s
  fps = mph*5280/3600;
%Combine the mph and ft/s vectors into a matrix
  table = [mph;fps]
%Create a table title
  disp('Velocity Conversion Table')
%Create column headings
  disp('  mph   f/s')
%Display the table
  fprintf('%8.0f  %8.2f \n',table)
```

If you put some time into your planning, you probably won't need to change the pseudocode much, once you start programming.

Flowcharts alone, or flowcharts combined with pseudocode, are especially appropriate for more complicated programming tasks. You can create a "big picture" of your program graphically, then convert your project to pseudocode suitable to enter into the program as comments. Before you can start flowcharting, you'll need to be introduced to some standard flowcharting symbols (see Table 8.3).

FLOWCHART
A pictorial representation of a computer program

Table 8.3 Flowcharting for Designing Computer Programs

(oval)	An oval is used to indicate the beginning or the end of a section of code.
(parallelogram)	A parallelogram is used to indicate input or output processes.
(diamond)	A diamond indicates a decision point.
(rectangle)	Calculations are placed in rectangles.

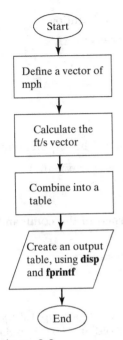

Figure 8.2
Flowcharts make it easy to visualize the structure of a program.

PSEUDOCODE
A list of programming tasks necessary to create a program

KEY IDEA
Logical functions are often more efficient programming tools than traditional selection structures.

Figure 8.2 is an example of a flowchart for the mph-to-ft/s problem. For a problem this simple, you would probably never actually create a flowchart. However, as problems become more complicated, flowcharts become an invaluable tool, allowing you to organize your thoughts.

Once you've created a flowchart, you should transfer the ideas into comment lines in an M-file, then add the appropriate code between the comments.

Remember, both flowcharts and pseudocode are tools intended to help you create better computer programs. They can also be used effectively to illustrate the structure of a program to nonprogrammers, since they emphasize the logical progression of ideas over programming details.

8.3 LOGICAL FUNCTIONS

MATLAB® offers both traditional selection structures, such as the family of `if` functions, and a series of logical functions that perform much the same task. The primary logical function is `find`, which can often be used in place of both traditional selection structures and loops.

8.3.1 Find

The `find` command searches a matrix and identifies which elements in that matrix meet a given criterion. For example, the U.S. Naval Academy requires applicants to be at least 5′6″ (66″) tall. Consider this list of applicant heights:

```
height = [63,67,65,72,69,78,75]
```

You can find the index numbers of the elements that meet our criterion by using the `find` command:

```
accept = find(height>=66)
```

This command returns

```
accept =
    2   4   5   6   7.
```

The `find` function returns the index numbers from the matrix that meet the criterion. If you want to know what the actual heights are, you can call each element, using the index number:

```
height(accept)
ans =
    67   72   69   78   75
```

An alternative approach would be to nest the commands:

```
height(find(height>=66))
```

You could also determine which applicants do *not* meet the criterion. Use

```
decline = find(height<66)
```

which gives

```
decline =
    1   3.
```

To create a more readable report, use the `disp` and `fprintf` functions:

```
disp('The following candidates meet the height requirement');
    fprintf('Candidate # %4.0f is %4.0f
    inches tall \n', [accept;height(accept)])
```

These commands return the following table in the command window:

```
The following candidates meet the height requirement
Candidate #  2 is   67 inches tall
Candidate #  4 is   72 inches tall
Candidate #  5 is   69 inches tall
Candidate #  6 is   78 inches tall
Candidate #  7 is   75 inches tall
```

Clearly, you could also create a table of those who do not meet the requirement:

```
disp('These candidates do not meet the height requirement')
fprintf('Candidate # %4.0f is %4.0f inches tall \n',
    [decline;height(decline)])
```

Similar to the previous code, the following table is returned in the command window:

```
These candidates do not meet the height requirement
Candidate #  1 is   63 inches tall
Candidate #  3 is   65 inches tall
```

You can create fairly complicated search criteria that use the logical operators. For example, suppose the applicants must be at least 18 years old and less than 35 years old. Then, your data might look like this:

Height (inches)	Age (years)
63	18
67	19
65	18
72	20
69	36
78	34
75	12

Now, we define the matrix and find the index numbers of the elements in column 1 that are greater than 66. Then we find which of those elements in column 2 are also greater than or equal to 18, and less than or equal to 35. We use the commands

```
applicants = [ 63, 18; 67, 19; 65, 18; 72, 20; 69, 36; 78,
        34; 75, 12]
pass = find(applicants(:,1)>=66 & applicants(:,2)>=18
        & applicants(:,2) < 35)
```

which return

```
pass =
    2
    4
    6
```

the list of applicants that meet all the criteria. We could use fprintf to create a nicer output. First, create a table of the data to be displayed:

```
results = [pass,applicants(pass,1),applicants(pass,2)]';
```

Then use fprintf to send the results to the command window:

```
fprintf('Applicant # %4.0f is %4.0f inches tall and
    %4.0f years old\n',results)
```

The resulting list is

```
Applicant    2 is    67 inches tall and 19 years old
Applicant    4 is    72 inches tall and 20 years old
Applicant    6 is    78 inches tall and 34 years old.
```

So far, we've used `find` only to return a single index number. If we define two outputs from `find`, as in

`[row, col] = find(criteria)`

it will return the appropriate row and column numbers (also called the row and column index numbers or subscripts).

Now, imagine that you have a matrix of patient temperature values measured in a clinic. The column represents the number of the stations where the temperature was taken. Thus, the command

`temp = [95.3, 100.2, 98.6; 97.4,99.2, 98.9; 100.1,99.3, 97]`

gives

```
temp =
    95.3000    100.2000    98.6000
    97.4000     99.2000    98.9000
   100.1000     99.3000    97.0000
```

and

`element = find(temp>98.6)`

gives us the element number for the single-index representation:

```
element =
     3
     4
     5
     6
     8
```

When the `find` command is used with a two-dimensional matrix, it uses an element-numbering scheme that works down each column one at a time. For example, consider our 3×3 matrix. The element index numbers are shown in Figure 8.3. The elements that contain values greater than 98.6 are shown in bold.

In order to determine the row and column numbers, we need the syntax

`[row, col] = find(temp>98.6)`

which gives us the following row and column numbers:

```
row =
     3
     1
     2
     3
     2
```

KEY IDEA
MATLAB® is column
dominant.

Figure 8.3
Element-numbering
sequence for a matrix.

1, 1	**1, 2**	1, 3
2, 1	**2, 2**	**2, 3**
3, 1	**3, 2**	3, 3

Figure 8.4
Row, element designation for a 3 × 3 matrix. The elements that meet the criterion are shown in bold.

```
col =
     1
     2
     2
     2
     3
```

Together, these numbers identify the elements shown in Figure 8.4. Using `fprintf`, we can create a more readable report. For example,

```
fprintf('Patient%3.0f at station%3.0f had a temp of%6.1f
    \n', [row,col,temp(element)]')
```

returns

```
Patient 3 at station 1 had a temp of 100.1
Patient 1 at station 2 had a temp of 100.2
Patient 2 at station 2 had a temp of 99.2
Patient 3 at station 2 had a temp of 99.3
Patient 2 at station 3 had a temp of 98.9.
```

8.3.2 Flowcharting and Pseudocode for Find Commands

The `find` command returns only one answer: a vector of the element numbers requested. For example, you might flowchart a sequence of command, as shown in Figure 8.5. If you use `find` multiple times to separate a matrix into categories, you may choose to employ a diamond shape, indicating the use of `find` as a selection structure.

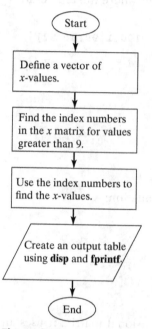

Figure 8.5
Flowchart illustrating the `find` command.

```
%Define a vector of x-values
 x = [1,2,3; 10, 5,1; 12,3,2;8, 3,1]
%Find the index numbers of the values in x>9
 element = find(x>9)
%Use the index numbers to find the x-values
%greater than 9 by plugging them into x
 values = x(element)
% Create an output table
 disp('Elements greater than 9')
 disp('Element # Value')
 fprintf('%8.0f %3.0f \n', [element';values'])
```

EXAMPLE 8.1

Figure 8.6
Oscilloscopes are widely used in signal-processing applications. (SPL/Science Source)

SIGNAL PROCESSING USING THE SINC FUNCTION

The `sinc` function is used in many engineering applications, but especially in signal processing (see Figure 8.6). Unfortunately, this function has two widely accepted definitions:

$$f_1(x) = \frac{\sin(\pi x)}{\pi x} \text{ and } f_2(x) = \frac{\sin(x)}{x}$$

Both of these functions have an indeterminate form of 0/0 when $x = 0$. In this case, l'Hôpital's theorem from calculus can be used to prove that both functions are equal to 1 when $x = $ zero. For values of x not equal to zero, the two functions have a similar form. The first function, $f_1(x)$, crosses the x-axis when x is an integer; the second function crosses the x-axis when x is a multiple of π.

Suppose you would like to define a function called sinc_x that uses the second definition. Test your function by calculating values of sinc_x for x from -5π to $+5\pi$ and plotting the results.

1. State the problem

   Create and test a function called sinc_x, using the second definition:

$$f_2(x) = \frac{\sin(x)}{x}$$

2. Describe the input and output

Input	Let x vary from -5π to $+5\pi$. to
Output	Create a plot of sinc_x versus **x**

3. Develop a hand example
4. Develop a MATLAB® solution

   Outline your function in a flowchart, as shown in Figure 8.7. Then convert the flowchart to pseudocode comments, and insert the appropriate MATLAB® code.

Figure 8.7
Flowchart of the sinc function.

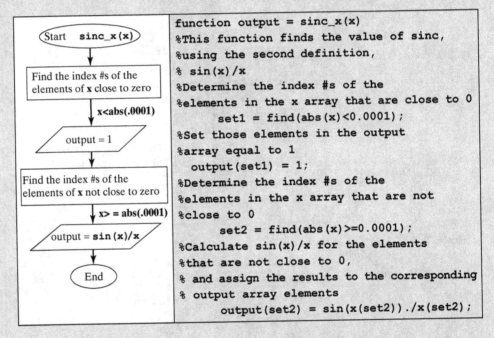

Once we've created the function, we should test it in the command window:

```
sinc_x(0)
ans =
        1
sinc_x(pi/2)
ans =
        0.6366
sinc_x(pi)
ans =
        3.8982e-017
sinc_x(-pi/2)
ans =
        0.6366
```

(continued)

Table 8.4 Calculating the Sinc Function

x	sin(x)	sinc_x(x) = sin(x)/x
0	0	$0/0 = 1$
$\pi/2$	1	$1/(\pi/2) = 0.637$
π	0	0
$-\pi/2$	-1	$-1/(\pi/2) = -0.637$

Notice that `sinc_x(pi)` equals a very small number, but not zero. That is because MATLAB® treats π as a floating-point number and uses an approximation of its real value (see Table 8.4).

5. Test the solution

When we compare the results with those of the hand example, we see that the answers match. Now we can use the function confidently in our problem. We have

```
%Example 8.1
      clear, clc
%Define an array of angles
      x = -5*pi:pi/100:5*pi;
%Calculate sinc_x
      y = sinc_x(x);
%Create the plot
      plot(x,y)
      title('Sinc Function'), xlabel('angle,
      radians'),ylabel('sinc')
```

which generates the plot in Figure 8.8.

Figure 8.8
The `sinc` function.

The plot also supports our belief that the function is working properly. Testing `sinc_x` with one value at a time validated its answers for a scalar input; however, the program that generated the plot sent a vector argument to the function. The plot confirms that it also performs properly with vector input.

If you have trouble understanding how this function works, remove the semi-colons that are suppressing the output, then run the program. Understanding the output from each line will help you understand the program logic better.

In addition to `find`, MATLAB® offers two other logical functions: `all` and `any`. The `all` function checks to see if a logical condition is true for *every* member of an array, and the `any` function checks to see if a logical condition is true for *any* member of an array. Consult MATLAB®'s built-in `help` function for more information.

PRACTICE EXERCISE 8.1

The correct answers can be found on the Pearson website. Consider the following matrices:

$$x = \begin{bmatrix} 1 & 10 & 42 & 6 \\ 5 & 8 & 78 & 23 \\ 56 & 45 & 9 & 13 \\ 23 & 22 & 8 & 9 \end{bmatrix} \quad y = \begin{bmatrix} 1 & 2 & 3 \\ 4 & 10 & 12 \\ 7 & 21 & 27 \end{bmatrix} \quad z = [10 \quad 22 \quad 5 \quad 13]$$

1. Using single-index notation, find the index numbers of the elements in each matrix that contain values greater than 10.
2. Find the row and column numbers (sometimes called subscripts) of the elements in each matrix that contain values greater than 10.
3. Find the values in each matrix that are greater than 10.
4. Using single-index notation, find the index numbers of the elements in each matrix that contain values greater than 10 and less than 40.
5. Find the row and column numbers for the elements in each matrix that contain values greater than 10 and less than 40.
6. Find the values in each matrix that are greater than 10 and less than 40.
7. Using single-index notation, find the index numbers of the elements in each matrix that contain values between 0 and 10 or between 70 and 80.
8. Use the `length` command together with results from the `find` command to determine how many values in each matrix are between 0 and 10 or between 70 and 80.

8.4 SELECTION STRUCTURES

Most of the time, the `find` command can and should be used instead of an `if` statement. In some situations, however, the `if` statement is required. This section describes the syntax used in `if` statements.

8.4.1 The Simple `if`

A simple `if` statement has the following form:

```
if      comparison
        statements
end
```

If the comparison (a logical expression) is true, the statements between the `if` statement and the `end` statement are executed. If the comparison is false, the program jumps immediately to the statement following `end`. It is good programming practice to indent the statements within an `if` structure for readability. However, recall that MATLAB® ignores white space. Your programs will run regardless of whether you do or do not indent any of your lines of code.

Here's a simple example of an `if` statement:

```
if G<50
  disp('G is a small value equal to:')
  disp(G);
end
```

This statement (from `if` to `end`) is easy to interpret if G is a scalar. If **G** is less than 50, then the statements between the `if` and the `end` lines are executed. For example, if **G** has a value of 25, then

```
G is a small value equal to:
   25
```

is displayed on the screen. However, if **G** is not a scalar, then the **if** statement considers the comparison true *only if it is true for every element!* Thus, if G is defined from 0 to 80,

```
G = 0:10:80;
```

the comparison is false, and the statements inside the `if` statement are not executed! In general, `if` statements work best when dealing with scalars.

8.4.2 The `if/else` Structure

The simple `if` allows us to execute a series of statements if a condition is true, and to skip those steps if the condition is false. The `else` clause allows us to execute one set of statements if the comparison is true, and a different set if the comparison is false. Suppose you would like to take the logarithm of a variable *x*. You know from basic algebra classes that the input to the `log` function must be greater than 0. Here's a set of `if/else` statements that calculates the logarithm if the input is positive, and sends an error message if the input to the function is 0 or negative:

```
if x >0
   y = log(x)
else
   disp('The input to the log function must be positive')
end
```

Notice that there is no logical comparison on the `else` line. This section of code executes only when the if statement is negative, so an additional comparison (for example, x < = 0) is not needed.

When **x** is a scalar, this code segment is easy to interpret. However, when **x** is a matrix, the comparison is true only if it is true for every element in the matrix. So, if

```
x = 0:0.5:2;
```

then the elements in the matrix are not all greater than 0. Therefore, MATLAB® skips to the `else` portion of the statement and displays the error message. The `if/else` statement is probably best confined to use with scalars, although you may find it to be of limited use with vectors.

HINT

MATLAB® includes a function called `beep` that causes the computer to "beep" at the user. You can use this function to alert the user to an error. For example, in the `if/else` clause, you could add a beep to the portion of the code that includes an error statement:

```
x = input('Enter a value of x greater than 0: ');
if x >0
    y = log(x)
else
    beep
    disp('The input to the log function must be positive')
end
```

This segment of code mimics the `error` function, the only difference being that the `error` function causes the program to abort—whereas the code segment above simply results in an error message going to the command window.

```
x = input('Enter a value of x greater than 0: ');
if x >0
    y = log(x)
else
    error('The input to the log function must be positive')
end
```

Try both code segments in MATLAB® to observe their behavior.

8.4.3 The `elseif` Structure

When we nest several levels of `if/else` statements, it may be difficult to determine which logical expressions must be true (or false) in order to execute each set of statements. The `elseif` function allows you to check multiple criteria while keeping the code easy to read. Consider the following lines of code that evaluate whether to issue a driver's license, based on the applicant's age:

```
if age<16
    disp('Sorry - You'll have to wait')
elseif age<18
    disp('You may have a youth license')
elseif age<70
    disp('You may have a standard license')
else
    disp('Drivers over 70 require a special license')
end
```

In this example, MATLAB® first checks to see if `age < 16`. If the comparison is true, the program executes the next line or set of lines, displays the message `Sorry—You'll have to wait`, and then exits the `if` structure. If the comparison is false, MATLAB® moves on to the next `elseif` comparison, checking to see if `age < 18` this time. The program continues through the if structure until it finally finds a true comparison, or until it encounters the else. Notice that the else line does not include a comparison. The only way for the executing code to reach the else line is if the elseif immediately before it is false.

The flowchart for this sequence of commands (see Figure 8.9) uses the diamond shape to indicate a selection structure.

This structure is easy to interpret if age is a scalar. If it is a matrix, the comparison must be true for every element in the matrix. Consider this age matrix

age = [15,17,25,55,75]

The first comparison, if age<16, is false, because it is not true for every element in the array. The second comparison, elseif age<18, is also false. The third comparison, elseif age<70, is false as well, since not all of the ages are below 70. The result is Drivers over 70 require a special license—a result that won't please the other drivers in the group.

HINT

One common mistake new programmers make when using if statements is to overspecify the criteria. In the preceding example, it is enough to state that age < 18 in the elseif clause, because age cannot be less than 16 and still reach this statement. You don't need to specify age < 18 & age > = 16. If you overspecify the criteria, you risk defining a path for which there is no correct answer. For example, in the code

```
if age<16
    disp('Sorry - You"ll have to wait')
```

Figure 8.9

Flowchart using multiple if statements.

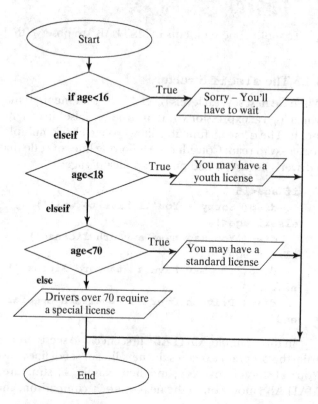

```
      elseif age<18 & age>16
         disp('You may have a youth license')
   elseif age<70 & age>18
         disp('You may have a standard license')
   elseif age>70
         disp('Drivers over 70 require a special license')

   end
```

there is no correct choice for age = 16, 18, or 70.

In general, elseif structures work well for scalars, but find is probably a better choice for matrices. Here's an example that uses find with an array of ages and generates a table of results in each category:

```
age = [15,17,25,55,75];
set1 = find(age<16);
set2 = find(age>=16 & age<18);
set3 = find(age>=18 & age<70);
set4 = find(age>=70);
fprintf('Sorry - You"ll have to wait - you"re only %3.0f
  \n',age(set1))
fprintf('You may have a youth license because you"re %3.0f
  \n',age(set2))
fprintf('You may have a standard license because you"re
  %3.0f \n',age(set3))
fprintf('Drivers over 70 require a special license. You"re
  %3.0f \n',age(set4))
```

These commands return

```
Sorry - You'll have to wait - you're only 15
You may have a youth license because you're 17
You may have a standard license because you're 25
You may have a standard license because you're 55
Drivers over 70 require a special license. You're 75
```

Since every find in this sequence is evaluated, it is necessary to specify the range completely (for example, age>=16 & age<18).

EXAMPLE 8.2

ASSIGNING GRADES

The if family of statements is used most effectively when the input is a scalar. Create a function to determine test grades based on the score and assuming a single input into the function. The grades should be based on the following criteria:

Grade	Score
A	90 to 100
B	80 to 90
C	70 to 80
D	60 to 70
E	<60

(*continued*)

1. State the problem
   Determine the grade earned on a test.
2. Describe the input and output

   Input   Single score, not an array

   Output   Letter grade

3. Develop a hand example
   85 should be a B
   But should 90 be an A or a B? We need to create more explicit criteria.

Grade	Score
A	≥90 to 100
B	≥80 and <90
C	≥70 and <80
D	≥60 and <70
E	>60

4. Develop a MATLAB® solution
   Outline the function, using the flowchart shown in Figure 8.10.

Figure 8.10
Flowchart for a grading scheme.

5. Test the solution

Now test the function in the command window:

```
grade(25)
ans =
E
grade(80)
ans =
B
grade(-52)
ans =
E
grade(108)
ans =
A
```

Notice that although the function seems to work properly, it returns grades for values over 100 and values less than 0. If you'd like, you can now go back and add the logic to exclude those values:

```
function results = grade(x)
%This function requires a scalar input
  if(x>=0 & x<=100)
    if(x>=90)
        results = 'A';
    elseif(x>=80)
        results = 'B';
    elseif(x>=70)
        results = 'C';
    elseif(x>=60)
        results = 'D';
    else
        results = 'E';
    end
  else
    results = 'Illegal Input';
end
```

An alternative strategy would be to use the error function.

```
function results = grade(x)
%This function requires a scalar input
  if(x<0 | x>100)
  error('Illegal Input')
  end
    if(x>=90)
      results = 'A';
    elseif(x>=80)
      results = 'B';
    elseif(x>=70)
      results = 'C';
    elseif(x>=60)
      results = 'D';
```

(*continued*)

```
                else
                    results = 'E';
            end
```

We can test the function again in the command window:

```
grade(-10)
ans =
Illegal Input
grade(108)
ans =
Illegal Input
```

This function will work great for scalars, but if you send a vector to the function, you may get some unexpected results, such as

```
score = [95,42,83,77];
grade(score)
ans =
E
```

PRACTICE EXERCISE 8.2

The `if` family of functions is particularly useful in functions. Write and test a function for each of these problems, assuming that the input to the function is a scalar. The correct answers can be found on the Pearson website.

1. Suppose the legal drinking age is 21 in your state. Write and test a function to determine whether a person is old enough to drink. If the user enters a negative age, use the `error` function to exit the function and to return an error message.

2. Many rides at amusement parks require riders to be a certain minimum height. Assume that the minimum height is 48″ for a certain ride. Write and test a function to determine whether the rider is tall enough. If the user enters a negative height, use the `error` function to exit the function and to return an error message.

3. When a part is manufactured, the dimensions are usually specified with a tolerance. Assume that a certain part needs to be 5.4 cm long, plus or minus 0.1 cm (5.4 ± 0.1 cm). Write a function to determine whether a part is within these specifications. If the user enters a negative length, use the `error` function to exit the function and to return an error message.

4. Unfortunately, the United States currently uses both metric and English units. Suppose the part in Exercise 3 was inspected by measuring the length in inches instead of centimeters. Write and test a function that determines whether the part is within specifications and that accepts input into the function in inches. If the user enters a negative length, use the `error` function to exit the function and to return an error message.

5. Many solid-fuel rocket engines consist of three stages. Once the first stage burns out, it separates from the missile and the second stage lights. Then the second stage burns out and separates, and the third stage lights. Finally,

once the third stage burns out, it also separates from the missile. Assume that the following data approximately represent the times during which each stage burns:

Stage 1	0–100 seconds
Stage 2	100–170 seconds
Stage 3	170–260 seconds

Write and test a function to determine whether the missile is in Stage 1 flight, Stage 2 flight, Stage 3 flight, or free flight (unpowered). If the user enters a negative time, use the `error` function to exit the function and to return an error message.

8.4.4 switch and case

The `switch/case` structure is often used when a series of programming path options exists for a given variable, depending on its value. The `switch/case` is similar to the `if/else/elseif`. As a matter of fact, anything you can do with `switch/case` could be done with `if/else/elseif`. However, the code is a bit easier to read with `switch/case`, a structure that allows you to choose between multiple outcomes, based on some criterion. The criterion can be either a scalar (a number) or a string. In practice, it is used more with strings than with numbers. The structure of `switch/case` is

```
switch  variable
case  option1
   code to be executed if variable is equal to option 1
case option2
   code to be executed if variable is equal to option 2
case option_n
   code to be executed if variable is equal to option n
otherwise
   code to be executed if variable is not equal to any of
      the options
end
```

Here's an example: Suppose you want to create a function that tells the user what the airfare is to one of three different cities:

```
city = input('Enter the name of a city in single quotes: ')
switch city
   case 'Boston'
     disp('$345')
   case 'Denver'
     disp('$150')
   case 'Honolulu'
     disp('Stay home and study')
   otherwise
     disp('Not on file')
end
```

If, when you run this script, you reply `'Boston'` at the prompt, MATLAB® responds

```
city =
Boston
$345
```

You can tell the `input` command to expect a string by adding "s" in a second field. This relieves the user of the awkward requirement of adding single quotes around any string input. With the added "s," the preceding code now reads:

```
city = input('Enter the name of a city: ','s')
switch city
 case 'Boston'
   disp('$345')
 case 'Denver'
   disp('$150')
 case 'Honolulu'
   disp('Stay home and study')
 otherwise
   disp('Not on file')
end
```

The `otherwise` portion of the **switch/case** structure is not required for the structure to work. However, you should include it if there is any way that the user could input a value not equal to one of the cases.

Switch/case structures are flowcharted exactly the same as `if/else` structures.

HINT

If you are a C programmer, you may have used `switch/case` in that language. One important difference in MATLAB® is that once a "true" case has been found, the program does not check the other cases.

EXAMPLE 8.3

BUYING GASOLINE

Figure 8.11
Gasoline is sold in both liters and gallons.

Four countries in the world do not officially use the metric system: the United States, the United Kingdom, Liberia, and Myanmar. Even in the United States, the practice is that some industries are almost completely metric, and others still use the English system of units. For example, any shade-tree mechanic will tell you that although older cars have a mixture of components—some metric and others English—newer cars (any car built after 1989) are almost completely metric. Wine is packaged in liters, but milk is packaged in gallons. Americans measure distance in miles, but power in watts. Confusion between metric and English units is common. American travelers to Canada are regularly confused because gasoline is sold by the liter in Canada, but by the gallon in the United States.

Imagine that you want to buy gasoline (see Figure 8.11). Write a program that:

- Asks the user whether he or she wants to request the gasoline in liters or in gallons.
- Prompts the user to enter how many units he or she wants to buy.
- Calculates the total cost to the user, assuming that gasoline costs $2.89 per gallon.

Use a `switch/case` structure.

1. State the problem
   Calculate the cost of a gasoline purchase.

2. Describe the input and output

Input	Specify gallons or liters
	Number of gallons or liters
Output	Cost in dollars, assuming $2.89 per gallon

3. Develop a hand example

If the volume is specified in gallons, the cost is

$$\text{volume} \times \$2.89.$$

So, for 10 gallons,

$$\text{cost} = 10 \text{ gallons} \times \$2.89/\text{gallon} = \$28.90.$$

If the volume is specified in liters, we need to convert liters to gallons and then calculate the cost:

$$\text{volume} = \text{liters} \times 0.264 \text{ gallon/liter}$$
$$\text{cost} = \text{volume} \times \$2.89$$

So, for 10 liters,

$$\text{volume} = 10 \text{ liters} \times 0.264 \text{ gallon/liter} = 2.64 \text{ gallons}$$
$$\text{cost} = 2.64 \text{ gallons} \times 2.89 = \$7.63.$$

4. Develop a MATLAB® solution

First create a flowchart (see Figure 8.12). Then convert the flowchart into pseudocode comments. Finally, add the MATLAB® code:

```
clear,clc
%Define the cost per gallon
 rate = 2.89;
%Ask the user to input gallons or liters
 unit = input('Enter gallons or liters\n ','s');
%Use a switch/case to determine the conversion factor
 switch unit
  case 'gallons'
     factor = 1;
  case 'liters'
    factor = 0.264;
  otherwise
    error('Not available')
end

%Ask the user how much gas he/she would like to buy
  volume = input( ['Enter the volume you would like to buy
  in ',unit,': \n'] );
  %Calculate the cost of the gas
    cost = volume * factor*rate;
  %Send the results to the screen
  fprintf('That will be $ %5.2f for %5.1f %s
          \n',cost,volume,unit)
```

There are several things to notice about this solution. First, the variable `unit` contains an array of character information. If you check the workspace window

(continued)

Figure 8.12
Flowchart to determine the cost of gasoline, using the `switch/case` structure.

after you run this program, you'll notice that `unit` is either a 1×6 character array (if you entered liters) or a 1×7 character array (if you entered gallons). On the line

```
unit = input('Enter gallons or liters ','s');
```

the second field, `'s'`, tells MATLAB® to expect a string as input. This allows the user to enter gallons or liters without the surrounding single quotes. On the line

```
volume = input('Enter the volume you would like to buy in
            ',unit,':'] );
```

we created a character array out of three components:

- The string `'Enter the volume you would like to buy in'`
- The character variable `unit`
- The string `':'`

By combining these three components, we were able to make the program prompt the user with either

```
Enter the volume you would like to buy in liters:
```

or

```
Enter the volume you would like to buy in gallons:
```

In the `fprintf` statement, we included a field for string input by using the placeholder `%s`:

```
fprintf('That will be $ %5.2f for %5.1f %s
        \n',cost,volume,unit)
```

This allowed the program to tell the users that the gasoline was measured either in gallons or in liters.

Finally, we used an **if** statement with the `error` function, so that if the user entered something besides gallons or liters, no calculations were performed and the program terminated.

5. Test the solution

We can test the solution by running the program three separate times, once for gallons, once for liters, and once for some unit not supported. The interaction in the command window for gallons is

```
Enter gallons or liters
gallons
Enter the volume you would like to buy in gallons:
10
That will be $ 28.90 for 10.0 gallons
```

For liters, the interaction is

```
Enter gallons or liters
liters
Enter the volume you would like to buy in liters:
10
That will be $ 7.63 for 10.0 liters
```

Finally, if you enter anything besides gallons or liters, the program sends an error message to the command window:

```
Enter gallons or liters
quarts
Not available
```

Since the program results are the same as the hand calculation, it appears that the program works as planned.

8.4.5 Menu

KEY IDEA

Graphical user interfaces like the menu box reduce the opportunity for user errors, such as spelling mistakes.

The `menu` function is often used in conjunction with a `switch/case` structure. This function causes a menu box to appear on the screen, with a series of buttons defined by the programmer.

```
input = menu('Message to the user','text for button
    1',' text for button 2', etc.)
```

Figure 8.13

The pop-up menu window.

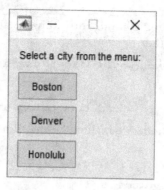

We can use the menu option in our previous airfare example to ensure that the user chooses only cities about which we have information. This also means that we don't need the otherwise syntax, since it is not possible to choose a city "not on file."

```
city = menu('Select a city from the menu:
   ','Boston','Denver','Honolulu')
switch city
    case 1
        disp('$345')
    case 2
        disp('$150')
    case 3
        disp('Stay home and study')
end
```

Notice that a case number has replaced the string in each case line. When the script is executed, the menu box shown in Figure 8.13 appears and waits for the user to select one of the buttons. If you choose Honolulu, MATLAB® will respond

```
city =
    3
Stay home and study.
```

Of course, you could suppress the output from the menu command, which was included here for clarity.

EXAMPLE 8.4

BUYING GASOLINE: A MENU APPROACH

In Example 8.3, we used a switch/case approach to determine whether the customer wanted to buy gasoline measured in gallons or liters. One problem with our program is that if the user can't spell, the program won't work. For example, if, when prompted for gallons or liters, the user enters

```
litters
```

The program will respond

```
Not available.
```

We can get around this problem by using a menu; then the user need only press a button to make a choice. We'll still use the switch/case structure, but will combine it with the menu.

1. **State the problem**
   Calculate the cost of a gasoline purchase.
2. **Describe the input and output**

   Input   Specify gallons or liters, using a menu
                  Number of gallons or liters

   Output   Cost in dollars, assuming $2.89 per gallon

3. **Develop a hand example**
   If the volume is specified in gallons, the cost is
   $$\text{volume} \times \$2.89.$$

   So, for 10 gallons,
   $$\cos t = 10 \text{ gallons} \times \$2.89/\text{gallon} = \$28.90.$$

   If the volume is specified in liters, we need to convert liters to gallons, then calculate the cost:
   $$\text{volume} = \text{liters} \times 0.264 \text{ gallon/liter}$$
   $$\cos t = \text{volume} \times \$2.89$$

   So, for 10 liters,
   $$\text{volume} = 10 \text{ liters} \times 0.264 \text{ gallon/liter} = 2.64 \text{ gallons}$$
   $$\cos t = 2.64 \text{ gallons} \times 2.89 = \$7.63$$

4. **Develop a MATLAB® solution**
   First, create a flowchart (see Figure 8.14). Then, convert the flowchart into pseudocode comments. Finally, add the MATLAB® code:

```
%Example 8.4 clear,clc
%Define the cost per gallon
 rate = 2.89;
%Ask the user to input gallons or liters, using a menu
 disp('Use the menu box to make your selection ')
 choice = menu('Measure the gasoline in liters or
gallons?','gallons','liters');
%Use a switch/case to determine the conversion factor
switch choice
   case 1
     factor = 1;
     unit = 'gallons'
   case 2
     factor = 0.264;
     unit = 'liters'
end

%Ask the user how much gas he/she would like to buy
 volume = input(['&#x2018;Enter the volume you would like to
  buy in ',unit,': \n'] );
%Calculate the cost of the gas
 cost = volume * factor*rate;
%Send the results to the screen
 fprintf('That will be $ %5.2f for %5.1f %s
\n',cost,volume,unit)
```

(continued)

Figure 8.14
Flowchart to determine
the cost of gasoline,
using a menu.

This solution is simpler than the one in Example 8.3 because there is no chance for bad input. There are a few things to notice, however.

When we define the choice by using the menu function, the result is a number, not a character array:

```
choice = menu('Measure the gasoline in liters or
gallons?','gallons','liters');
```

You can check this by consulting the workspace window, in which the choice is listed as a 1 × 1 double-precision number.

Because we did not use the input command to define the variable unit, which is a string (a character array), we needed to specify the value of unit as part of the case calculations:

```
case 1
  factor = 1;
  unit = 'gallons'
case 2
  factor = 0.264;
  unit = 'liters'
```

Doing this allows us to use the value of unit in the output to the command window, both in the disp command and in fprintf.

5. Test the solution

As in Example 8.3, we can test the solution by running the program, but this time we need to try it only twice—once for gallons and once for liters. The interaction in the command window for gallons is

```
Use the menu box to make your selection
```

```
Enter the volume you would like to buy in gallons:
10
That will be $ 28.90 for 10.0 gallons
```

For liters, the interaction is

```
Use the menu box to make your selection
Enter the volume you would like to buy in liters:
10
That will be $ 7.63 for 10.0 liters
```

These values match those in the hand solution, and have the added advantage that you can't misspell any of the input.

PRACTICE EXERCISE 8.3

Use the `switch/case` structure to solve these problems. The correct answers can be found on the Pearson website.

1. Create a program that prompts the user to enter his or her year in school—freshman, sophomore, junior, or senior. The input will be a string. Use the `switch/case` structure to determine which day finals will be given for each group—Monday for freshmen, Tuesday for sophomores, Wednesday for juniors, and Thursday for seniors.

2. Repeat Exercise 1, but this time with a menu.

3. Create a program to prompt the user to enter the number of candy bars he or she would like to buy. The input will be a number. Use the `switch/case` structure to determine the bill, where

$$1 \text{ bar} = \$0.75$$
$$2 \text{ bars} = \$1.25$$
$$3 \text{ bars} = \$1.65$$

more than 3 bars = $\$1.65 + \$0.30$ (number ordered $- 3$).

Figure 8.15
Using debugging tools is an effective way to evaluate how MATLAB® moves through the code as it executes.

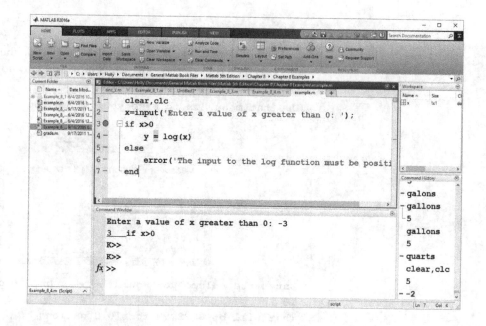

8.5 DEBUGGING

As the code we are writing becomes more complicated, the debugging tools available in MATLAB® become more valuable. Consider the simple program shown in Figure 8.15 that demonstrates the use of the if/else structure. A breakpoint has been added on line three. When the code is executed by selecting the save and run icon, it will first pause on line two waiting for the user to enter a number. Once the number has been entered, the program moves to line three and stops because the breakpoint has been encountered. Selecting the **Step** icon will progress the execution through the code one line at a time, allowing the programmer to observe the effect of each line of code.

Also notice that the folding capability available in MATLAB® has been activated for if/else structures. This was accomplished by selecting the Home tab then

Preferences -> Editor/Debugger -> Code Folding

and activating code folding for if/else structures. A visual cue is created, making it easier to keep track of which lines of code are included in the structure.

SUMMARY

Sections of computer code can be categorized as sequences, selection structures, and repetition structures. Sequences are lists of instructions that are executed in order. Selection structures allow the programmer to define criteria (conditional statements) that the program uses to choose execution paths. Repetition structures define loops in which a sequence of instructions is repeated until some criterion is met (also defined by conditional statements).

MATLAB® uses the standard mathematical relational operators, such as greater than (>) and less than (<). The not-equal-to (~=) operator's form is not usually seen in mathematics texts. MATLAB® also includes logical operators such as *and* (&)

and *or* ($|$). These operators are used in conditional statements, allowing MATLAB® to make decisions regarding which portions of the code to execute.

The `find` command is unique to MATLAB®. It allows the user to specify a condition by using both logical and relational operators. The command is then used to identify elements of a matrix that meet the condition.

Although the `if`, `else`, and `elseif` commands can be used for both scalars and matrix variables, they are useful primarily for scalars. These commands allow the programmer to identify alternative computing paths on the basis of the results of conditional statements.

The following MATLAB® summary lists and briefly describes all the special characters, commands, and functions that were defined in this chapter:

Special Characters	
$<$	less than
$<=$	less than or equal to
$>$	greater than
$>=$	greater than or equal to
$==$	equal to
$\sim=$	not equal to
$\&$	and
$|$	or
$\sim$	not
$\&\&$	short circuit and (used with scalars)
$||$	short circuit or (used with scalars)

MATLAB® SUMMARY

Commands and Functions	
`all`	checks to see if a criterion is met by all the elements in an array
`any`	checks to see if a criterion is met by any of the elements in an array
`case`	selection structure
`else`	defines the path if the result of an if statement is false
`elseif`	defines the path if the result of an if statement is false and specifies a new logical test
`end`	identifies the end of a control structure
`error`	sends a message to the command window and aborts the program
`find`	determines which elements in a matrix meet the input criterion
`if`	checks a condition, resulting in either true or false
`menu`	creates a menu to use as an input vehicle
`otherwise`	part of the case selection structure
`switch`	part of the case selection structure

KEY TERMS

code folding	logical condition	repetition
control structure	logical operator	selection
index	loop	sequence
local variable	relational operator	subscript

PROBLEMS

Logical Operators: `Find`

8.1 A sensor that monitors the temperature of a backyard hot-tub records the data shown in Table P8.1.

Table P8.1 Hot-Tub Temperature Data

Time of Day	Temperature (°F)
00:00	100
01:00	101
02:00	102
03:00	103
04:00	103
05:00	104
06:00	104
07:00	105
08:00	106
09:00	106
10:00	106
11:00	105
12:00	104
13:00	103
14:00	101
15:00	100
16:00	99
17:00	100
18:00	102
19:00	104
20:00	106
21:00	107
22:00	105
23:00	104
24:00	104

(a) The temperature should never exceed 105°F. Use the `find` function to find the index numbers of the temperatures that exceed the maximum allowable temperature.

(b) Use the `length` function with the results from part (a) to determine how many times the maximum allowable temperature was exceeded.

(c) Determine at what times the temperature exceeded the maximum allowable temperature, using the index numbers found in part (a).

(d) The temperature should never be lower than 102°F. Use the `find` function together with the `length` function to determine how many times the temperature was less than the minimum allowable temperature.

(e) Determine at what times the temperature was less than the minimum allowable temperature.

(f) Determine at what times the temperature was within the allowable limits (i.e., between 102°F and 105°F, inclusive).

Figure P8.3
Solid-fuel rocket booster to a Titan missile. (NASA Headquarters)

(g) Use the max function to determine the maximum temperature reached and the time at which it occurred.

8.2 The height of a rocket (in meters) can be represented by the following equation:

$$\text{height} = 2.13\,t^2 - 0.0013\,t^4 + 0.000034\,t^{4.751}\}$$

Create a vector of time (t) values from 0 to 100 at 2-second intervals.

(a) Use the find function to determine when the rocket hits the ground to within 2 seconds. (*Hint:* The value of height will be positive for all values until the rocket hits the ground.)

(b) Use the max function to determine the maximum height of the rocket and the corresponding time.

(c) Create a plot with t on the horizontal axis and height on the vertical axis for times until the rocket hits the ground. Be sure to add a title and axis labels.*

8.3 Solid-fuel rocket engines are used as boosters for the space shuttle, in satellite launch vehicles, and in weapons systems (see Figure P8.3). The propellant is a solid combination of fuel and oxidizer, about the consistency of an eraser. For the space shuttle, the fuel component is aluminum and the oxidizer is ammonium perchlorate, held together with an epoxy resin "glue." The propellant mixture is poured into a motor case, and the resin is allowed to cure under controlled conditions. Because the engines are extremely large, they are cast in segments, each requiring several "batches" of propellant to fill. (Each engine contains over 1.1 million pounds of propellant!) This casting–curing process is sensitive to temperature, humidity, and pressure. If the conditions aren't just right, the fuel could ignite or the properties of the propellant grain (which means its shape; the term *grain* is borrowed from artillery) might be degraded. Solid-fuel rocket engines are extremely expensive as well as dangerous and clearly must work right every time, or the results will be disastrous. Failures can cause loss of human life and irreplaceable scientific data and equipment. Highly public failures can destroy a company. Actual processes are tightly monitored and controlled. However, for our purposes, consider these general criteria:

> The temperature should remain between 115°F and 125°F.
> The humidity should remain between 40% and 60%.
> The pressure should remain between 100 and 200 Torr.

Imagine that the data in Table P8.3 were collected during a casting–curing process.

Table P8.3 Casting–Curing Data

Batch Number	Temperature (°F)	Humidity (%)	Pressure (Torr)
1530	116	45	110
1240	114	42	115
2380	118	41	120
1470	124	38	95
3590	126	61	118

Source: Pearson Education

---

*From Etter, Kuncicky, and Moore, *Introduction to Matlab* 7 (Upper Saddle River, NJ: Pearson/Prentice Hall, 2005).

(a) Use the `find` command to determine which batches did and did not meet the criterion for temperature.

(b) Use the `find` command to determine which batches did and did not meet the criterion for humidity.

(c) Use the `find` command to determine which batches did and did not meet the criterion for pressure.

(d) Use the `find` command to determine which batches failed for any reason and which passed.

(e) Use your results from the previous questions, along with the `length` command, to determine what percentage of engines passed or failed on the basis of each criterion and to determine the total passing rate.

8.4 Two gymnasts are competing with each other. Their scores are shown in Table P8.4.

Table P8.4 Gymnastics Scores

Event	Gymnast 1	Gymnast 2
Pommel horse	9.821	9.700
Vault	9.923	9.925
Floor	9.624	9.83
Rings	9.432	9.987
High bar	9.534	9.354
Parallel bars	9.203	9.879

(a) Write a program that uses `find` to determine how many events each gymnast won.

(b) Use the `mean` function to determine each gymnast's average score.

8.5 Use find to create a function called **f** that satisfies the following criteria:

$$\text{For values of } x > 2, f(x) = x^2$$
$$\text{For values of } x \le 2, f(x) = 2x$$

Plot your results for values of x from -3 to 5. Choose your spacing to create a smooth curve. You should notice a break in the curve at $x = 2$. What happens if you try to do this problem using an `if/else` structure.

8.6 Create a function called g that satisfies the following criteria:

$$\text{For } x < -\pi, \qquad\qquad g(x) = -1$$
$$\text{For } x \ge -\pi \text{ and } x \le \pi, \qquad g(x) = \cos(x)$$
$$\text{For } x > \pi, \qquad\qquad g(x) = -1$$

Plot your results for values of x from -2π to $+2\pi$. Choose your spacing to create a smooth curve.

8.7 A file named **temp.dat** contains information collected from a set of thermocouples. The data in the file are shown in Table P8.7. The first column consists of time measurements (one for each hour of the day), and the remaining columns correspond to temperature measurements at different points in a process.

(a) Write a program that prints the index numbers (rows and columns) of temperature data values greater than 85.0. (*Hint:* You'll need to use the find command.)

(b) Find the index numbers (rows and columns) of temperature data values less than 65.0.

Table P8.7 Temperature Data

Hour	Temp1	Temp2	Temp3
1	68.70	58.11	87.81
2	65.00	58.52	85.69
3	70.38	52.62	71.78
4	70.86	58.83	77.34
5	66.56	60.59	68.12
6	73.57	61.57	57.98
7	73.57	67.22	89.86
8	69.89	58.25	74.81
9	70.98	63.12	83.27
10	70.52	64.00	82.34
11	69.44	64.70	80.21
12	72.18	55.04	69.96
13	68.24	61.06	70.53
14	76.55	61.19	76.26
15	69.59	54.96	68.14
16	70.34	56.29	69.44
17	73.20	65.41	94.72
18	70.18	59.34	80.56
19	69.71	61.95	67.83
20	67.50	60.44	79.59
21	70.88	56.82	68.72
22	65.99	57.20	66.51
23	72.14	62.22	77.39
24	74.87	55.25	89.53

(c) Find the maximum temperature in the file, and the corresponding hour value and thermocouple number.

8.8 The amount of sea ice surrounding the Antarctic continent varies dramatically during the year, and from year to year (see Figure P8.8).

Figure P8.8
Antarctic sea ice extent changes dramatically through the year. (National Snow and Ice Data Center)

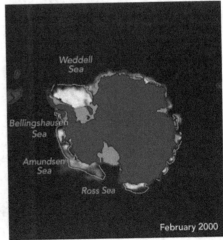

The following data, shown in Table P8.8, were obtained from the NOAA National Centers for Environmental Information website and represent the extent of the sea ice during September when the maximum usually occurs, and February when the minimum usually occurs.

(a) Plot both the September values and February values versus the year, and add a line representing the average ice extent for 1979–2010 of 3.04 million square kilometres for February and 18.79 million square kilometres for September.

Table P8.8 Antarctic Sea Ice Extent

Year	September Average Extent (millions of square kilometers)	February Average Extent (millions of square kilometers)
1979	18.40	3.10
1980	19.06	2.83
1981	18.90	2.87
1982	18.63	3.11
1983	18.84	3.03
1984	18.65	2.71
1985	19.02	2.78
1986	17.97	3.19
1987	18.65	3.24
1988	18.64	2.83
1989	18.27	2.99
1990	18.44	3.01
1991	18.56	3.07
1992	18.41	2.86
1993	18.67	2.46
1994	18.96	3.15
1995	18.73	3.49
1996	18.86	2.89
1997	19.15	2.42
1998	19.14	2.99
1999	19.02	2.90
2000	19.12	2.84
2001	18.40	3.73
2002	18.18	2.86
2003	18.57	3.87
2004	19.13	3.59
2005	19.14	2.93
2006	19.36	2.65
2007	19.25	2.88
2008	18.50	3.87
2009	19.20	2.92
2010	19.22	3.16
2011	18.95	2.49
2012	19.43	3.57
2013	19.82	3.87
2014	20.10	3.86
2015	18.69	3.69
2016		2.75

(b) Use the `find` command to determine which years exceeded the average September values for 1979–2010.

(c) Use the `find` command to determine which years were lower than the average February values for 1979–2010.

8.9 Sea ice in the Arctic Ocean increases and decreases annually. Declines have even made it possible for shipping to occur through the "Northwest Passage" in recent summer seasons (see Figure P8.9).

Figure P8.9

The extent of arctic sea ice varies dramatically during the year. Recent decreases in the summer extent have opened up the "Northwest Passage" from the Atlantic to the Pacific oceans. (NOAA)

The data shown in Table P8.9 were obtained from the NOAA National Centers for Environmental Information website and represent the extent of the sea ice during September when the minimum usually occurs, and March when the maximum usually occurs.

(a) Plot both the September values and March values versus the year, and add a line representing the average ice extent for 1979–2010 of 15.52 million square kilometres for March and 6.51 million square kilometres for September.

(b) Use the `find` command to determine which years exceeded the average September values for 1979–2010.

(c) Use the `find` command to determine which years were lower than the average March values for 1979–2010.

Table P8.9 Arctic Sea Ice Extent

Year	September Average Extent (millions of square kilometers)	March Average Extent (millions of square kilometers)
1979	7.19	16.48
1980	7.83	16.15
1981	7.24	15.65
1982	7.44	16.17
1983	7.51	16.13
1984	7.10	15.65

(*continued*)

Table P8.9 (continued)

Year	September Average Extent (millions of square kilometers)	March Average Extent (millions of square kilometers)
1985	6.91	16.09
1986	7.53	16.10
1987	7.47	15.99
1988	7.48	16.16
1989	7.03	15.54
1990	6.23	15.90
1991	6.54	15.52
1992	7.54	15.50
1993	6.50	15.90
1994	7.18	15.62
1995	6.12	15.35
1996	7.87	15.16
1997	6.73	15.61
1998	6.55	15.69
1999	6.23	15.45
2000	6.31	15.30
2001	6.74	15.64
2002	5.95	15.46
2003	6.13	15.52
2004	6.04	15.08
2005	5.56	14.77
2006	5.91	14.45
2007	4.29	14.66
2008	4.72	15.27
2009	5.38	15.16
2010	4.92	15.14
2011	4.61	14.60
2012	3.62	15.26
2013	5.35	15.10
2014	5.28	14.83
2015	4.63	14.39
2016		14.43

8.10 The Colorado River Drainage Basin covers parts of seven western states. A series of dams has been constructed on the Colorado River and its tributaries to store runoff water and to generate low-cost hydroelectric power (see Figure P8.10). The ability to regulate the flow of water has made the growth of agriculture and population in these arid desert states possible. Even during periods of extended drought, a steady, reliable source of water and electricity has been available to the basin states. Lake Powell is one of these reservoirs. The file **lake_powell.dat** contains data on the water level in the reservoir for the 8 years from 2008 to 2015. These data are shown in Table P8.10. Use the data in the file to answer the following questions:

(a) Determine the average elevation of the water level for each year, and for the 8-year period over which the data were collected.

Figure P8.10

Glen Canyon Dam at Lake Powell. (David Toussaint/ Getty images, Inc.)

Table P8.10 Water-Level Data for Lake Powell, Measured in Feet above Sea Level

	2008	2009	2010	2011	2012	2013	2014	2015
January	3590.66	3614.17	3622.14	3620.55	3636.91	3604.42	3578.69	3593.57
February	3590.66	3612.05	3620.16	3614.95	3635.28	3601.47	3575.55	3592.23
March	3589.77	3610.43	3619.41	3610.73	3635.33	3598.96	3574.76	3591.02
April	3594.09	3611.26	3620.5	3611.93	3635.76	3596.53	3577.56	3590.18
May	3610.81	3629.09	3625.96	3623.13	3636.83	3599.44	3589.38	3597.27
June	3631.05	3640.49	3638.82	3648.98	3633.9	3600.07	3609.19	3613.54
July	3633	3641.14	3636.52	3660.86	3628.45	3594.17	3608.05	3612.62
August	3629.55	3637.5	3634.55	3655.34	3623.62	3589.64	3605.82	3609.07
September	3626.9	3635.37	3633.66	3653.01	3621.56	3591.25	3605.53	3606.01
October	3623.82	3633.52	3634.08	3650.27	3619.46	3590.88	3605.57	3606.44
November	3621.9	3631.1	3630.31	3645.67	3615.1	3587.9	3601.87	3605.47
December	3617.89	3626.22	3626.54	3639.75	3609.82	3584.43	3597.75	3600.8

(b) Determine how many months each year exceed the overall average for the 8-year period.

(c) Create a report that lists the month (number) and the year for each of the months that exceed the overall average. For example, June is month 6.

(d) Determine the average elevation of the water for each month for the 8-year period.

Note: This problem should be solved using the `find` function, the `mean` function, and the `length` function. Programmers with previous experience may be tempted to use a loop structure, which is not required.

IF STRUCTURES

8.11 Create a program that prompts the user to enter a scalar value of temperature. If the temperature is greater than 98.6°F, send a message to the command window telling the user that he or she has a fever.

8.12 Create a program that first prompts the user to enter a value for **x** and then prompts the user to enter a value for y. If the value of **x** is greater than the value of y, send a message to the command window telling the user that **x > y**. If **x** is less than or equal to y, send a message to the command window telling the user that **y > = x**.

8.13 The inverse sine (asin) and inverse cosine (acos) functions are valid only for inputs between -1 and $+1$, because both the sine and the cosine have values only between -1 and $+1$ (see Figure P8.13). MATLAB® interprets the result of asin or acos for a value outside the range as a complex number. For example, we might have

```
acos(-2)
ans =
    3.1416 - 1.3170i
```

which is a questionable mathematical result. Create a function called my_asin that accepts a single value of **x** and checks to see if it is between -1 and $+1$ ($-1 <= x <= 1$). If x is outside the range, send an error message to the screen. If it is inside the allowable range, return the value of asin.

Figure P8.13
The sine function varies between -1 and $+1$. Thus, the inverse sine (asin) is not defined for values greater than 1 and values less than -1.

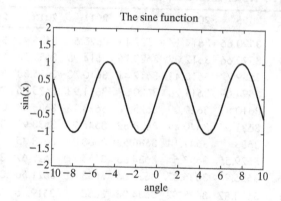

8.14 Create a program that prompts the user to enter a scalar value for the outside air temperature. If the temperature is equal to or above 80°F, send a message to the command window telling the user to wear shorts. If the temperature is between 60°F and 80°F, send a message to the command window telling the user that it is a beautiful day. If the temperature is equal to or below 60°F, send a message to the command window telling the user to wear a jacket or coat.

8.15 Suppose the following matrix represents the number of saws ordered from your company each month over the last year:

```
saws = [1,4,5,3,7,5,3,10,12,8,7,4]
```

All the numbers should be zero or positive.

(a) Use an if statement to check whether any of the values in the matrix are invalid. (Evaluate the whole matrix at once in a single if statement.) Send the message "All valid" or else "Invalid number found" to the screen, depending on the results of your analysis.

(b) Change the saws matrix to include at least one negative number, and check your program to make sure that it works for both cases.

8.16 Most large companies encourage employees to save by matching their contributions to a 401(k) plan. The government limits how much you can save in these plans, because they shelter income from taxes until the money is withdrawn during your retirement. The amount you can save is tied to your income, as is the amount your employer can contribute. The government will allow you to save additional amounts without the tax benefit. These plans change from year to year, so this example is just a made-up "what if."

Suppose the Quality Widget Company has the savings plan described in Table P8.16. Create a function that finds the total yearly contribution to your savings plan, based on your salary and the percentage you contribute. Remember, the total contribution consists of the employee contribution and the company contribution.

SWITCH/CASE

Table P8.16 Quality Widget Company Savings Plan

Income	Maximum You Can Save Tax Free	Maximum the Company Will Match
Up to $30,000	10%	10%
Between $30,000 and $60,000	10%	10% of the first $30,000 and 5% of the amount above $30,000
Between $60,000 and $100,000	10% of the first $60,000 and 8% of the amount above $60,000	10% of the first $30,000 and 5% of the amount between $30,000 and $60,000; nothing for the remainder above $60,000
Above $100,000	10% of the first $60,000 and 8% of the amount between $60,000 and $100,000; nothing on the amount above $100,000	Nothing—highly compensated employees are exempt from this plan and participate in stock options instead

Figure P8.17
Regular polygons.

8.17 In order to have a closed geometric figure composed of straight lines (see Figure P8.17), the angles in the figure must add to

$$(n - 2)(180 \text{ degrees})$$

where n is the number of sides.

(a) Prove this statement to yourself by creating a vector called **n** from 3 to 6 and calculating the angle sum from the formula. Compare what you know about geometry with your answer.

(b) Write a program that prompts the user to enter one of the following:

  triangle
  square
  pentagon
  hexagon

Use the input to define the value of **n** via a switch/case structure; then use **n** to calculate the sum of the interior angles in the figure.

(c) Reformulate your program from part (b) so that it uses a menu.

8.18 At a local university, each engineering major requires a different number of credits for graduation. For example, recently the requirements were as follows:

Civil Engineering	130
Chemical Engineering	130
Computer Engineering	122
Electrical Engineering	126.5
Mechanical Engineering	129

Prompt the user to select an engineering program from a menu. Use a switch/case structure to send the minimum number of credits required for graduation back to the command window.

8.19 The easiest way to draw a star in MATLAB® is to use polar coordinates. You simply need to identify points on the circumference of a circle, and draw lines between those points. For example, to draw a five-pointed star, start at the top of the circle ($\theta = \pi/2$, $r = 1$) and work counterclockwise (see Figure P8.19).

Figure P8.19
Steps required to draw a five-pointed star in polar coordinates.

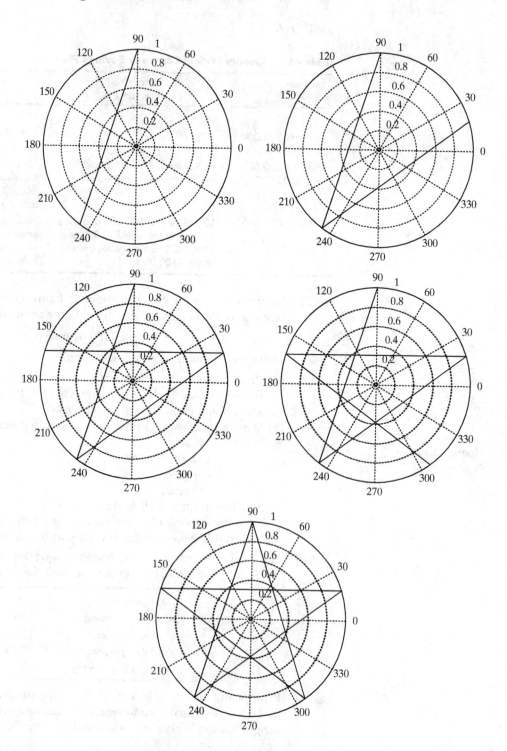

Prompt the user to specify either a five-pointed or a six-pointed star, using a menu. Then create the star in a MATLAB® figure window. Note that a six-pointed star is made of three triangles and requires a strategy different from that used to create a five-pointed star.

CHALLENGE PROBLEMS

8.20 Most major airports have separate lots for long-term and short-term parking. The cost to park depends on the lot you select, and how long you stay. Consider this rate structure from the Salt Lake International Airport during the summer of 2016.

- Long-Term (Economy) Parking
  - The first hour is $2.00, and each additional hour or fraction thereof is $1.00
  - Daily maximum $9.00
  - Weekly maximum $60.00
- Short-Term Parking
  - The first 30 minutes are $2.00 and each additional 20 minutes or fraction thereof is $1.00
  - Daily maximum $32.00

Write a program that asks the user the following:

- Which lot are you using?
- How many weeks, hours, days, and minutes did you park? Your program should then calculate the parking bill.

9 Repetition Structures

Objectives

After reading this chapter, you should be able to:

- Write and use `for` loops.
- Write and use `while` loops.
- Create midpoint break structures.
- Measure the time required to execute program components.
- Understand how to improve program execution times.

INTRODUCTION

A way to think of a computer program (not just MATLAB®) is to consider how the statements that compose it are organized. Usually, sections of computer code can be categorized as *sequences, selection structures,* and *repetition structures.* The previous chapter described selection structures; in this chapter, we will focus on repetition structures. As a rule of thumb, if a section of code is repeated more than three times, it is a good candidate for a repetition structure.

Repetition structures are often called loops. All loops consist of five basic parts:

- A parameter to be used in determining whether or not to end the loop
- Initialization of this parameter
- A way to change the parameter each time through the loop. (If you don't change it, the loop will never stop executing.)
- A comparison, using the parameter, to a criterion used to decide when to end the loop
- Calculations to do inside the loop

KEY IDEA

Loops allow you to repeat sequences of commands until some criterion is met.

KEY IDEA

Use for loops when you know how many times you need to repeat a sequence of commands.

KEY IDEA

Use while loops when you don't know how many times a sequence of commands will need to be repeated.

MATLAB® supports two different types of loops: the for loop, and the while loop. Two additional commands, break and continue, can be used to create a third type of loop, called a midpoint break loop. The for loop is the easiest choice when you know how many times you need to repeat the loop. While loops are the easiest choice when you need to keep repeating the instructions until a criterion is met. Midpoint break loops are useful for situations where the commands in the loop must be executed at least once, but where the decision to exit the loop is based on some criterion. If you have previous programming experience, you may be tempted to use loops extensively. However, in many cases you can compose MATLAB® programs that avoid loops, either by using the find command or by vectorizing the code. (In vectorization, we operate on entire vectors at a time instead of one element at a time.) It's a good idea to avoid loops if a vectorized solution is possible, because vectorized programs run faster and often require fewer programming steps.

9.1 FOR LOOPS

The structure of the for loop is simple. The first line identifies the loop and defines an index, which is a number that changes on each pass through the loop, and is used to determine when to end the repetitions. After the identification line comes the group of commands we want to execute. Finally, the end of the loop is identified by the command end. Thus, the structure of a for loop can be summarized as

```
for index = [matrix]
        commands to be executed
end.
```

The loop is executed once for each element of the index matrix identified in the first line. Here's a really simple example:

```
for k = [1,3,7]
  k
end
```

During the first pass through the loop, k is assigned a value of 1, the first value in the k matrix. During the next pass the value of k is modified to 3, the second value in the k matrix. Each time through the loop, k is modified and assigned to subsequent values from the index matrix. This example code returns

```
k =
  1
k =
  3
k =
  7 .
```

The index in this case is k. Programmers often use k as an index variable, as a matter of style. The index matrix can also be defined with the colon operator or, in a number of other ways as well. Here's an example of code that finds the value of 5 raised to powers between 1 and 3:

```
for
k = 1:3
    a = 5^k
end
```

On the first line, the index, k, is defined as the matrix [1, 2, 3]. The first time through the loop, k is assigned a value of 1, and 5^1 is calculated. Then the loop repeats, but now k is equal to 2, and 5^2 is calculated. The last time through the loop, k is equal to 3, and 5^3 is calculated. Because the statements in the loop are repeated three times, the value of a is displayed three times in the command window:

```
a =
    5
a =
    25
a =
    125
```

Although we defined k as a matrix in the first line of the for loop, because k is an index number when it is used in the loop, it can equal only one value at a time. After we finish executing the loop, if we call for k, it has only one value: the value of the index the final time through the loop. For the preceding example,

```
k
```

returns

```
k =
    3.
```

Notice that k is listed as a 1×1 matrix in the workspace window.

A common way to use a for loop is in defining a new matrix. Consider, for example, the following code:

```
for
k = 1:5
    a (k) = k^2
end
```

This loop defines a new matrix, **a**, one element at a time. Since the program repeats its set of instructions five times, a new element is added to the **a** matrix each time through the loop, with the following output in the command window:

```
a =
    1
a =
    1    4
a =
    1    4    9
a =
    1    4    9    16
a =
    1    4    9    16    25
```

HINT

Most computer programs do not have MATLAB®'s ability to handle matrices so easily; therefore, they rely on loops similar to the one just presented to define arrays. It would be easier to create the vector a in MATLAB® with the code

```
k = 1:5
a = k.^2
```

which returns

```
k =
    1    2    3    4    5
a =
    1    4    9   16   25
```

This is an example of *vectorizing* the code.

Another common use for a for loop is to combine it with an if statement and determine how many times something is true. For example, in the list of test scores shown in the first line, how many are above 90?

```
scores [76,45,98,97];
count = 0;
for k=1:length(scores)
  if scores(k)>90
     count = count + 1;
  end
end
disp (count)
```

The variable count is initialized as zero, then each time through the loop, if the score is greater than 90, the count is incremented by 1. Notice that the length function was used to determine how many times the for loop should repeat. In this case

```
length (scores)
```

is equal to four, the number of values in the *scores* array.

Most of the time, for loops are created, which use an index matrix that is a single row. However, if a two-dimensional matrix is defined in the index specification, MATLAB® uses an entire column as the index each time through the loop. For example, suppose we define the index matrix as

$$k = \begin{bmatrix} 1 & 2 & 3 \\ 1 & 4 & 9 \\ 1 & 8 & 27 \end{bmatrix}$$

Then

```
for k = [1, 2, 3; 1, 4, 9; 1, 8, 27]
  a = k'
end
```

returns

```
a =
    1    1    1
a =
    2    4    8
a =
    3    9   27.
```

Notice that k was transposed when it was set equal to a, so our results are rows instead of columns. We did this to make the output easier to read.

We can summarize the use of for loops with the following rules:

- The loop starts with a for statement and ends with the word end.
- The first line in the loop defines the number of times the loop will repeat, using an index matrix.
- The index of a for loop must be a variable. (The index is the number that changes each and every time through the loop.) Although k is often used as the symbol for the index, any variable name may be employed. The use of k is a matter of style.
- Any of the techniques learned to define a matrix can be used to define the index matrix. One common approach is to use the colon operator, as in

    for index = start:inc:final

- If the expression is a row vector, the elements are used one at a time—once for each time through the loop.
- If the expression is a two-dimensional matrix (this alternative is not common), each time through the loop, the index will contain the next *column* in the matrix. This means that the index will be a column vector.
- Once you've completed a for loop, the index variable retains the last value used.
- for loops can often be avoided by vectorizing the code.

The basic flowchart for a for loop includes a diamond, which reflects the fact that a for loop starts each pass with a check to see if there is a new value in the index matrix (see Figure 9.1). If there isn't, the loop is terminated, and the program continues with the statements after the loop.

Figure 9.1
Flowchart for a for loop.

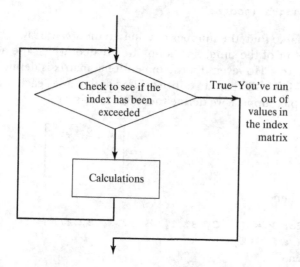

EXAMPLE 9.1

CREATING A DEGREES-TO-RADIANS TABLE

Although it would be much easier to use MATLAB®'s vector capability to create a degrees-to-radians table, we can demonstrate the use of `for` loops with this example.

1. **State the problem**
   Create a table that converts angle values from degrees to radians, from 0 to 360 degrees, in increments of 10 degrees.
2. **Describe the input and output**

   Input   An array of angle values in degrees

   Output   A table of angle values in both degrees and radians

3. **Develop a hand example**
   For 10 degrees,

$$\text{Radians} = (10)\frac{\pi}{180} = 0.1745.$$

4. **Develop a MATLAB® solution**
   First develop a flowchart (see Figure 9.2) to help you plan your code.

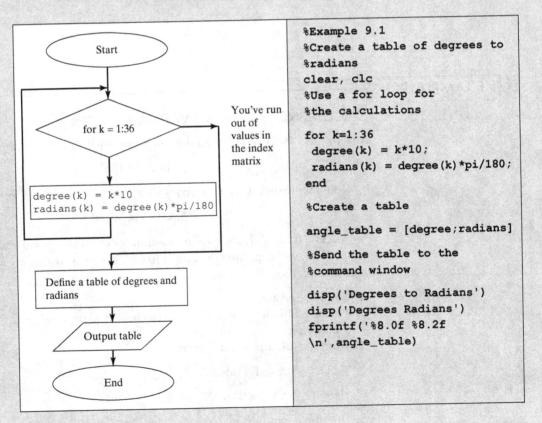

Figure 9.2
Flowchart for changing degrees to radians.

(continued)

The command window displays the following results:

```
Degrees to Radians

Degrees    Radians
   10       0.17
   20       0.35
   30       0.52        etc.
```

5. Test the solution

The value for 10 degrees calculated by MATLAB® is the same as the hand calculation.

Clearly, it is much easier to use MATLAB®'s vector capabilities for this calculation. You get exactly the same answer, and it takes significantly less computing time. This approach is called vectorization of your code, and is one of the strengths of MATLAB®. The vectorized code is

```
degrees = 0:10:360;
radians = degrees*pi/180;
angle_table = [degrees;radians]
disp('Degrees to Radians')
disp('Degrees Radians')
fprintf('%8.0f %8.2f \n',angle_table)
```

EXAMPLE 9.2

CALCULATING FACTORIALS WITH A FOR LOOP

A factorial is the product of all the integers from 1 to N. For example, 5 factorial is

$$1 \cdot 2 \cdot 3 \cdot 4 \cdot 5.$$

In mathematics texts, factorial is usually indicated with an exclamation point:

5! is five factorial.

MATLAB® contains a built-in function for calculating factorials, called `factorial`. However, suppose you would like to program your own factorial function called `fact`.

1. State the problem

Create a function called `fact` to calculate the factorial of any number. Assume scalar input.

2. Describe the input and output

Input   A scalar value N

Output   The value of N!

3. Develop a hand example

$$5! = 1 \cdot 2 \cdot 3 \cdot 4 \cdot 5 = 120$$

4. **Develop a MATLAB® solution**

   First develop a flowchart (see Figure 9.3) to help you plan your code.

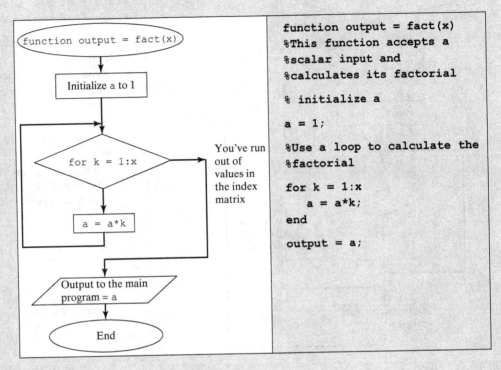

Figure 9.3
Flowchart for finding a factorial, using a `for` loop.

5. **Test the solution**

   Test the function in the command window:

   ```
   fact(5)
   ans =
       120
   ```

   This function works only if the input is a scalar. If an array is entered, the `for` loop does not execute, and the function returns a value of 1:

   ```
   x=1:10;
   fact(x)
   ans =
       1
   ```

   You can add an `if` statement to confirm that the input is a positive integer and not an array, as shown in the flowchart in Figure 9.4 and the accompanying code. Check the new function in the command window:

   ```
   fact(-4)
   Error using fact (line 8)
   Input must be a positive integer
   fact(x)
   Error using fact (line 8)
   Input must be a positive integer
   ```

   (continued)

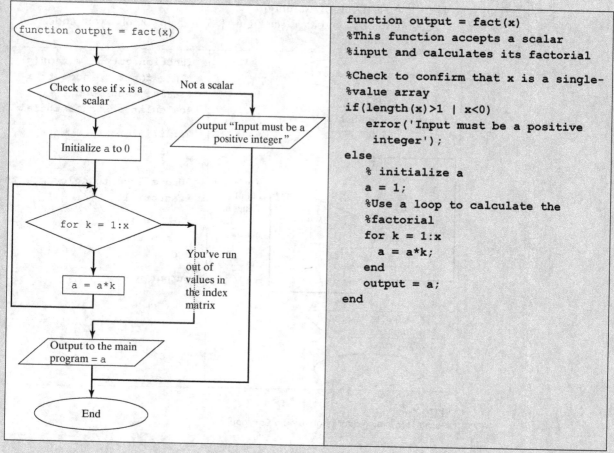

```
function output = fact(x)
%This function accepts a scalar
%input and calculates its factorial

%Check to confirm that x is a single-
%value array
if(length(x)>1 | x<0)
    error('Input must be a positive
    integer');
else
    % initialize a
    a = 1;
    %Use a loop to calculate the
    %factorial
    for k = 1:x
        a = a*k;
    end
    output = a;
end
```

In the flowchart:

- function output = fact(x)
- Check to see if x is a scalar — Not a scalar → output "Input must be a positive integer"
- Initialize a to 0
- for k = 1:x → You've run out of values in the index matrix
- a = a*k
- Output to the main program = a
- End

Figure 9.4
Flowchart for finding a factorial, including error checking.

PRACTICE EXERCISE 9.1

Use a `for` loop to solve the following problems. The correct answers can be found on the Pearson website.

1. Create a table that converts inches to feet.
2. Consider the following matrix of values:

$$x = [45, 23, 17, 34, 85, 33]$$

How many values are greater than 30? (Use a counter.)
3. Repeat Exercise 2, this time using the `find` command.
4. Use a `for` loop to sum the elements of the matrix in Problem 2. Check your results with the `sum` function. (Use the help feature if you don't know or remember how to use `sum`.)

5. Use a `for` loop to create a vector containing the first 10 elements in the harmonic series, that is,

$$1/1 \quad 1/2 \quad 1/3 \quad 1/4 \quad 1/5...1/10$$

6. Use a `for` loop to create a vector containing the first 10 elements in the alternating harmonic series, that is,

$$1/1 \quad -1/2 \quad 1/3 \quad -1/4 \quad 1/5...-1/10$$

9.2 WHILE LOOPS

`While` loops are similar to `for` loops. The big difference is the way MATLAB® decides how many times to repeat the loop. `While` loops continue until some criterion is met. The format for a `while` loop is as follows:

```
while  criterion
  commands to be executed
end
```

Here's an example:

```
k = 0;
while k<3
 k = k+1
end
```

In this case, we initialized a counter, k, before the loop. Then the loop repeated as long as k was less than 3. We incremented k by 1 every time through the loop, so that the loop repeated three times, giving

```
k =
  1
k =
  2
k =
  3.
```

Notice that when k=3, the criterion in the `while` statement

```
k<3
```

is false. Thus, when MATLAB® checks to see if it should make another pass through the loop, the program makes the decision (based on the criterion) to skip to the end of the structure.

We could use k as an index number to define a matrix or just as a counter. Most `for` loops can also be coded as `while` loops. Recall the `for` loop in the previous section used to calculate the first three powers of 5. The following `while` loop accomplishes the same task:

```
k = 0;
while k<3
  k = k+1;
  a(k) = 5^k
end
```

KEY IDEA

Any problem that can be solved using a `while` loop could also be solved using a `for` loop.

The code returns

```
a =
    5
a =
    5    25
a =
    5    25    125
```

Each time through the loop, another element is added to the matrix a. As another example, first initialize a:

```
a = 0;
```

Then find the first multiple of 3 that is greater than 10:

```
while(a<10)
    a = a + 3
end;
```

The first time through the loop, a is equal to 0, so the comparison is true. The next statement (a = a + 3) is executed, and the loop is repeated. This time a is equal to 3 and the condition is still true, so execution continues. In succession, we have

```
a =
    3
a =
    6
a =
    9
a =
   12.
```

The last time through the loop, a starts out as 9, then becomes 12 when 3 is added to 9. The comparison is made one final time, but since a is now equal to 12—which is greater than 10—the program skips to the end of the while loop and no longer repeats.

While loops can also be used to count how many times a condition is true by incorporating an if statement. Recall the test scores we counted in a for loop earlier. We can also count them with a while loop:

```
scores = [76,45,98,97];
count = 0;
k = 0;
while k<length(scores)
    k = k+1;
    if scores(k)>90
        count = count + 1;
    end
end
disp(count)
```

The variable count is used to count how many values are greater than 90. The variable k is used to count how many times the loop is executed.

The basic flow chart for a while loop (see Figure 9.5) is the same as that for a for loop (see Figure 9.4).

Figure 9.5
Flowchart for a while loop.

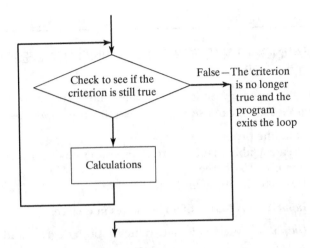

One common use for a while loop is error checking of user input. Consider a program where we prompt the user to input a positive number, and then we calculate the log base 10 of that value. We can use a while loop to confirm that the number is positive, and if it is not, to prompt the user to enter an allowed value. The program keeps on prompting for a positive value until the user finally enters a valid number.

```
x = input('Enter a positive value of x')
while (x<=0)
  disp('log(x) is not defined for negative numbers')
  x = input('Enter a positive value of x')
end
  y = log10(x);
fprintf('The log base 10 of %4.2f is %5.2f \n',x,y)
```

If, when the code is executed, a positive value of x is entered, the while loop does not execute (since x is not less than 0). If, instead, a zero or negative value is entered, the while loop is executed, an error message is sent to the command window, and the user is prompted to reenter the value of x. The while loop continues to execute until a positive value of x is finally entered.

KEY IDEA
It is easy to create an infinite loop with a while structure.

HINT

The variable used to control the while loop must be updated every time through the loop. If not, you'll generate an infinite loop. When a calculation is taking a long time to complete, you can confirm that the computer is really working on it by checking the lower left-hand corner for the "busy" indicator. If you want to exit the calculation manually, type Ctrl c. (Depress the Ctrl and c key at the same time.) Make sure that the command window is the active window when you execute this command.

HINT

Many computer texts and manuals indicate the control key with the ^symbol. This is confusing at best. The command ^C usually means to strike the Ctrl key and the c key at the same time.

EXAMPLE 9.3

CREATING A TABLE FOR CONVERTING DEGREES TO RADIANS WITH A WHILE LOOP

Just as we used a `for` loop to create a table for converting degrees to radians in Example 9.2, we can use a `while` loop for the same purpose.

1. State the problem

Create a table that converts degrees to radians, from 0 to 360 degrees, in increments of 10 degrees.

2. Describe the input and output

Input An array of angle values in degrees

Output A table of angle values in both degrees and radians

3. Develop a hand example

For 10 degrees,

$$\text{radians} = (10)\frac{\pi}{180} = 0.1745$$

4. Develop a MATLAB® solution

First develop a flowchart (see Figure 9.6) to help you plan your code.

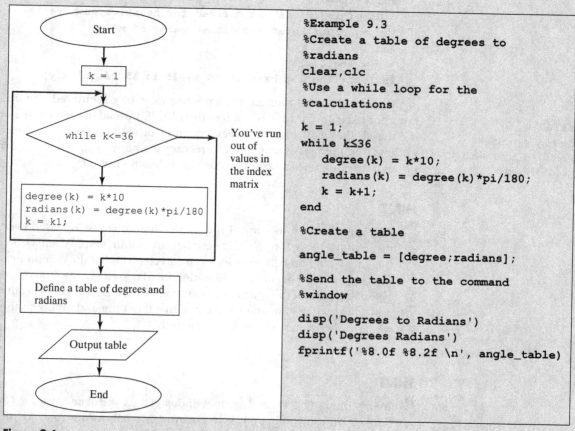

Figure 9.6

Flowchart for converting degrees to radians with a `while` loop.

The command window displays the following results:

```
Degrees to Radians

Degrees     Radians
   10         0.17
   20         0.35
   30         0.52        etc.
```

5. Test the solution
The value for 10 degrees calculated by MATLAB® is the same as the hand calculation.

EXAMPLE 9.4

CALCULATING FACTORIALS WITH A WHILE LOOP

Create a new function called `fact2` that uses a `while` loop to find *N*!. Include an `if` statement to check for negative numbers and to confirm that the input is a scalar.

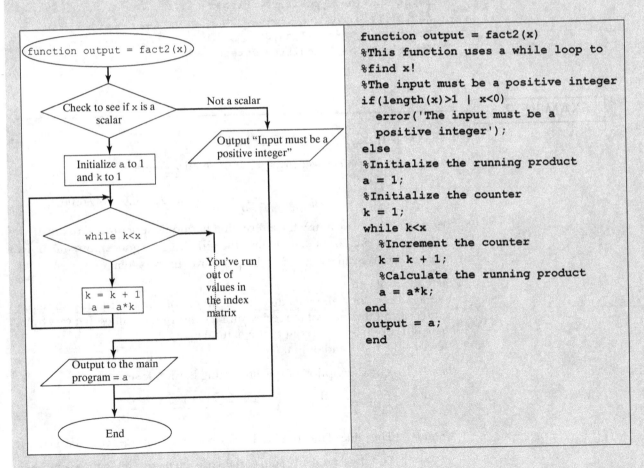

Figure 9.7
Flowchart for finding a factorial with a `while` loop.

(*continued*)

1. State the problem
   Create a function called `fact2` to calculate the factorial of any number.
2. Describe the input and output

   Input   A scalar value N

   Output   The value of $N!$

3. Develop a hand example

$$5! = 1 \cdot 2 \cdot 3 \cdot 4 \cdot 5 = 120$$

4. Develop a MATLAB® solution
   First develop a flowchart (see Figure 9.7) to help you plan your code.
5. Test the solution
6. Test the function in the command window:

```
fact2(5)
ans =
  120
fact2(-10)
Error using fact (line 8)
Input must be a positive integer
fact2([1:10])
Error using fact (line 8)
Input must be a positive integer
```

EXAMPLE 9.5

THE ALTERNATING HARMONIC SERIES

The *alternating harmonic series* converges to the natural log of 2:

$$\sum_{k=1}^{\infty} \frac{(-1)^{k+1}}{k} = 1 - \frac{1}{2} + \frac{1}{3} - \frac{1}{4} + \frac{1}{5} - \cdots = \ln(2) = 0.6931471806$$

Because of this, we can use the alternating harmonic series to approximate the $\ln(2)$. But how far out do you have to take the series to get a good approximation of the final answer? We can use a `while` loop to solve this problem.

1. State the problem
   Use a `while` loop to calculate the members of the alternating harmonic sequence and the value of the series until it converges to values that vary by less than .001. Compare the result to the natural log of 2.
2. Describe the input and output

   Input   The description of the alternating harmonic series

$$\sum_{k=1}^{\infty} \frac{(-1)^{k+1}}{k} = 1 - \frac{1}{2} + \frac{1}{3} - \frac{1}{4} + \frac{1}{5} - \cdots \frac{1}{\infty}$$

   Output   The value of the truncated series, once the convergence criterion is met.

   Plot the cumulative sum of the series elements, up to the point where the convergence criterion is met.

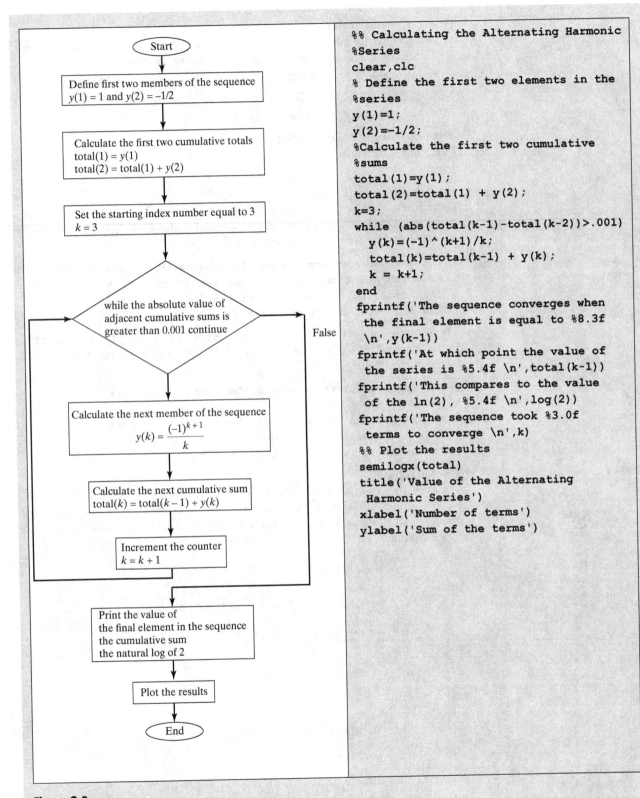

Figure 9.8
Flowchart to evaluate the alternating harmonic series until it converges.

(*continued*)

3. Develop a hand example

Let's calculate the value of the alternating harmonic series for 1 to 5 terms. First, find the value for each of the first five terms in the sequence

$$1.0000 \qquad -0.5000 \qquad 0.3333 \qquad -0.2500 \qquad 0.2000$$

Now, calculate the sum of the series assuming 1 to 5 terms

$$1.0000 \qquad 0.5000 \qquad 0.8333 \qquad 0.5833 \qquad 0.7833$$

The calculated sums are getting closer together, as we can see if we find the difference between adjacent pairs

$$-0.5000 \qquad 0.3333 \qquad -0.2500 \qquad 0.2000$$

4. Develop a MATLAB® solution

First, develop a flowchart (see Figure 9.8) to help you plan your code, then convert it to a MATLAB® program. When we run the program, the following results are displayed in the command window.

```
The sequence converges when the final element is equal to 0.001
At which point the value of the series is 0.6936
This compares to the value of the ln(2), 0.6931
The sequence took 1002 terms to converge
```

The series is quite close to the $\ln(2)$, but perhaps we could get closer with more terms. If we change the convergence criterion to 0.0001 and run the program, we get the following results:

```
The sequence converges when the final element is equal to
 -0.000
At which point the value of the series is 0.6931
This compares to the value of the ln(2), 0.6931
The sequence took 10001 terms to converge
```

5. Test the solution

Compare the result of the hand solution to the MATLAB® solution, by examining the graph (see Figure 9.9). The first five values for the series match those displayed in the graph. We can also see that the series seems to be converging to approximately 0.69, which is approximately the natural log of 2.

Figure 9.9

The alternating harmonic series converges slowly to the ln(2).

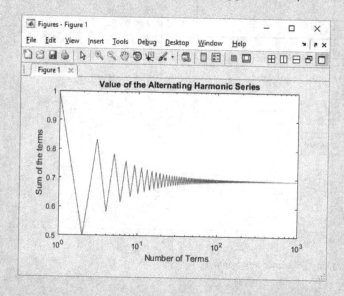

PRACTICE EXERCISE 9.2

Use a `while` loop to solve the following problems. The correct answers can be found on the Pearson website.

1. Create a conversion table of inches to feet.
2. Consider the following matrix of values:

$$x = [45, 23, 17, 34, 85, 33]$$

   How many values are greater than 30? (Use a counter.)
3. Compare your solution to Exercise 2 to the solutions you created in Practice Exercise 9.1, where you used both a `for` loop and the `find` function to solve the same problem.
4. Use a `while` loop to sum the elements of the matrix in Exercise 2. Check your results with the `sum` function. (Use the help feature if you don't know or remember how to use `sum`.)
5. Use a `while` loop to create a vector containing the first 10 elements in the harmonic series, that is,

$$1/1 \quad 1/2 \quad 1/3 \quad 1/4 \quad 1/5...1/10$$

6. Use a `while` loop to create a vector containing the first 10 elements in the alternating harmonic series, that is,

$$1/1 \quad -1/2 \quad 1/3 \quad -1/4 \quad 1/5...-1/10$$

HINT

To make the signs in a sequence of numbers alternate, raise -1 to a power. For example, to generate the values in a vector

```
-1 2 -3 4 -5
```

use the following loop

```
for k = 1:5
  a(k) = (-1)^k*k
end
```

Note: Order of operation is important. The result of

```
(-1)^k
```

alternates the sign depending on the value of k. Without the parentheses, the result of

```
-1^k
```

is always -1.

9.3 BREAK AND CONTINUE

The `break` command can be used to terminate a loop prematurely (while the comparison in the first line is still true). A `break` statement will cause termination of the smallest enclosing `while` or `for` loop. Here's an example:

```
n = 0;
while(n<10)
   n = n+1;
   a = input('Enter a value greater than 0:');
   if(a<=0)
      disp('You must enter a positive number')
      disp('This program will terminate')
      break
   end
      disp('The natural log of that number is')
      disp(log(a))
end
```

INITIALIZE

Define a starting value
for a variable that will be
changed later

In this program, the value of n is initialized outside the loop. Each time through, the input command is used to ask for a positive number. The number is checked, and if it is zero or negative, an error message is sent to the command window and the program jumps out of the loop. If the value of a is positive, the program continues and another pass through the loop occurs, until n is finally greater than 10.

The continue command is similar to break; however, instead of terminating the loop, the program just skips to the next pass:

```
n=0;
while(n<10)
   n=n+1;
   a=input('Enter a value greater than 0:');
   if(a<=0)
      disp('You must enter a positive number')
      disp('Try again')
      continue
   end
   disp('The natural log of that number is')
   disp(log(a))
end
```

In this example, if you enter a negative number, the program lets you try again—until the value of n is finally greater than 10.

9.4 MIDPOINT BREAK LOOPS

The loops described in the previous sections are examples of *midpoint break loops*. In these constructs, the loop is entered, calculations are processed, and a decision is made at some arbitrary point in the loop whether or not to exit. Then, additional calculations are processed, and the loop repeats. This strategy can be used either with a for loop or a while loop.

In a while structure, the loop continues to repeat until the criterion specified in the first line of the loop is false. For example

```
while (x>.001)
   . . . do some calculations that result in updating x
end
```

When the comparison between x and 0.001 is evaluated, either a 1 (for true) or a zero (for false) is returned. If the result is 0, the loop is terminated. One potential problem with this structure is that if the original value of x is very small, for example, in this case 0.0005, the loop will never execute. A way around this is to force the result to true, and add an if statement and corresponding break structure

```
while(1)
    . . . do some calculations
    if (x<=.001)
       break
    end
    . . . do any additional calculations or information
       processing
end
```

Recall that if a comparison is true, MATLAB® returns the number 1, so saying while(1) is equivalent to always making the comparison that starts a pass through the while loop true. The while(1) implementation allows the loop to continue executing for an infinite number of iterations. The decision to exit the loop is then controlled by the if/break structure. When would this be useful? One example is error checking, similar to the example in the previous problem. Consider another MATLAB® program that prompts the user to enter the number of candy bars purchased, and then finds the cost to the user. If the user enters a negative number, the program should prompt the user to try again. If a positive number is entered, the program completes the calculations and exits the loop.

```
while(1)
    candy_bars = input('Enter the number of candy bars ');
    if candy_bars<0
        disp('Must be a positive number')
    else
        total = candy_bars *.75;
        fprintf('The total cost is %5.2f dollars \n',total)
        break
    end
end
```

Here's the command window interaction when the program is executed.

```
Enter the number of candy bars -3
Must be a positive number
Enter the number of candy bars 5
The total cost is 3.75 dollars
```

One issue with this strategy is that the loop need never end. In this program, if the user keeps replying with a negative number, the program will continue to prompt for a positive value. One way to get around this is to use a for loop, which has a preset number of iterations. In this example, we've defined 3 as the maximum number of passes through the loop.

```
for k=1:3
    candy_bars = input('Enter the number of candy bars');
    if candy_bars<0
    disp('Must be a positive number')
    else
```

```
          total = candy_bars *.75;
          fprintf('The total cost is %5.2f dollars \n',total)
          break
       end
    end
```

Here's the command window interaction.

```
Enter the number of candy bars -3
Must be a positive number
Enter the number of candy bars -2
Must be a positive number
Enter the number of candy bars -5
Must be a positive number
```

After three iterations, the loop ends.

These may seem like trivial examples. A more complicated case is described in Example 9.6.

EXAMPLE 9.6

Calculating the value of the alternating harmonic series in order to approximate the value of $\ln(2)$ (as illustrated in Example 9.5) is an example of a numerical method. Many functions that you use routinely, such as `sine` and `cosine`, are approximated using similar series, called Taylor series or Maclaurin series. The alternating harmonic series is an example of a series that converges, but not every series does. For example, simply changing the alternating negative signs in the alternating harmonic series to positive numbers (the harmonic series vs. the alternating harmonic series) results in a series that diverges—it just keeps getting bigger and bigger with every new term. In cases such as these, we would want to specify a maximum number of iterations in our problem before giving up and exiting the loop.

A less obvious example of a series that diverges is

$$1 - 2 + 3 - 4 + 5 - 6 \ldots + (n-1) - n$$

which can be expressed mathematically as

$$\sum_{k=1}^{n} (-1)^{\wedge}(k+1)*k$$

Write a program that calculates the value of the summation. Assume that we don't know that it diverges, and specify an exit from the loop if two adjacent values of the cumulative sum are less than 0.001. Also, specify a maximum of 50 iterations.

1. State the problem
   Calculate the sum of the alternating series, assuming it converges, to within 0.001

2. Describe the input and output

   Input $\sum_{1}^{n} (-1)^{\wedge}(k+1)*k$

   Output   Find the cumulative sum of the series for each iteration

   Create a plot of the cumulative sums versus the number of terms

3. Develop a hand example
   The first six terms in the series are

   $$1 - 2 + 3 - 4 + 5 - 6$$

Thus, the first six cumulative sums are

$n = 1$	total = 1
$n = 2$	total = $1 - 2 = -1$
$n = 3$	total = $1 - 2 + 3 = 2$
$n = 4$	total = $1 - 2 + 3 - 4 = -2$
$n = 5$	total = $1 - 2 + 3 - 4 + 5 = 3$
$n = 6$	total = $1 - 2 + 3 - 4 + 5 - 6 = -3$

4. Develop a MATLAB® solution

Outline your program in a flowchart, as shown in Figure 9.10. Next, convert the flowchart to pseudocode comments, and insert the appropriate MATLAB® code.

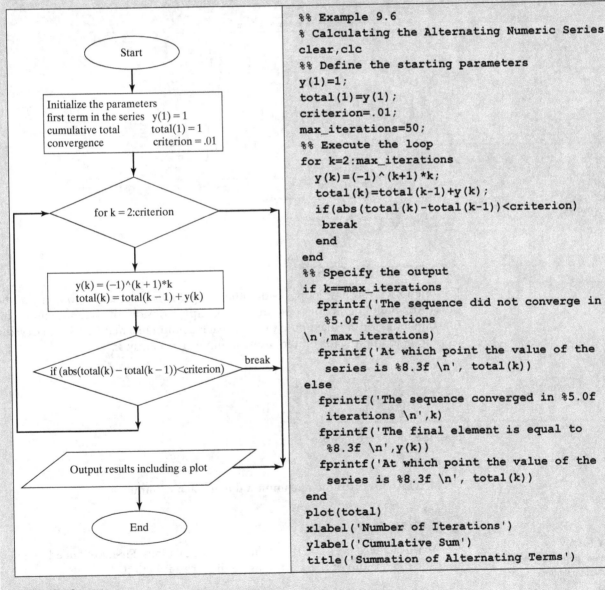

```matlab
%% Example 9.6
% Calculating the Alternating Numeric Series
clear,clc
%% Define the starting parameters
y(1)=1;
total(1)=y(1);
criterion=.01;
max_iterations=50;
%% Execute the loop
for k=2:max_iterations
    y(k)=(-1)^(k+1)*k;
    total(k)=total(k-1)+y(k);
    if(abs(total(k)-total(k-1))<criterion)
      break
    end
end
%% Specify the output
if k==max_iterations
  fprintf('The sequence did not converge in
    %5.0f iterations
\n',max_iterations)
  fprintf('At which point the value of the
    series is %8.3f \n', total(k))
else
  fprintf('The sequence converged in %5.0f
    iterations \n',k)
  fprintf('The final element is equal to
    %8.3f \n',y(k))
  fprintf('At which point the value of the
    series is %8.3f \n', total(k))
end
plot(total)
xlabel('Number of Iterations')
ylabel('Cumulative Sum')
title('Summation of Alternating Terms')
```

Figure 9.10

Flowchart for calculating the cumulative sums of the alternating numeric series.

(*continued*)

When this program is executed, the result in the command window is:

```
The sequence did not converge in 50 iterations
At which point the value of the series is -25.000
```

The resulting plot is shown in Figure 9.11.

5. Test the solution

The MATLAB® solution matches the hand calculations for the first six terms of the series. If we had not programmed in a maximum number of iterations, in the form of a `for` loop structure, the program would have entered an infinite loop.

Figure 9.11
The cumulative sum of the alternating numeric series does not converge, but rather oscillates around zero.

9.5 NESTED LOOPS

It is often useful to nest loops inside other loops. This is actually how many of the MATLAB® built-in functions operate. For example, consider the `max` function. This function looks for the maximum value for each column in a matrix. We can develop a program to find the maximum, using a simple 4×4 array, x.

```
x = [1     2     6     3;
     4     8     2     1;
     12    18    3     5;
     6     4     2     13]
```

If we use the `max` function

```
max(x)
```

MATLAB® returns the maximum value in each column

```
ans =
   12 18 6 13
```

KEY IDEA
Nested loops are used to evaluate multidimensional data.

We can achieve the same result with nested `for` loops. First, we'll need to determine the dimensions of the x array, using the `size` function.

```
[rows,cols]=size(x);
```

Now, we can use that information to create the external `for` loop, which we program to execute once for each column in the array. Then, we define a provisional value for the maximum, based on the first value in each column. Finally, we can use an internal `for` loop, which will execute once for each row in the array.

```
for k=1:cols                    External for loop
    maximum(k)=x(1,k);          Internal for  loop
        for j=1:rows            If structure
            if x(j,k)>maximum(k)
            maximum(k)=x(j,k);
        end
    end
end
maximum % Sends the results to the screen
```

9.6 IMPROVING THE EFFICIENCY OF LOOPS

KEY IDEA

Loops are generally less efficient than vectorized calculations.

In general, using a `for` loop (or a `while` loop) is less efficient in MATLAB® than using array operations. We can test this assertion by timing the multiplication of the elements in a long array. First, we create a matrix **A** containing 1,000,000 ones; the `ones` command creates an $n \times n$ matrix of ones:

```
ones(1000);
```

The result is a 1000×1000 matrix of ones (1,000,000 total values). Now, we can compare the results of multiplying each element by π, using array multiplication first and then a `for` loop. You can time the results by using the `clock` function and the function `etime`, which measures elapsed time. If you have a fast computer, you may need to use a larger array. The structure of the clocking code is

```
t0 = clock;
. . . code to be timed
etime (clock, t0)
```

The `clock` function polls the computer clock for the current time. The `etime` function compares the current time with the initial time, and subtracts the two values to give the elapsed time.

For our problem,

```
clear, clc
A = ones(1000); %Creates a 1000 x 1000 matrix of ones
t0 = clock;
    B = A*pi;
time = etime(clock, t0)
```

gives a result of

```
time =
    0
```

The array calculation took 0 seconds, simply meaning that it happened very quickly. Every time you run these lines of code, you should get a different answer. The `clock` and `etime` functions used here measure how long the CPU worked between receiving the original and final timing requests. However, the CPU is doing other things besides our problem: At a minimum, it is performing system tasks, and it may be running other programs in the background.

To measure the time required to perform the same calculation with a loop, we need to clear the memory and re-create the array of ones:

```
clear
A = ones(1000);
```

This ensures that we are comparing calculations from the same starting point. Now, we code

```
t0 = clock;
    for k = 1:length(A(:))
B(k) = A(k)*pi;
        end
time = etime(clock, t0)
```

which gives the result

```
time =
    1.6130
```

It took almost two seconds to perform the same calculation! (This was on an older computer—your result will depend on the machine you use.) The number of iterations through the for loop was determined by finding how many elements are in **A**. This was accomplished with the length command. Recall that length returns the largest array dimension, which is 1000 for our array and isn't what we want. To find the total number of elements, we used the colon operator (:) to represent **A** as a single list, 1 million elements long, and then used length, which returned 1,000,000. Each time through the for loop, a new element was added to the **B** matrix. This is the step that took all the time, since the computer must allocate additional memory 1,000,000 times. We can reduce the time required for this calculation by creating the **B** matrix first (so that the memory allocation process takes place only once) and then replacing the values one at a time. The code is

```
clear
A = ones(1000);
t0 = clock;
%Create a B matrix of ones
  B = A;
  for k = 1:length(A(:))
  B(k) = A(k)*pi;
  end
time = etime(clock, t0)
```

which gives the result

```
time =
    1.0830
```

This is obviously a big improvement. You could see an even bigger difference between the first example, a simple multiplication of the elements of an array, and the last example if you created a bigger matrix. By contrast, the intermediate example, in which we did not initialize **B**, would take a prohibitive amount of time to execute.

MATLAB® also includes a set of commands called tic and toc that can be used in a manner similar to the clock and etime functions to time a piece of code. Thus, the code

```
clear
A = ones(1000);
tic
  B = A;
  for k = 1:length(A(:))
    B(k) = A(k)*pi;
  end
toc
```

returns

```
Elapsed time is 1.09 seconds.
```

The difference in execution time is expected, since the computer is busy doing different background tasks each time the program is executed. As with `clock/etime`, the `tic/toc` commands measure elapsed time, not the time devoted to just this program's execution.

Both the `clock/etime` sets of functions are programmatic—they must be embedded in the MATLAB script. Run times can also be determined using the **Run and Time** icon found on the Editor toolstrip. (See Figures 9.12 and 9.13.)

HINT

Be sure to suppress intermediate calculations when you use a loop. Printing those values to the screen will greatly increase the amount of execution time. If you are brave, repeat the preceding example, but delete the semicolons inside the loop just to check out this claim. Don't forget that you can stop the execution of the program with `Ctrl c`. Be sure the command window is the active window when you execute `Ctrl c`.

Figure 9.12
MATLAB® allows you to measure execution times using the **Run and Time** icon from the Editor toolstrip.

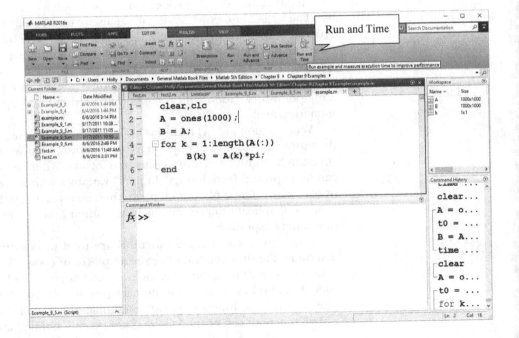

Figure 9.13
The Profile Summary is generated when a script is executed using the **Run and Time** icon from the Editor toolstrip.

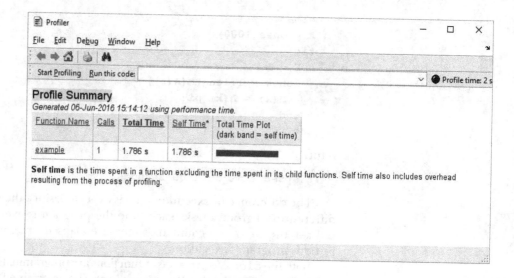

SUMMARY

Repetition structures (loops) are used when a section of code needs to be repeated several times. As a rule of thumb, if you find yourself repeating a section of code more than three times, it probably should be in a repetition structure. MATLAB® supports two types of repetition structures: the for loop and the while loop. In addition, the break and continue commands can be used to modify either type of loop to create a *midpoint break loop.*

For loops are used mainly when the programmer knows how many times a sequence of commands should be executed. While loops are used when the commands should be executed until a condition is met. Most problems can be structured so that either for or while loops are appropriate.

The break and continue statements are used to exit a loop prematurely. They are usually used in conjunction with if statements. The break command causes a jump out of a loop and execution of the remainder of the program. The continue command skips execution of the current pass through a loop, but allows the loop to continue until the completion criterion is met. This type of structure is called a midpoint break loop, and is commonly used in many applications, especially in numerical analysis.

Vectorization of MATLAB® code allows it to execute much more efficiently and, therefore, more quickly. Loops, in particular, should be avoided in MATLAB® if the code can be formulated into a vectorized format. When loops are unavoidable, they can be improved by defining "dummy" variables with placeholder values, such as ones or zeros. These placeholders can then be replaced in the loop. Doing this will result in significant improvements in execution time, a fact that can be confirmed with timing experiments.

The clock and etime functions are used to poll the computer clock and determine the time required to execute pieces of code. The time calculated is the "elapsed" time. During this time, the computer not only has been running MATLAB® code, but also has been executing background jobs and housekeeping functions. The tic and toc functions perform a similar task. Either the tic/toc or clock/ etime functions can be used to compare execution time for different code options.

MATLAB® SUMMARY

Commands and Functions	
break	causes the execution of a loop to be terminated
clock	determines the current time on the CPU clock
continue	terminates the current pass through a loop, but proceeds to the next pass
end	identifies the end of a control structure
error	terminates the program and sends a message to the screen
etime	finds elapsed time
for	generates a loop structure
ones	creates a matrix of ones
tic	starts a timing sequence
toc	stops a timing sequence
while	generates a loop structure

KEY TERMS

converge
diverge
for loop
infinite loop

loop
repetition
midpoint break loop
nested loops

while loop
series
vectorization

PROBLEMS

9.1 Use a for loop to sum the elements in the following vector:

$$x = [1, 23, 43, 72, 87, 56, 98, 33]$$

Check your answer with the sum function.

9.2 Repeat the previous problem, this time using a while loop.

9.3 Use a for loop to create a vector of the squares of the numbers 1 through 5.

9.4 Use a while loop to create a vector of the squares of the numbers 1 through 5.

9.5 Use the primes function to create a list of all the primes below 100. Now use a for loop to multiply adjacent values together. For example, the first four prime numbers are

2   3   5   7.

Your calculation would be

2*3   3*5   5*7

which gives

6   15   35.

9.6 A Fibonacci sequence is composed of elements created by adding the two previous elements. The simplest Fibonacci sequence starts with 1, 1, and proceeds as follows:

1, 1, 2, 3, 5, 8, 13, . . .

Figure P9.6

Chambered nautilus. (Colin Keates © Dorling Kindersley, Courtesy of the natural history museum, London.)

However, a Fibonacci sequence can be created with any two starting numbers. Fibonacci sequences appear regularly in nature. For example, the shell of the chambered nautilus (see Figure P9.6) grows in accordance with a Fibonacci sequence.

Prompt the user to enter the first two numbers in a Fibonacci sequence, and the total number of elements requested for the sequence. Find the sequence and store it in an array by using a `for` loop. Now plot your results on a `polarplot` graph. Use the element number for the angle, and the value of the element in the sequence for the radius.

9.7 Repeat the preceding problem, this time using a `while` loop.

9.8 One interesting property of a Fibonacci sequence is that the ratio of the values of adjacent members of the sequence approaches a number called "the golden ratio" or Φ (phi). Create a program that accepts the first two numbers of a Fibonacci sequence as user input, then calculates additional values in the sequence until the ratio of adjacent values converges to within 0.001. You can do this in a `while` loop by comparing the ratio of element k to element k - 1, and the ratio of element k - 1 to element k - 2. If you call your sequence **x**, then the code for the `while` statement is

$$\text{while abs}(x(k)/x(k-1) - x(k-1)/x(k-2))>0.001$$

9.9 Recall from trigonometry that the tangent of both $\pi/2$ and $-\pi/2$ is infinity. This may be seen from the fact that

$$\tan(\theta) = \sin(\theta)/\cos(\theta)$$

and since

$$\sin(\pi/2) = 1$$

and

$$\cos(\pi/2) = 0,$$

it follows that

$$\tan(\pi/2) = \text{infinity}.$$

Because MATLAB® uses a floating-point approximation of π, it calculates the tangent of $\pi/2$ as a very large number, but not infinity.

Prompt the user to enter an angle θ between $\pi/2$ and $-\pi/2$, inclusive. If it is between $\pi/2$ and $-\pi/2$, but not equal to either of those values, calculate $\tan(\theta)$ and display the result in the command window. If it is equal to $\pi/2$ or $-\pi/2$, set the result equal to `Inf` and display the result in the command window. If it is outside the specified range, send the user an error message in the command window and prompt the user to enter another value. Continue prompting the user for a new value of theta until he or she enters a valid number.

9.10 Imagine that you are a proud new parent. You decide to start a college savings plan now for your child, hoping to have enough in 18 years to pay the sharply rising cost of education. Suppose that your folks give you $1000 to get started and that each month you can contribute $100. Suppose also that the interest rate is 6% per year compounded monthly, which is equivalent to 0.5% each month.

Because of interest payments and your contribution, each month your balance will increase in accordance with the formula

new balance = old balance + interest + your contribution

Use a `for` loop to find the amount in the savings account each month for the next 18 years. (Create a vector of values.) Plot the amount in the account as a function of time. (Plot time on the horizontal axis, and dollars on the vertical axis.)

9.11 Imagine that you have a crystal ball and can predict the percentage increases in tuition for the next 22 years. The following vector `increase` shows your predictions, in percent, for each year:

```
increase = [10, 8, 10, 16, 15, 4, 6, 7, 8, 10, 8, 12,
            14, 15, 8, 7, 6, 5, 7, 8, 9, 8]
```

Use a `for` loop to determine the cost of a four-year education, assuming that the current cost for one year at a state school is $7000.

9.12 Use an `if` statement to compare your results from the previous two problems. Are you saving enough? Send an appropriate message to the command window.

9.13 Edmond Halley (the astronomer famous for discovering Halley's comet) invented a fast algorithm for computing the square root of a number, A. Halley's algorithm approximates $\sqrt{A}$ as follows:

Start with an initial guess x_1. The new approximation is then given by

$$Y_n = \frac{1}{A} x_n^2$$

$$x_{n+1} = \frac{x_n}{8}(15 - y_n(10 - 3y_n))$$

These two calculations are repeated until some convergence criterion, ε, is met.

$$\left| x_{n+1} - x_n \right| \le \varepsilon$$

Write a MATLAB® function called `my_sqrt` that approximates the square root of a number. It should have two inputs, the initial guess and the convergence criterion.

Test your function by approximating the square root of 5 and comparing it to the value calculated with the built-in MATLAB® function, `sqrt`.

9.14 The value of $\cos(x)$ can be approximated using a Maclaurin series

$$\cos(x) = 1 - \frac{x^2}{2!} + \frac{x^4}{4!} - \frac{x^6}{6!} + \cdots$$

which can be expressed more compactly as

$$\sum_{k=1}^{\infty} (-1)^{k-1} \frac{x^{(k-1)*2}}{((k-1)*2)!}$$

(recall that the symbol ! stands for factorial).

Use a midpoint break loop to determine how many terms must be included in the summation, in order to find the correct value of $\cos(2)$ within an error of .001. Limit the number of iterations to a maximum of 10.

9.15 The value of $\sin(x)$ can be approximated as

$$\sin(x) = x - \frac{x^3}{3!} + \frac{x^5}{5!} - \frac{x^7}{7!} + \cdots$$

Create a function called `my_sin`, using a midpoint break loop to approximate the value of $\sin(x)$. Determine convergence by comparing successive values of the summation as you add additional terms. These successive sums should be within an absolute value of 0.001 of each other. Test your function by evaluating the `my_sin(2)` and comparing it to the built-in MATLAB® sine function.

9.16 The value of π can be approximated with the Gregory–Leibniz series summation

$$\frac{\pi}{4} = 1 - \frac{1}{3} + \frac{1}{5} - \frac{1}{7} + \frac{1}{9} - \cdots$$

or

$$\pi = 4 - \frac{4}{3} + \frac{4}{5} - \frac{4}{7} + \frac{4}{9} - \cdots$$

The series converges very slowly. Calculate π, using a midpoint break loop. Determine convergence by comparing successive values of the summation as you add additional terms until the difference between successive sums is less than 0.001. Set the maximum number of iterations to 3000.

9.17 A store owner asks you to write a program for use in the checkout process. The program should:

- Prompt the user to enter the cost of the first item.
- Continue to prompt for additional items, until the user enters 0.
- Display the total.
- Prompt for the dollar amount the customer submits as payment.
- Display the change due.

Nested Loops

9.18 In the previous chapter, the Lake Powell water elevation data were evaluated using the `find` function. Repeat the calculations, using a nested loop structure. The file **lake_powell.dat** contains the data listed in Table 8.10.

Faster Loops

9.19 Whenever possible, it is better to avoid using `for` loops, because they are slow to execute.

(a) Generate a 100,000-item vector of random digits called x; square each element in this vector and name the result y; use the commands `tic` and `toc` to time the operation.

(b) Next, perform the same operation element by element in a `for` loop. Before you start, clear the values in your variables with

```
clear x y
```

Use `tic` and `toc` to time the operation.

Depending on how fast your computer runs, you may need to stop the calculations by issuing the `Ctrl c` command in the command window.

(c) Now convince yourself that suppressing the printing of intermediate answers will speed up execution of the code by allowing these same operations to run and print the answers as they are calculated. You will almost undoubtedly need to cancel the execution of this loop because of the large amount of time it takes. *Recall that* `Ctrl c` *terminates the program.*

(d) If you are going to use a constant value several times in a `for` loop, calculate it once and store it, rather than calculating it each time through the loop. Demonstrate the increase in speed of this process by adding `(sin(0.3) + cos(pi/3))*5!` to every value in the long vector in a `for` loop. (Recall that ! means factorial, which can be calculated with the MATLAB® function `factorial`.)

(e) As discussed in this chapter, if MATLAB® must increase the size of a vector every time through a loop, the process will take more time than if the vector were already the appropriate size. Demonstrate this fact by repeating part (b) of this problem. Create the following vector of *y*-values, in which every element is equal to zero before you enter the `for` loop:

```
y = zeros(1,100000);
```

You will be replacing the zeros one at a time as you repeat the calculations in the loop.

Challenge Problems

9.20 (a) Create a function called `polygon` that draws a polygon in a polar plot. Your function should have a single input parameter—the number of sides.

(b) Use a `for` loop to create a figure with four subplots, showing a triangle in the first subplot, a square in the second subplot, a pentagon in the third subplot, and a hexagon in the fourth subplot. You should use the function you created in part (a) to draw each polygon. Use the index parameter from the `for` loop to specify the subplot in which each polygon is drawn, and in an expression to determine the number of sides used as input to the `polygon` function.

9.21 Consider the following method to approximate the mathematical constant, *e*. Start by generating *K* uniform random integers between 1 and *K*. Compute *J*, the number of integers between 1 and *K*, which were never generated. We then approximate *e* by the ratio

$$\frac{K}{J}$$

Consider the following example for $K = 5$. Assume that the following five integers are randomly generated between 1 and 5.

$$1 \quad 1 \quad 2 \quad 3 \quad 2$$

The number of times the integers are generated is given by

Integers	1	2	3	4	5
Number of instances	2	2	1	0	0

In this example, there are two integers, namely 4 and 5, which were never generated. This means that $J = 2$. Consequently, *e* is approximated by

$$\frac{5}{2} = 2.5$$

Write a function called `eapprox` that takes the value of K as input, and which then approximates e using the method described above. Test your function several times with different values of K, and compare the result to the value of e calculated using the built-in MATLAB® function.

$$\mathrm{exp(1)}$$

HINT

Use the randi function to create an array of random integers.

9.22 Vectorize (replace loops with a single statement) the calculations in the function created in the previous problem, by using the built-in MATLAB® functions `histcounts` and `sum`.

Index